A Treasury of Scientific Prose

A Treasury of Scientific Prose

A Nineteenth-Century Anthology

Edited by

HOWARD MUMFORD JONES

and

I. BERNARD COHEN

with the assistance of
Everett Mendelsohn

LITTLE, BROWN AND COMPANY · BOSTON · TORONTO

Published simultaneously in Canada
by Little, Brown & Company (Canada) Limited

PRINTED IN THE UNITED STATES OF AMERICA

Contents

[v]

CONTENTS

[vi]

A Treasury of Scientific Prose

Introduction

THE quality of expository prose has apparently become of lessening interest to literary critics in the twentieth century, who devote most of their attention to fiction, poetry, and drama. It requires no great knowledge of literary history, however, to realize that the novel and the short story as conceived by the moderns are virtually products of yesterday, and that the great bulk of the world's prose is nonfictional. From Plato to Darwin, prose, though it has from time to time graciously admitted matter of fiction to its rich empire, has chiefly devoted itself to commemoration, to persuasion, to exposition, or to matters of fact. Its uses have been historical, hortatory, and explanatory. Prose matured as history, as dialogues, as sermon, as oratory, as instruction, as explanation. The great names of Herodotus, Thucydides, Cicero, Seneca, St. Augustine, Aquinas, Dante, Galileo, Bacon, Bossuet, Sir Thomas Browne, Gibbon, Burke, and Schopenhauer are representative of this simple, yet fundamental, truth.

The tradition of English prose is likewise historical, moral, and expository. Fiction in the English Renaissance is negligible, but the amount of nonfictional prose is enormous and frequently splendid, as in the case of Hakluyt's *Voyages*, Bacon's *Advancement of Learning*, Raleigh's *History of the World*, and the sermons of John Donne. The great prose achievements of the seventeenth century run from Bacon through Milton to Dryden and Swift, and there is not a novelist of stature in the lot, for one can scarcely call *Pilgrim's Progress* a novel, and *Robinson Crusoe* (over the edge of the century), like most of Defoe's concoctions, purports to be autobiography. The point of *Gulliver's Travels* is not its narrative charm but its philosophy. When in the eighteenth century the novel really begins, it starts by pretending to be something else — a collection of letters, a comic epic in prose, a confession, an autobiography, a philosophic tract. Meanwhile the great tradition of nonfictional prose moves on with Addison, Steele, and Goldsmith for its light skirmishers, and Bishop Butler, Johnson, Gibbon, Burke, Reynolds, Franklin, and their kind in its main column.

Of this mighty stream the prose of science and of thinking about science is an important confluent. Because science, until the last quarter of the nineteenth century, was thought of as natural philosophy, it was written with the large discourse it inherited from the days of Elizabeth and of the Stuarts. The quality of largeness is easier to feel than to define, but it can be sensed by anybody who will turn from the pages of a present-day scientific journal to read Burton on melancholia or Boyle's *Sceptical Chymist*.

In the seventeenth century a great battle over style took place, in which science played a central role. The outcome was modern English prose. Begun by Bacon, this stylistic revolution turned in large measure upon the intellectual significance of the "New Philosophy," of which the Royal Society, chartered in 1662, became the embodiment. Bacon warned his readers not to mistake words for things, a truth at once so simple and so pro-

[4]

found that it became the basis of British empiricism. The debate over the experimental method got itself involved with other complicated issues that had but an indirect relation to the question of how best to write a report on a scientific experiment. Among such issues were the antinomy of scepticism and religious belief, the supposed superiority of the ancients over the moderns (an issue that seems to us entirely empty), and the relation between imagination and fancy on the one hand and reason and wit on the other — terms that scores of divines, philosophers, scholars, and literary men struggled to make clear. The victory of a plain style was not easily won. The fact that some of the experiments reported in the early days of the Royal Society were fantastic, even in seventeenth-century terms, did not escape the hostile conservatives such as Samuel Butler and Jonathan Swift; and opponents of the Society did not hesitate to confuse the stylistic and the epistemological problems. The Royal Society felt the matter to be of such crucial importance that in 1664–1665 it appointed John Wilkins, cryptographer, bishop, and author of an *Essay toward a Real Character and a Philosophical Language,* to discuss with twenty-one members of the Society means of improving the English tongue as a medium for science. The best-known product of this program of propaganda is Bishop Thomas Sprat's *History of the Royal Society* (1667), a book so clearly written that even Swift, who made fun of "projectors" in *Gulliver's Travels,* called it "the best book in the English language."

The aim of the reform was plainness and simplicity. Simplicity, however, is not enough to explain the excellence of the scientific writers, selections from whom are given in this collection. The quality of largeness characteristic of English prose about science until relatively recent decades is obviously something more than a product of simplicity. Seventeenth-century scientific prose was, to be sure, under compulsion to rid itself of the fantastic attributes Bacon complained of, and this was a great benefit. But it benefited even more from a continuing controversy. From Bacon to the present, science has been charged with atheism, scepticism, agnosticism, materialism, and amoralism. Battling in England against an Established Church that long controlled Oxford and Cambridge, British science since Bacon's time has never been able to dodge what may be called the cosmological problem. It has had to assume that the scientist, like the divine, the poet, and the metaphysician, sees life steadily and sees it whole. It could not be content with merely technical explanations. Hence it is that such characteristic scientific geniuses as Newton and Darwin have also been philosophers concerned with the general shape of things in the universe and not merely with statements of technical problems.

This cultural fact has been of immense benefit to British scientific prose. Newton's odd concern with the prophecies of Daniel is from this point of view not eccentricity but a symbol of the need either of working out a harmony of science and belief (as in the cases of Paley and Chambers in this anthology) or of demonstrating that honest scientists, if they are true to their profession, will not (as some of the eighteenth-century French materialist *philosophes* wanted to do) go out of their way to damage the profession of the theologian. Lyell and Darwin are representative of this British attitude. So characteristic is this of British scientific writing up to 1859 or a little later that even Herbert Spencer, who fancied he knew science and who was the philosopher of empiricism, begins the *Synthetic Philosophy* not by calling God into question but by declaring with the Psalmist that God is the Unknowable. This attitude was to change, of course, with Huxley and Tyndall, the one an admirer of Hume and the other in the tradition of French materialism.

But the point is not to argue that all scientists should become believers (or stay so) or to deny that an atheist can do brilliant scientific work; the point is to make clear the context in which scientific writing was done during the decades represented in this anthology. The scientific writer from 1802 to 1858, the years this book illustrates, was more often than not under a kind of public commitment to general truth. He had to show, if not God, then Order, or Law, or Organization, or Meaning. The terms in which he wrote were, so to speak, terms of respect for these cosmological notions. He had, in short, to be both a philosopher and a professional workman in science. There are of course exceptions, but the generalization seems empirically sound.

This philosophical responsibility entailed a second one that at first sight looks like a defect. One of the striking facts about British science during most of the nineteenth century was what one may call its amateur standing. The Royal Society had begun as a gentlemen's club. Oxford and Cambridge were long innocent of modern scientific laboratories. In the history of Great Britain scientist after scientist did something else for a living or, if not that, had sufficient private income to follow science as a sort of hobby. There were no foundations to which to appeal, no fellowship aids, no government boards of consequence until late in the century (and those that existed were more often than not "practical" in their outlook), and very few learned and scientific periodicals. Conditions of this sort may have held back the development of British science, but, oddly enough, they enriched British scientific writing.

The scientist had nobody to appeal to, outside his own small circle, except the literate public. The need to make science clear, to make it persuasive, and to make it comprehensible to the largest possible audience followed almost of necessity from the cultural situation. It must be remembered that modern science played but a small role in standard British education. One cannot forget that when Matthew Arnold toured America in 1884–1885, it was in the character of a man laying about him mightily to protect a humanistic education against the supposed assaults of Thomas Henry Huxley, who had helped inaugurate The Johns Hopkins University in 1876. Not only did the writers represented in this collection have to make science clear to laymen, they had to make it clear to laymen who were products of a conservative, essentially nonscientific pattern of education. One who reads Harcourt's plea of 1833 for the creation of the British Association for the Advancement of Science soon discovers that Harcourt is addressing an audience possessing what may be described as a strong infusion of amateurism as one of its chief cultural characteristics. Charles Dickens, who as a newspaper reporter had to know a thing or two about British life, in Chapter One of *Pickwick Papers* records Mr. Pickwick's contribution to the theory of tittlebats. This was in 1836. It is burlesque, but it is a burlesque of the kind of activity Harcourt was dealing with seriously in 1833.

There are a good many things wrong with the amateur spirit, but its profound effect upon British scientific writing — especially during the first sixty years of the nineteenth century — is that it kept scientific writing within the realm of public dis-

course. Not everyone understood every word of the selections
here reprinted nor of the larger units out of which they are
taken, but it was assumed as a matter of course by the nineteenth-century men that anybody could with application understand them. Probably the finest creation of this interesting cultural situation is that masterpiece of direct scientific exposition
for the lay mind, Faraday's *Chemical History of a Candle.*

The assumption that the scientist had a duty to the informed
general public did not disappear with the publication of *The
Origin of Species* in 1859. On the contrary, the polemic and
expository essays of Huxley and the popular discourses of William Kingdon Clifford continued the tradition. But it was, in
the increasing volume of scientific writing, a weakening tradition. After 1859 the trend to mathematicization got the upper
hand in the physical sciences — a trend evident in the fact that
the selection from Clerk Maxwell in this collection has to be
broken off at the point where mathematics takes over. The result was both technical exclusion and technical exclusiveness.
The lay reader was warned off, the specialist was invited in. Inevitably an interest in the prose of science declined. Witnessing
the transformation of his own ideas (which he had not expressed
in mathematics) into the mathematical equations of Maxwell,
Faraday wrote to Maxwell as early as 1857, saying:

There is one thing I would be glad to ask you. When a mathematician engaged in investigating physical actions and results has
arrived at his own conclusions, may they not be expressed in common language as fully, clearly, and definitely as in mathematical
formulae? If so, would it not be a great boon to such as we to express them so — translating them out of their hieroglyphics so that
we also might work upon them by experiment. I think it must be

so, because I have always found that you could convey to me a perfectly clear idea of your conclusions, which though they may give me no full understanding of the steps of your process, gave me the results neither above nor below the truth, and so clear in character that I can think and work from them.

If this be possible, would it not be good thing, if mathematicians, writing on these subjects, were to give us their results in this popular useful working state as well as in that which is their own and proper to them?

Here, in a sense, the older and the younger generation of scientists confront each other.

Maxwell felt the difficulty, and, addressing a meeting of the British Association for the Advancement of Science at Liverpool in 1870, he was compelled to recognize the existence of two distinct types of mind:

For the sake of persons of these different types scientific truth should be presented in different forms, and should be regarded as equally scientific, whether it appears in a robust form in the vivid colouring of a physical illustration, or in the tenuity and paleness of a symbolical expression.

Perhaps. But the central dilemma was the uses of mathematics and the uses of prose. Maxwell inevitably and rightly had to employ the sharper and more nearly accurate instrument of mathematical expression, and so do we.

It is therefore said that contemporary science is too complex, too technical, too specialized to permit living scientists, even if they wrote better than most of them write, to do what Robert Brown, Playfair, Bell and the others accomplished during the first two thirds of the last century. And this is in large measure a fair statement. On the other hand, any rack of paperback books is bound to contain a good many titles about contemporary science that laymen seem to want to read; and, moreover, complexity is always relative. A written letter is a technological mystery to a savage, the multiplication table is awe-inspiring to a tot who doesn't know his numbers, and the operation of an electric typewriter is a miracle of dexterity to one who uses a pencil only with much difficulty. If one were a literary Englishman of the 1850's with a classical education in one's background, one would have found a good many baffling words and phrases in this prose.

The difference between Darwin and the writers represented in this collection, and the modern scientific specialist is that the earlier scientists often felt it their duty to use technical language only when they were forced to and, using it, to make it as clear as possible, whereas the modern specialist is too often impatient with the English language, and is inclined to think that what he does is none of the public's business anyway. This is not to indict modern scientists as a class; it is, however, to lament the failure of many modern scientists to live up to the responsibility implicit in the thought of Charles S. Peirce (and for that matter, Faraday): how to make our ideas clear.

The selections that follow are representative of a rich library of scientific prose appearing principally between 1800 and 1859. Huxley is not represented because in the period from which these selections are drawn Huxley was still working as a taxonomic biologist, and, like his contemporaries Richard Owen and Joseph Dalton Hooker, mainly producing technical reports. But the authors here represented help to explain why *The Origin of Species* is both a classic of science and a classic of literature. They illustrate the expository and philosophical tradition Darwin inherited, one which, after Darwin and Maxwell, as we have said, tended to dwindle. To anyone with an ear for prose cadence, a feeling for exactitude in language, and an interest in ideas, these selections ought to prove a delight, for they show how excellent a medium of expression English can be when it is written not by the aesthetically minded, but by mature men with something intellectual to present.

I

Natural Theology

WILLIAM PALEY

Natural Theology*

William Paley (1743–1805) was not an active scientist but rather a lecturer on moral and religious philosophy at Cambridge, and later Archdeacon of Carlisle. The *Natural Theology* (1802), in its forceful argument for design in nature as evidence of God's direct intervention in earthly affairs, is one of the more successful volumes in a long series of works by theological naturalists. What struck these observers was the care bestowed by the Creator on even the least of animals or most minute of parts; and the manifold ways in which organisms were adapted to their environment. The arguments from design to the Deity, which reached their height in the Bridgewater Treatises of the 1830's, were all but forgotten by the close of the century. The edition utilized was edited by Henry Lord Brougham and Sir Charles Bell in 1836. Several of their explicatory notes are included and are indicated by asterisks. Bell, as indicated by the selections in this volume, was much influenced by the type of thinking found in Paley's *Natural Theology*.

STATE OF THE ARGUMENT.

IN CROSSING a heath, suppose I pitched my foot against a *stone,* and were asked how the stone came to be there, I might possibly answer, that, for anything I knew to the contrary, it had lain there for ever; nor would it, perhaps, be very easy to show the absurdity of this answer. But suppose I had found a *watch* upon the ground, and it should be inquired how the watch happened to be in that place, I should hardly think of the

* From *Natural Theology, or the Evidences of the Existence and Attributes of the Deity, Collected from the Appearances of Nature* (1802).

answer which I had before given — that, for anything I knew, the watch might have always been there. Yet why should not this answer serve for the watch as well as for the stone? why is it not as admissible in the second case as in the first? For this reason, and for no other, viz., that, when we come to inspect the watch, we perceive (what we could not discover in the stone) that its several parts are framed and put together for a purpose, e.g. that they are so formed and adjusted as to produce motion, and that motion so regulated as to point out the hour of the day; that, if the different parts had been differently shaped from what they are, of a different size from what they are, or placed after any other manner, or in any other order than that in which they are placed, either no motion at all would have been carried on in the machine, or none which would have answered the use that is now served by it. To reckon up a few of the plainest of these parts, and of their offices, all tending to one result:— We see a cylindrical box containing a coiled elastic spring, which, by its endeavour to relax itself, turns round the box. We next observe a flexible chain (artificially wrought for the sake of flexure) communicating the action of the spring from the box to the fusee. We then find a series of wheels, the teeth of which catch in, and apply to, each other, conducting the motion from the fusee to the balance, and from the balance to the pointer, and, at the same time, by the size and shape of those wheels, so regulating that motion as to terminate in causing an index, by an equable and measured progression, to pass over a given space in a given time. We take notice that the wheels are made of brass, in order to keep them from rust; the springs of steel, no other metal being so elastic; that over the face of the watch there is placed a glass, a material employed in no other part of the work, but in the room of which, if there had been any other than a transparent substance, the hour could not be seen without opening the case. This mechanism being observed, (it requires indeed an examination of the instrument, and perhaps some previous knowledge of the subject, to perceive and understand it; but being once, as we have said, observed and understood,) the inference, we think, is inevitable, that the watch must have had a maker: that there must have existed, at some time, and at some place or other, an artificer or artificers who formed it for the purpose which we find it actually to answer; who comprehended its construction, and designed its use.

I. Nor would it, I apprehend, weaken the conclusion, that we had never seen a watch made; that we had never known an artist capable of making one; that we were altogether incapable of executing such a piece of workmanship ourselves, or of understanding in what manner it was performed; all this being no more than what is true of some exquisite remains of ancient art, of some lost arts, and, to the generality of mankind, of the more curious productions of modern manufacture. Does one man in a million know how oval frames are turned? Ignorance of this kind exalts our opinion of the unseen and unknown artist's skill, if he be unseen and unknown, but raises no doubt in our minds of the existence and agency of such an artist, at some former time, and in some place or other. Nor can I perceive that it varies at all the inference, whether the question arise concerning a human agent, or concerning an agent of a different species, or an agent possessing, in some respect, a different nature.

II. Neither, secondly, would it invalidate our conclusion, that the watch sometimes went wrong, or that it seldom went exactly right. The purpose of the machinery, the design, and the designer, might be evident, and, in the case supposed, would be evident, in whatever way we accounted for the irregularity of the movement, or whether we could account for it or not. It is not necessary that a machine be perfect, in order to show with what design it was made: still less necessary, where the only question is, whether it were made with any design at all.

III. Nor, thirdly, would it bring any uncertainty into the argument, if there were a few parts of the watch, concerning which we could not discover, or had not yet discovered, in what manner they conduced to the general effect; or even some parts, concerning which we could not ascertain whether they conduced to that effect in any manner whatever. For, as to the first branch of the case, if by the loss, or disorder, or decay of the parts in question, the movement of the watch were found in fact to be stopped, or disturbed, or retarded, no doubt would remain in our minds as to the utility or intention of these parts, although we should be unable to investigate the manner according to which, or the connexion by which, the ultimate effect depended upon their action or assistance; and the more complex is the machine, the more likely is this obscurity to arise. Then, as to the second thing supposed, namely, that there were parts which might be spared without prejudice to the movement of the watch, and that he had proved this by experiment, these superfluous parts, even if we were completely assured that they were such, would not vacate the reasoning which we had instituted concerning other parts. The indication of contrivance remained, with respect to them, nearly as it was before.

IV. Nor, fourthly, would any man in his senses think the

existence of the watch, with its various machinery, accounted for, by being told that it was one out of possible combinations of material forms; that whatever he had found in the place where he found the watch, must have contained some internal configuration or other; and that this configuration might be the structure now exhibited, viz., of the works of a watch, as well as a different structure.

V. Nor, fifthly, would it yield his inquiry more satisfaction, to be answered, that there existed in things a principle of order, which had disposed the parts of the watch into their present form and situation. He never knew a watch made by the principle of order; nor can he even form to himself an idea of what is meant by a principle of order, distinct from the intelligence of the watchmaker.

VI. Sixthly, he would be surprised to hear that the mechanism of the watch was no proof of contrivance, only a motive to induce the mind to think so:

VII. And not less surprised to be informed, that the watch in his hand was nothing more than the result of the laws of *metallic* nature. It is a perversion of language to assign any law as the efficient, operative cause of anything. A law presupposes an agent; for it is only the mode according to which an agent proceeds: it implies a power; for it is the order according to which that power acts. Without this agent, without this power, which are both distinct from itself, the *law* does nothing, is nothing. The expression, "the law of metallic nature," may sound strange and harsh to a philosophic ear; but it seems quite as justifiable as some others which are more familiar to him, such as "the law of vegetable nature," "the law of animal nature," or, indeed, as "the law of nature" in general, when assigned as the cause of phenomena, in exclusion of agency and power, or when it is substituted into the place of these.*

VIII. Neither, lastly, would our observer be driven out of his conclusion, or from his confidence in its truth, by being told that he knew nothing at all about the matter. He knows enough for his argument: he knows the utility of the end: he knows the subserviency and adaptation of the means to the end. These points being known, his ignorance of other points, his doubts concerning other points, affect not the certainty of his reasoning. The consciousness of knowing little need not beget a distrust of that which he does know. . . .

PROSPECTIVE CONTRIVANCES.

I can hardly imagine to myself a more distinguishing mark, and, consequently, a more certain proof of design, than *preparation, — i. e.*, the providing of things beforehand, which are not to be used for a considerable time afterwards: for this implies a contemplation of the future, which belongs only to intelligence.

Of these *prospective* contrivances, the bodies of animals furnish various examples.

* When philosophers and naturalists observe a certain succession in the phenomena of the universe, they consider the uniformity to exist through a *law of nature*. If they discover the order of events, or phenomena, they say they have discovered the law: for example, the law of affinities, of gravitation, &c. It is a loose expression; for to obey a law supposes an understanding and a will to comply. The phrase also implies that we know the nature of the governing power which is in operation, and in the present case both conditions are wanting.

The "law" is the mode in which the power acts, and the term should infer, not only an acquiescence in the existence of the power, but of Him who has bestowed the power and enforced the law.

The term "force" is generally used instead of power, when the intensities are measurable in their mechanical results.

I. The human teeth afford an instance, not only of prospective contrivance, but of the completion of the contrivance being
designedly suspended. They are formed within the gums, and
there they stop; the fact being, that their farther advance to
maturity would not only be useless to the new-born animal, but
extremely in its way; as it is evident that the act of *sucking,* by
which it is for some time to be nourished, will be performed
with more ease both to the nurse and to the infant, whilst the
inside of the mouth and edges of the gums are smooth and soft,
than if set with hard-pointed bones. By the time they are
wanted the teeth are ready. They have been lodged within the
gums for some months past, but detained, as it were, in their
sockets, so long as their farther protrusion would interfere with
the office to which the mouth is destined. Nature, namely, that
intelligence which was employed in creation, looked beyond the
first year of the infant's life: yet, whilst she was providing for
functions which were after that term to become necessary, was
careful not to incommode those which preceded them. What
renders it more probable that this is the effect of design, is, that
the teeth are imperfect, whilst all other parts of the mouth are
perfect. The lips are perfect, the tongue is perfect; the cheeks,
the jaws, the palate, the pharynx, the larynx, are all perfect: the
teeth alone are not so. This is the fact with respect to the human mouth: the fact also is, that the parts above enumerated
are called into use from the beginning; whereas the teeth would
be only so many obstacles and annoyances, if they were there.
When a contrary order is necessary, a contrary order prevails.
In the worm of the beetle, as hatched from the egg, the teeth are
the first things which arrive at perfection. The insect begins to

gnaw as soon as it escapes from the shell, though its other parts be only gradually advancing to their maturity.

What has been observed of the teeth, is true of the *horns* of animals; and for the same reason. The horn of a calf or a lamb does not bud, or at least does not sprout to any considerable length, until the animal be capable of browsing upon its pasture; because such a substance upon the forehead of the young animal would very much incommode the teat of the dam in the office of giving suck.

But in the case of the *teeth* — of the human teeth at least, the prospective contrivance looks still farther. A succession of crops is provided, and provided from the beginning; a second tier being originally formed beneath the first, which do not come into use till several years afterwards. And this double or suppletory provision meets a difficulty in the mechanism of the mouth, which would have appeared almost insurmountable. The expansion of the jaw (the consequence of the proportionable growth of the animal, and of its skull) necessarily separates the teeth of the first set, however compactly disposed, to a distance from one another, which would be very inconvenient. In due time, therefore, *i. e.*, when the jaw has attained a great part of its dimensions, a new set of teeth springs up, (loosening and pushing out the old ones before them,) more exactly fitted to the space which they are to occupy, and rising also in such close ranks, as to allow for any extension of line which the subsequent enlargement of the head may occasion.

II. It is not very easy to conceive a more evidently prospective contrivance than that which, in all viviparous animals, is found in the *milk* of the female parent. At the moment the young animal enters the world there is its maintenance ready for it. The particulars to be remarked in this economy are neither few nor slight. We have, first, the nutritious quality of the fluid, unlike, in this respect, every other excretion of the body: and in which nature hitherto remains unimitated, neither cookery nor chemistry having been able to make milk out of grass: we have, secondly, the organ for its reception and retention: we have, thirdly, the excretory duct annexed to that organ: and we have, lastly, the determination of the milk to the breast at the particular juncture when it is about to be wanted. We have all these properties in the subject before us; and they are all indications of design. The last circumstance is the strongest of any. If I had been to guess beforehand, I should have conjectured, that at the time when there was an extraordinary demand for nourishment in one part of the system, there would be the least likelihood of a redundancy to supply another part. The advanced pregnancy of the female has no intelligible tendency to fill the breasts with milk. The lacteal system is a constant wonder: and it adds to other causes of our admiration, that the number of the teats or paps in each species is found to bear a proportion to the number of the young. In the sow, the bitch, the rabbit, the cat, the rat, which have numerous litters, the paps are numerous, and are disposed along the whole length of the belly: in the cow and mare they are few. The most simple account of this, is to refer it to a designing Creator.

But in the argument before us, we are entitled to consider not only animal bodies when framed, but the circumstance under which they are framed: and in this view of the subject, the constitution of many of their parts is most strictly prospective.

III. The eye is of no use, at the time when it is formed. It is an optical instrument made in a dungeon; constructed for the refraction of light to a focus, and perfect for its purpose, before a ray of light has had access to it; geometrically adapted to the properties and action of an element, with which it has no communication. It is about indeed to enter into that communication: and this is precisely the thing which evidences intention. It is *providing* for the *future* in the closest sense which can be given to these terms; for it is providing for a future change; not for the then subsisting condition of the animal; nor for any gradual progress or advance in that same condition; but for a new state, the consequence of a great and sudden alteration, which the animal is to undergo at its birth. Is it to be believed that the eye was formed, or, which is the same thing, that the series of causes was fixed by which the eye is formed, without a view to this change; without a prospect of that condition, in which its fabric, of no use at present, is about to be of the greatest; without a consideration of the qualities of that element, hitherto entirely excluded, but with which it was hereafter to hold so intimate a relation? A young man makes a pair of spectacles for himself against he grows old; for which spectacles he has no want or use whatever at the time he makes them. Could this be done without knowing and considering the defect of vision to which advanced age is subject? Would not the precise suitableness of the instrument to its purpose, of the remedy to the defect, of the convex lens to the flattened eye, establish the certainty of the conclusion, that the case, afterwards to arise, had been considered beforehand, speculated upon, provided for? all which are exclusively the acts of a reasoning mind. The eye formed in one state, for use only in another state, and in a different state, affords a proof no less clear of destination to a future purpose; and a proof proportionably stronger, as the ma-

chinery is more complicated, and the adaptation more exact.
IV. What has been said of the eye, holds equally true of the
lungs. Composed of air-vessels, where there is no air; elaborately
constructed for the alternate admission and expulsion of an
elastic fluid, where no such fluid exists; this great organ, with
the whole apparatus belonging to it, lies collapsed in the fœtal
thorax; yet in order, and in readiness for action, the first moment that the occasion requires its service. This is having a
machine locked up in store for future use; which incontestably
proves, that the case was expected to occur in which this use
might be experienced; but expectation is the proper act of intelligence. Considering the state in which an animal exists before its birth, I should look for nothing less in its body than a
system of lungs. It is like finding a pair of bellows in the bottom
of the sea; of no sort of use in the situation in which they are
found: formed for an action which was impossible to be exerted; holding no relation or fitness to the element which surrounds them, but both to another element in another place.

As part and parcel of the same plan ought to be mentioned,
in speaking of the lungs, the provisionary contrivances of the
foramen ovale and *ductus arteriosus*. In the fœtus pipes are laid
for the passage of the blood through the lungs; but, until the
lungs be inflated by the inspiration of air, that passage is im-
pervious, or in a great degree obstructed. What then is to be
done? What would an artist, what would a master, do upon the
occasion? He would endeavour, most probably, to provide a
temporary passage, which might carry on the communication
required, until the other was open. Now this is the thing which
is actually done in the heart. Instead of the circuitous route
through the lungs which the blood afterwards takes before it get

from one auricle of the heart to the other, a portion of the blood passes immediately from the right auricle to the left, through a hole placed in the partition which separates these cavities. This hole anatomists call the *foramen ovale*. This is likewise another cross cut, answering the same purpose, by what is called the *ductus arteriosus*, lying between the pulmonary artery and the aörta. But both expedients are so strictly temporary, that after birth the one passage is closed, and the tube which forms the other shrivelled up into a ligament. If this be not contrivance, what is?

But, forasmuch as the action of the air upon the blood in the lungs appears to be necessary to the perfect concoction of that fluid, *i. e.* to the life and health of the animal, (otherwise the shortest route might still be the best,) how comes it to pass that the *fœtus* lives, and grows, and thrives without it? The answer is, that the blood of the fœtus is the mother's; that it has undergone that action in her habit; that one pair of lungs serves for both. When the animals are separated a new necessity arises; and to meet this necessity as soon as it occurs an organization is prepared. It is ready for its purpose; it only waits for the atmosphere; it begins to play the moment the air is admitted to it.

OF THE GOODNESS OF THE DEITY.

The proof of the *divine goodness* rests upon two propositions: each, as we contend, capable of being made out by observations drawn from the appearances of nature.

The first is, "that in a vast plurality of instances in which contrivance is perceived, the design of the contrivance is *beneficial*."

The second, "that the Deity has superadded *pleasure* to animal sensations, beyond what was necessary for any other purpose, or when the purpose, so far as it was necessary, might have been effected by the operation of pain."

First, "in a vast plurality of instances in which contrivance is perceived, the design of the contrivance is *beneficial*."

No productions of nature display contrivance so manifestly as the parts of animals; and the parts of animals have all of them, I believe, a real, and, with very few exceptions, all of them a known and intelligible subserviency to the use of the animal. Now, when the multitude of animals is considered, the number of parts in each, their figure and fitness, the faculties depending upon them, the variety of species, the complexity of structure, the success, in so many cases, and felicity of the result, we can never reflect without the profoundest adoration, upon the character of that Being from whom all these things have proceeded: we cannot help acknowledging what an exertion of benevolence creation was; of a benevolence how minute in its care, how vast in its comprehension!

When we appeal to the parts and faculties of animals, and to the limbs and senses of animals in particular, we state, I conceive, the proper medium of proof for the conclusion which we wish to establish. I will not say, that the insensible parts of nature are made solely for the sensitive parts: but this I say, that, when we consider the benevolence of the Deity, we can only consider it in relation to sensitive being. Without this reference, or referred to any thing else, the attribute has no object; the term has no meaning. Dead matter is nothing. The parts, therefore, especially the limbs and senses, of animals, although they constitute, in mass, and quantity, a small portion of the

WILLIAM PALEY

material creation, yet, since they alone are instruments of perception, they compose what may be called the whole of visible nature, estimated with a view to the disposition of its Author. Consequently, it is in *these* that we are to seek his character. It is by these that we are to prove that the world was made with a benevolent design.

Nor is the design abortive. It is a happy world after all. The air, the earth, the water teem with delighted existence. In a spring noon, or a summer evening, on whichever side I turn my eyes, myriads of happy beings crowd upon my view. "The insect youth are on the wing." Swarms of new-born *flies* are trying their pinions in the air. Their sportive motions, their wanton mazes, their gratuitous activity, their continual change of place without use or purpose, testify their joy, and the exultation which they feel in their lately discovered faculties. A *bee* amongst the flowers in spring is one of the most cheerful objects that can be looked upon. Its life appears to be all enjoyment; so busy, and so pleased; yet it is only a specimen of insect life, with which by reason of the animal being half domesticated, we happen to be better acquainted than we are with that of others. The *whole-winged* insect tribe, it is probable, are equally intent upon their proper employments, and, under every variety of constitution, gratified, and perhaps equally gratified, by the offices which the Author of their nature has assigned to them. But the atmosphere is not the only scene of enjoyment for the insect race. Plants are covered with aphides, greedily sucking their juices, and constantly, as it should seem, in the act of sucking. It cannot be doubted but that this is a state of gratification. What else should fix them so close to the operation, and so long? Other species are *running about*, with an alacrity in their motions which carries with it every mark of pleasure. Large patches of ground are sometimes half covered with these brisk and sprightly natures. If we look to what the *waters* produce, shoals of the fry of fish frequent the margins of rivers, of lakes, and of the sea itself. These are so happy, that they know not what to do with themselves. Their attitudes, their vivacity, their leaps out of the water, their frolics in it, (which I have noticed a thousand times with equal attention and amusement,) all conduce to show their excess of spirits, and are simply the effects of that excess. Walking by the sea-side, in a calm evening, upon a sandy shore, and with an ebbing tide, I have frequently remarked the appearance of a dark cloud, or, rather, very thick mist, hanging over the edge of the water, to the height, perhaps, of half a yard, and of the breadth of two or three yards, stretching along the coast as far as the eye could reach, and always retiring with the water. When this cloud came to be examined it proved to be nothing else than so much space filled with young *shrimps,* in the act of bounding into the air from the shallow margin of the water, or from the wet sand. If any motion of a mute animal could express delight, it was this: if they had meant to make signs of their happiness, they could not have done it more intelligibly. Suppose, then, what I have no doubt of, each individual of this number to be in a state of positive enjoyment; what a sum, collectively, of gratification and pleasure have we here before our view!

The *young* of all animals appear to me to receive pleasure simply from the exercise of their limbs and bodily faculties, without reference to any end to be attained, or any use to be answered by the exertion. A child, without knowing any thing of the use of language, is in a high degree delighted with being able to speak. Its incessant repetition of a few articulate sounds, or, perhaps, of the single word which it has learnt to pronounce, proves this point clearly. Nor is it less pleased with its first successful endeavours to walk, or rather to run (which precedes walking,) although entirely ignorant of the importance of the attainment to its future life, and even without applying it to any present purpose. A child is delighted with speaking, without having any thing to say, and with walking, without knowing where to go. And, prior to both these, I am disposed to believe, that the waking hours of infancy are ageeably taken up with the exercise of vision, or perhaps, more properly speaking, with learning to see.

But it is not for youth alone that the great Parent of creation hath provided. Happiness is found with the purring cat, no less than with the playful kitten; in the arm-chair of dozing age, as well as in either the sprightliness of the dance, or the animation of the chase. To novelty, to acuteness of sensation, to hope, to ardour of pursuit, succeeds, what is, in no inconsiderable degree, an equivalent for them all, "perception of ease." Herein is the exact difference between the young and the old. The young are not happy but when enjoying pleasure; the old are happy when free from pain. And this constitution suits with the degrees of animal power which they respectively possess. The vigour of youth was to be stimulated to action by impatience of rest; whilst to the imbecility of age, quietness and repose become positive gratifications. In one important respect the advantage is with the old. A state of ease is, generally speaking, more attainable than a state of pleasure. A constitution, therefore, which can enjoy ease, is preferable to that which can taste only pleasure. This same perception of ease often-times renders old age a condition of great comfort; especially when riding at its anchor after a busy or tempestuous life. It is well described by Rousseau, to be the interval of repose and enjoyment between the hurry and the end of life. How far the same cause extends to other animal natures cannot be judged of with certainty. The appearance of satisfaction with which most animals, as their activity subsides, seek and enjoy rest, affords reason to believe, that this source of gratification is appointed to advanced life, under all, or most, of its various forms. In the species with which we are best acquainted, namely our own, I am far, even as an observer of human life, from thinking that youth is its happiest season, much less the only happy one: as a Christian, I am willing to believe that there is a great deal of truth in the following representation given by a very pious writer, as well as excellent man: "To the intelligent and virtuous, old age presents a scene of tranquil enjoyments, of obedient appetite, of well-regulated affections, of maturity in knowledge, and of calm preparation for immortality. In this serene and dignified state, placed as it were on the confines of two worlds, the mind of a good man reviews what is past with the complacency of an approving conscience; and looks forward, with humble confidence in the mercy of God, and with devout aspirations towards his eternal and ever-increasing favour."[1]

What is seen in different stages of the same life, is still more exemplified in the lives of different animals. Animal enjoyments are infinitely *diversified*. The modes of life, to which the organization of different animals respectively determines them,

[1] Thomas Percival (1740–1804), Manchester physician and staunch Unitarian; author of *A Father's Instructions, Consisting of Moral Tales, Fables, and Reflections Designed to Promote the Love of Virtue, a Taste for Knowledge, and an Early Acquaintance with the Work of Nature* (London, 1775).

are not only of various but of opposite kinds. Yet each is happy in its own. For instance: animals of prey live much alone; animals of a milder constitution in society. Yet the herring, which lives in shoals, and the sheep, which lives in flocks, are not more happy in a crowd, or more contented amongst their companions, than the pike, or the lion, with the deep solitudes of the pool, or the forest.

But it will be said, that the instances which we have here brought forward, whether of vivacity or repose, or of apparent enjoyment derived from either, are picked and favourable instances. We answer, first, that they are instances, nevertheless, which comprise large provinces of sensitive existence; that every case which we have described is the case of millions. At this moment, in every given moment of time, how many myriads of animals are eating their food, gratifying their appetites, ruminating in their holes, accomplishing their wishes, pursuing their pleasures, taking their pastimes! In each individual, how many things must go right for it to be at ease; yet how large a proportion out of every species is so in every assignable instant! Secondly, we contend, in the terms of our original proposition, that throughout the whole of life, as it is diffused in nature, and as far as we are acquainted with it, looking to the average of sensations, the plurality and the preponderancy is in favour of happiness by a vast excess. In our own species, in which perhaps the assertion may be more questionable than any other, the prepollency of good over evil, of health, for example, and ease, over pain and distress, is evinced by the very notice which calamities excite. What inquiries does the sickness of our friends produce! what conversation their misfortunes! This shows that the common course of things is in favour of happiness; that happiness is the rule, misery the exception. Were the order reversed, our attention would be called to examples of health and competency, instead of disease and want.

One great cause of our insensibility to the goodness of the Creator, is the very *extensiveness* of his bounty. We prize but little what we share only in common with the rest, or with the generality of our species. When we hear of blessings, we think forthwith of successes, of prosperous fortunes, of honours, riches, preferments, *i. e.* of those advantages and superiorities over others, which we happen either to possess, or to be in pursuit of, or to covet. The common benefits of our nature entirely escape us. Yet these are the great things. These constitute what most properly ought to be accounted blessings of Providence; what alone, if we might so speak, are worthy of its care. Nightly rest and daily bread, the ordinary use of our limbs, and senses, and understandings, are gifts which admit of no comparison with any other. Yet because almost every man we meet with posesses these, we leave them out of our enumeration. They raise no sentiment; they move no gratitude. Now, herein is our judgement perverted by our selfishness. A blessing ought in truth to be the *more* satisfactory, the bounty at least of the donor is rendered more conspicuous, by its very diffusion, its commonness, its cheapness: by its falling to the lot, and forming the happiness, of the great bulk and body of our species, as well as of ourselves. Nay, even when we do not possess it, it ought to be matter of thankfulness that others do. But we have a different way of thinking. We court distinction. That is not the worst: we *see* nothing but what has distinction to recommend it. This necessarily contracts our views of the Creator's beneficence within a narrow compass; and most unjustly. It is in those things which are so common as to be no distinction, that the amplitude of the Divine benignity is perceived.

But pain, no doubt, and privations exist, in numerous instances, and to a great degree, which collectively would be very great, if they were compared with any other thing than with the mass of animal fruition. For the application, therefore, of our proposition to that *mixed* state of things which these exceptions induce, two rules are necessary, and both, I think, just and fair rules. One is, that we regard those effects alone which are accompanied with proofs of intention: The other, that when we cannot resolve all appearances into benevolence of design, we make the few give place to the many; the little to the great; that we take our judgement from a large and decided preponderancy, if there be one.

I crave leave to transcribe into this place what I have said upon this subject in my Moral Philosophy: — [2]

"When God created the human species, either he wished their happiness, or he wished their misery, or he was indifferent and unconcerned about either.

"If he had wished our misery, he might have made sure of his purpose, by forming our senses to be so many sores and pains to us, as they are now instruments of gratification and enjoyment; or by placing us amidst objects so ill suited to our perceptions, as to have continually offended us, instead of ministering to our refreshment and delight. He might have made, for example, every thing we tasted, bitter; every thing we saw, loathsome; every thing we touched, a sting; every smell a stench; and every sound, a discord.

[2] *Principles of Morals and Political Philosophy* (London, 1785). This book represents an expanded form of the very popular lectures given by Paley at Cambridge University.

"If he had been indifferent about our happiness or misery, we must impute to our good fortune (as all design by this supposition is excluded,) both the capacity of our senses to receive pleasure, and the supply of external objects fitted to produce it.

"But either of these, and still more, both of them, being too much to be attributed to accident, nothing remains but the first supposition, that God, when he created the human species, wished their happiness; and made for them the provision which he has made, with that view and for that purpose.

"The same argument may be proposed in different terms; *thus:* Contrivance proves design; and the predominant tendency of the contrivance indicates the disposition of the designer. The world abounds with contrivances; and all the contrivances which we are acquainted with are directed to beneficial purposes. Evil, no doubt, exists; but is never, that we can perceive, the *object* of contrivance. Teeth are contrived to eat, not to ache; their aching now and then is incidental to the contrivance, perhaps inseparable from it: or even, if you will, let it be called a defect in the contrivance; but it is not the object of it. This is a distinction which well deserves to be attended to. In describing implements of husbandry, you would hardly say of the sickle, that it is made to cut the reaper's hand: though from the construction of the instrument, and the manner of using it, this mischief often follows. But if you had occasion to describe instruments of torture, or execution, — this engine, you would say, is to extend the sinews; this to dislocate the joints; this to break the bones; this to scorch the soles of the feet. Here, pain and misery are the very objects of the contrivance. Now, nothing of this sort is to be found in the works of nature. We never discover a train of contrivance to bring about an evil

[35]

purpose. No anatomist ever discovered a system of organization calculated to produce pain and disease; or, in explaining the parts of the human body, ever said, this is to irritate; this to inflame; this duct is to convey the gravel to the kidneys; this gland to secrete the humour which forms the gout: if by chance he come at a part of which he knows not the use, the most he can say is, that it is useless; no one ever suspects that it is put there to incommode, to annoy, or to torment."

CHARLES BELL

The Hand As Evincing Design*

A Scot who received excellent training in anatomy at the University of Edinburgh, Charles Bell (1774–1842) was best known for his work on the nervous system. Through a series of careful dissections and experiments he distinguished two kinds of nerves — the sensory and the motor. Credit for this discovery is shared with a French anatomist-physiologist, François Magendie. *The Anatomy of Expression* was an early work completed during 1804. Its inspiration probably arose as diversion during his work with his brother John Bell for their jointly published *Anatomy of the Human Body* (1804). The volume on *The Hand* is the fourth Bridgewater Treatise, a series established by the will of the Right Honourable and Reverend Francis Henry, Earl of Bridgewater, who directed the Royal Society to publish works "on the power, wisdom, goodness of God, as manifested in the creation; illustrating such work by all reasonable arguments, as for instance the variety and formation of God's creatures in the animal, vegetable, and mineral kingdoms; the affect of digestion, and thereby conversion; the construction of the hand of man, and an infinite variety of other arguments; as also by discoveries ancient and modern in arts, sciences, and the whole extent of literature."

THE ARGUMENT PURSUED FROM THE COMPARATIVE ANATOMY.

SO FAR as we have hitherto proceeded, by examining objects in comparative anatomy which from their magnitude can not be misunderstood, we have been led to conclude that, independently of the system of parts marvellously to form the

* From *The Hand, Its Mechanism and Vital Endowments, as Evincing Design. The Bridgewater Treatises on the Power, Wisdom, and Goodness of God as Manifested in the Creation. Treatise IV* (1833).

[37]

individual animal, there is another, more comprehensive system, which embraces all animals; and which exhibits a certain uniformity in the functions of life, however different in form or bulk the creatures may be, or to whatever condition of the globe they may have been adapted. We have seen no accidental deviation or deformity, but that every change has been for a purpose, and every part has had its just relation. We have witnessed all the varieties moulded to such a perfect accommodation, and the alterations produced by such minute degrees, that all notion of external and accidental agency must be rejected.

We might carry our demonstration downward through the lower classes of animals; for example, we might trace the feet of insects from their most perfect or complex state, till they disappear; or, observing the changes in another direction, we might follow out the same parts from the smallest beginning to the most perfect condition of the member, where we see the thigh, leg, and tarsus of the fly. We might distinguish them at first as the fine cirri, like minute bristles, which on the bodies of worms take slight hold of the surface over which they creep. In the sea mouse, (*aphrodita*) we might notice these bristles standing out from distinct mammillary processes, which are furnished with appropriate muscles. Then in the *myriapodes*, the first order of insects, we might see the same "many feet," and each foot having a distinct articulation. From that, we might pass to the feet of those insects, where there is a thigh, leg, and foot, with the most perfect system of flexors, extensors, and adductor muscles, possessing, in fine, all that we most admire in the human anatomy. Nay, it is most curious to observe how the feet of the true insects are again changed or modified;

THE HAND AS EVINCING DESIGN

taking new offices, the anterior feet becoming feelers, organs of prehension, or *hands*. When, with such an object, we view the delicate and curiously adapted instruments of insects, we must perceive that it would be easy to trace almost every part through a succession of modifications. Among the *vertebrata*, we have seen the hand become a wing or a fin; so might we trace the wings of insects. If we begin with a fly, which has two delicate and perfect wings incased and protected, we find that the covers are raised to admit the expansion of the wings. In another, the case becomes a wing; and the fly is characterized by four wings. Proceed to examine a third example, and we shall discover that this anterior wing is larger and more perfect than the posterior: the fourth specimen has lost the posterior wings, and has only two perfect ones; and if we continue the examination, the next specimen will present an insect deprived of wings altogether. These are not freaks of nature, but new forms of the body; new appendages required for a different poising of the fly in its flight. They are adaptations in that regular series which we have observed to obtain in the larger animals, and where the intention can not be mistaken. A very natural question will force itself upon us, how are those varieties to be explained?

The curious adaptation of a member to different offices and to different conditions of the animal has led to a very extraordinary opinion in the present day, — that all animals consist of the same elements. It would be just to say that they consist of the same chemical elements, and that they attract and assimilate matter by the performance of the same vital functions, through every species of animals, however different in form and structure. But by the elements which are now mentioned, the authors of this new theory mean certain pieces which enter into the structure of the body, and which they illustrate by the analogy of the building materials of a house. If these materials, they say, are exhausted in the ornamental parts of the portico and vestibule, there must be a proportionate limitation of the apartments for the family!

This new theory has been brought forward with the highest pretensions; the authors of it have called upon us to mark the moment of its conception as the commencement of a new æra! They speak of the "elective affinities of organs," "the balancing of organs," "a new principle of connection," and a "new theory of analysis." — The hypothesis essentially is this, that when a part, which belongs to one animal, is missed in another, we are to seek for it in some neighbouring organ: and on such grounds they affirm, that this surpasses all former systems as a means of discovery. Now, the perfection or aggrandizement of any one organ of an animal is not attended with the curtailment or proportional deficiency of any other. Like ourselves, perhaps, the supporters of this theory dwell too much upon the bones; but even in them, we shall show that the system is untenable. In the mean time, we may ask, do additional parts connected with the stomach, making it highly complex, as in ruminating animals, shorten the intestinal canal, or make its form simpler? On the contrary, is not a complex stomach necessarily connected with a long and complicated intestine? — Does a complex intestinal canal throughout all its course render imperfect the solid viscera which are in juxtaposition to it? Is there any defect in them, because the organs of digestion are perfect, or complicated? Does the complex heart imply a more simple, or a more perfect condition of the lungs? In short, as animals rise in

the scale of existence, do we not find that the systems of digestion, circulation, respiration and sensation, bear ever a proportional increase? Is there any instance of an improvement in
one organ thrusting another out of its place, or diminishing its
volume?

Now, as to the osseous system, were we to follow these
theorists into the very stronghold of their position, the bones
of the skull, where the real intricacy of the parts allows them
some scope for their ingenuity, we might show how untenable
the principle is which they assume. But we must confine ourselves to our own subject.

In the higher orders of the vertebrata, we find that the bones
of the shoulder perform a double office; that they have an important share in the act of respiration, whilst they are perfect
as a foundation for the extremity. Now, let us take an instance
where the mode of respiration of the animal is inconsistent with
what we may term the original mechanism of the bones of the
shoulder. In the batrachian order,[1] the ribs are wanting: where
then are we to look for them? Shall we follow a system which
informs us that when a bone is wanting in the cavity of the
ear, we are to seek for it in the jaw; and which, yet, shall leave
us in the contemplation of this class of animals deficient in
thirty-two ribs, without pointing out where they are to be
found, or how their elements are built up in other structures?
If, on the contrary, we take the principle that parts are formed
or withdrawn, with a never-failing relation to the function
which is to be performed, we see that no sooner are the com-
pages of the chest removed, and the shoulder thus deprived of
support, than the bones to which the extremity is fixed are ex-

1 Batrachian — the amphibians.

panded and varied, both in form and articulation, so as to fulfil their main object of giving security and motion to the arm.

With respect to the instance which we have accidentally noticed regarding the mechanism of the jaw in birds, and which is brought forward so vauntingly as a proof of the excellence of the theory, it does, indeed, prove the reverse of what is assumed. The only effect of this hypothesis is to make us lose sight of the principle which ought to direct us in the observation of such curious structures, as well as of the conclusions to which an unbiassed mind would come. The matter to be explained is simply this: — the chain of bones in the ear, which is so curiously adapted in the mammalia to convey the vibrations of the membrane of the tympanum to the nerve of hearing, is not found in the organ of hearing in birds; but there is sub-stituted a mechanism entirely different. They choose to say that the incus, one of the bones of the chain, is wanting in the bird. Where shall we find it? — they ask. Here it is in the apparatus of the jaw or mandible; in that bone which is called *os quadratum.* I believe that the slight and accidental re-semblance which this bone (B.) in the bird has to the incus,[2] is the real origin of this fancy. Let us follow a juster mode of reasoning, and see how this hypothesis obscures the beauty of the subject. The first step of the investigation ought to be to inquire into the fact, if there be any imperfection in the hear-ing of birds. That is easily answered — the hearing of birds is most acute; the slightest noise alarms; and the nightingale, or other bird of song, in a summer evening, will answer to the note of his rival when he is out of our hearing. We have next to observe the imperfection in the organ — the want of an ex-

2 Incus — a small bone in the ear of mammals.

ternal ear; which, were it present, would be at variance with all that we have most to admire in the shape of the bird and the direction of the feathers, as conducing to its rapid passage through the air. With this obvious defect of the external ear, can we admit that the internal ear is also imperfect, notwithstanding the very remarkable acuteness of hearing, which we know to result from this internal structure, and from it alone? Now we do, in fact, find a different structure in the ear of birds; but, yet nothing is wanting. The *columella* is a shaft of bone of exquisite delicacy, which is extended from the outward membrane of the ear to the labyrinth or proper seat of the nerve of hearing. It occupies the place and office of the chain of four bones which belong to the ear of mammalia. We have no authority, however, for affirming that the incus is here wanting more than any other bone of the chain; — and if it be said that the os quadratum is the missing incus, why should not we find in the oviparous reptiles, where there is a *columella* in the ear, an os quadratum in the jaw?

From this mode of inquiry, we find that the sense of hearing is enjoyed in an exquisite degree in birds: that the organ of the sense is not imperfect, but is adapted to a new construction, and a varied apparatus — suited to the condition of the bird: and that there is no accidental dislocation or substitution of something less perfect than what we find in other classes of animals.

If we now look to the structure of the mandible of the bird, we shall find as curious, though a somewhat grosser example of mechanical relation. The bill of the bird, in some degree, pertains to our subject, as it is the organ of prehension and of touch. It is withal a fly trap — hence, its motions must be rapid:

and the velocity is increased by the most obvious means im-
aginable, — that is, by giving motion to both mandibles, instead of to one. When a dog snaps he throws back his head, and
thereby raises the upper jaw at the same time that the lower
jaw is dropped; but these are slow and clumsy motions, per-
taining to the muscles of the neck as well as of the jaws, and the
poor hound makes many attempts, before he catches the fly
that teazes him. But a swallow or fly-catcher makes no second
effort, so admirably suited is the apparatus of prehension to the
liveliness of the eye and the instinct. The adaptation of the
instrument consists in this, that the muscles which open the
lower mandible, by the same effort, open the upper one: A. is a

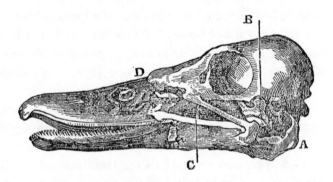

process of the lower mandible, projecting much behind the
centre of motion, and the muscle which is attached to it opens
the bill; — but at the same time, the lower mandible presses
upon the bone B., the *os quadratum:* now, there is attached to
this bone, projecting forwards, with its anterior extremity fixed
against the upper mandible, a shaft or process of bone C.; and
this receives the pressure of the *os quadratum,* when the muscle

[44]

acts; so that being thrust forwards, like a bolt, it opens the upper mandible, which moves upon the skull at D. Here, then, is a piece of mechanism as distinct as the lock of a gun, which is for the purpose, as we have said, of giving rapidity to the motions of the bill. Is it nearer the truth to consider this as a new apparatus, suiting the necessities of the creature, or an accidental result of the introduction of a bone, which in its proper office has nothing to do with the jaw?

But we have wandered somewhat from our subject. We have taken the bones of the shoulder, or those of the extremity which are nearest to the trunk; we may pursue the inquiry by noticing those which are most remote from it. In the bones of the hand, we have seen that the same system was variously modified so as to be adapted to every possible change in office. But as it is insisted that the number of parts continue the same, what can we say to the bones of the paddle in the saurian and chelonian tribes, which, as in the ichthyosurus for example, consist of sixty or seventy polygonous bones; whilst in the horse there are only fifteen bones; and in man, twenty-seven. Yet, with all those bones in the paddle,[3] there is still the full complement in the part that corresponds with the arm. If the system fail us in such an obvious instance as this, with what confidence can we prosecute the intricate bones of the spine and head under its guidance?

Seeking assistance from the works of distinguished naturalists, we do not always find that disposition of mind prevail, which we should be apt to suppose a necessary result of their peculiar

[3] Bones of the paddle, or limb serving the purpose of a fin or flipper, in e.g., turtle, whale or ichthyosaurus. Saurian — lizard-like reptiles. Chelonian — turtles and tortoises. Ichthyosaurus — extinct marine reptiles. Polygonous bones — multifaceted bones.

studies. We do not discover that combination of genius with sound sense, which distinguished Cuvier,[4] and the great men of science. It is, above all, surprising with what perverse ingenuity men seek to obscure the conception of a Divine Author, an intelligent, designing, and benevolent Being — rather clinging to the greatest absurdities, or interposing the cold and inanimate influence of the mere elements, in a manner to extinguish all feeling of dependance in our minds, and all emotions of gratitude.

Some will maintain that all the varieties which we see, are the result of a change of circumstances influencing the original animal; or that new organs have been produced by a desire and consequent effort of the animal to stretch and mould itself — that, as the leaves of a plant expand to light, or turn to the sun, or as the roots shoot to the appropriate soil, so do the exterior organs of animals grow and adapt themselves. We shall presently find that an opinion has prevailed that the organization of animals determines their propensities; but the philosophers, of whom we are now speaking, imagine the contrary, — that under the influence of new circumstances, organs have accommodated themselves, and assumed their particular forms.

It must be here remarked that there are no instances of the production of new organs by the union of individuals belonging to different species. Nor is there any foundation in observation for the opinion that a new species may be formed by the union of individuals of different families. But it is contended, that, although the species of animals have not changed in the last 5000 years, we do not know what might have been the

[4] Georges Cuvier (1769–1832) — an important student of comparative anatomy and palaeontology.

effect of the revolution before that time; that is, previous to the present condition of the world. But, on subjects of this nature, we must argue from what we know, and from what we see.

We do perceive surprising changes in the conformation of animals; some of them are very familiar to us; but all show a foreknowledge and a prospective plan, an alteration gradually taking place in preparation for the condition, never consequent upon it. It will be sufficient for our purpose, if we take the highest and the lowest examples. Man has two conditions of existence in the body. Hardly two creatures can be less alike than an infant and a man. The whole fœtal state is a preparation for birth. My readers would not thank me, were I to show how necessary all the proportions and forms of the infant are to his being born alive, — and yet nothing is so easy to demonstrate. Every one may see that from the moment of birth there is a new impulse given to the growth, so as finally to adapt the proportions of the body to the state of perfect manhood. Few, however, are aware that the fœtus has a *life* adapted to its condition, and that if the confinement of the womb were protracted beyond the appointed time, it must die! — from no defect of nourishment, but simply, because the time is come for a change in its whole economy![5]

Now, during all the long period of gestation, the organs are forming; the lungs are perfected before the admission of air — new tubes are constructed before the flood-gates, which are to admit the blood, are opened. But there are finer, and more curious, provisions than these. If we take any of the grand organs, as the heart, or the brain, and examine it through all its

[5] Economy is here used in the sense of the "animal economy," or ordering of the whole structure and function of the organism.

gradations of change in the embryo state, we shall recognize it simple, at first, and gradually developing, and assuming the peculiarities which finally distinguish it. So that it is affirmed, and not without the support of a most curious series of observations, that the human brain, in its earlier stage, resembles that of a fish: as it is developed, it resembles more the cerebral mass of the reptile; in its increase, it is like that of a bird, and slowly, and only after birth, does it assume the proper form and consistence of the human encephalon.[6] But in all these changes to which man is subject, we nowhere see the influence of the elements, or any other cause than that it has been so predestined. And if, passing over the thousand instances which might be gathered from the intermediate parts of the chain of animal existence, we take the lowest link, and look to the metamorphosis of insects, the conclusion will be the same.

For example, if we examine the larva of a winged insect, we shall see the provisions for its motion over the ground, in that condition, all admirably supplied in the arrangement of its muscles, and the distribution of its nervous system. But if, anticipating its metamorphosis, we dissect the same larva immediately before the change, we shall find a new apparatus in progress towards perfection; the muscles of its many feet are seen decaying; the nerves to each muscle are wasting; a new arrangement of muscles, with new points of attachment, directed to the wings instead of the feet, is now visible; and a new distribution of nerves is distinctly to be traced, accommodated to the parts which are now to be put in motion. Here is no budding and stretching forth under the influence of the surrounding elements; but a change operated on all the econ-

6 Encephalon — anatomic term for the brain.

omy, and prospective, that is, in reference to a condition which the creature has not yet attained.

These facts countenance the conclusion drawn from the comparative anatomy of the hand and arm — that with each new instrument, visible externally, there are a thousand internal relations established: a mechanical contrivance in the bones and joints, which alters every part of the skeleton: an arrangement of muscles, in just correspondence: a texture of nervous filaments, which is laid intermediate between the instrument and the very centre of life and motion; and, finally, as we shall discover from what follows, new sources of activity must be created in relation to the new organ, otherwise the part will hang a useless appendage.

It must now be apparent that nothing less than the Power, which originally created, is equal to the effecting of these changes on animals, which are to adapt them to their conditions: that their organization is predetermined, and not consequent on the condition of the earth or the surrounding elements. Neither can a property in the animal itself account for the changes which take place in the individual, any more than for the varieties which take place in the species. Every thing declares the species to have its origin in a distinct creation, not in a gradual variation from some original type; and any other hypothesis than that of a new creation of animals suited to the successive changes in the inorganic matter of the globe — the condition of the water, atmosphere, and temperature — brings with it only an accumulation of difficulties.

CHARLES BABBAGE

Argument in Favor of Design*

Charles Babbage (1792–1871), mathematician and pioneer in the field of calculating machines, was educated at Trinity College, Cambridge. Together with John Herschel and several others, he founded in 1812 the Analytical Society, which had as its primary aim to introduce the new methods of the calculus from the Continent into England. He was elected a Fellow of the Royal Society in 1816, and was active in the founding of the Astronomical Society in 1820. While at the University, Babbage had begun to conceive that calculating machines might be used for computing numerical tables, and he improved upon existing machines for calculation by the invention of what he called the "method of differences." A small model was shown to the Astronomical Society, which awarded Babbage a gold medal, following which he applied for the support of the Royal Society and obtained a grant from the Civil Contingencies Fund, so as to be able to make a full-scale computing machine. This machine, which eventually cost about £17,000 of public funds plus £6000 of the author's own money, was never completed. A small portion is in existence and is on exhibition in London. In the meanwhile, Babbage had designed a new type of machine, making use of today's punched cards, in which he once again showed himself a prophet far ahead of his time. Among many technical treatises and popular works, the *Ninth Bridgewater Treatise* (1837, second edition 1838) is one of the most fascinating to read today, even though it was never fully completed by the author, and was an extra volume not called for in the original series. It has been described as "one of the earliest attempts to reconcile breaches of continuity with the government of the universe by law," and it is notable for the attempt to show how mathematics may be used to bolster religious belief. As to whether the following presentation of miracles (used with singular effectiveness by Chalmers) is satisfying or not, each reader must decide for himself.

* From *The Ninth Bridgewater Treatise: A Fragment* (1838).

ARGUMENT IN FAVOUR OF DESIGN FROM THE CHANGING OF LAWS IN NATURAL EVENTS.

THE estimate we form of the intellectual capacity of our race, is founded on an examination of those productions which have resulted from the loftiest flights of individual genius, or from the accumulated labours of generations of men, by whose long-continued exertions a body of science has been raised up, surpassing in its extent the creative powers of any individual, and demanding for its development a length of time, to which no single life extends.

The estimate we form of the Creator of the visible world rests ultimately on the same foundation. Conscious that we each of us employ, in our own productions, *means* intended to accomplish the objects at which we aim, and tracing throughout the actions and inventions of our fellow-creatures the same intention, — judging also of their capacity by the fit selection they make of the means by which they work, we are irresistibly led, when we contemplate the natural world, to attempt to trace each existing fact presented to our senses to some pre-contrived arrangement, itself perhaps the consequence of a yet more general law; and where the most powerful aids by which we can assist our limited faculties fail in enabling us to detect such connexions, we still, and not the less, believe that a more extended inquiry, or higher powers, would enable us to discover them.

The greater the number of consequences resulting from any law, and the more they are foreseen, the greater the knowledge and intelligence we ascribe to the being by which it was ordained. In the earlier stages of our knowledge, we behold a multitude of distinct laws, all harmonizing to produce results which we deem beneficial to our own species: as science advances, many of these minor laws are found to merge into some more general principles; and with its higher progress these secondary principles appear, in their turn, the mere consequences of some still more general law. Such has been the case in two of the most curious and most elaborately cultivated branches of human knowledge, the sciences of astronomy and optics. All analogy leads us to infer, and new discoveries continually direct our expectation to the idea, that the most extensive laws to which we have hitherto attained, converge to some few simple and general principles, by which the whole of the material universe is sustained, and from which its infinitely varied phenomena emerge as the necessary consequences.

To illustrate the distinction between a system to which the restoring hand of its contriver is applied, either frequently or at distant intervals, and one which had received at its first formation the impress of the will of its author, foreseeing the varied but yet necessary laws of its action throughout the whole of its existence, we must have recourse to some machine, the produce of human skill. But far as all such engines[1] must ever be placed at an immeasurable interval below the simplest of Nature's works, yet, from the vastness of those cycles which even human contrivance in some cases unfolds to our view, we may perhaps be enabled to form a faint estimate of the magnitude of that lowest step in the chain of reasoning, which leads us up to Nature's God.

The illustration which I shall here employ will be derived

---

[1] The word "engine" is used in that older special sense where modern usage would demand "machine."

from the results afforded by the Calculating Engine;[2] and this I am the more disposed to use, because my own views respecting the extent of the laws of Nature were greatly enlarged by considering it, and also because it incidentally presents matter for reflection on the subject of inductive reasoning. Nor will any difficulty arise from the complexity of that engine; no knowledge of its mechanism, nor any acquaintance with mathematical science, are necessary for comprehending the illustration; it being sufficient merely to conceive that computations of great complexity *can* be effected by mechanical means.

Let the reader imagine that such an engine has been adjusted; that it is moved by a weight; and that he sits down before it, and observes a wheel, which moves through a small angle round its axis, at short intervals, presenting to his eye, successively, a series of numbers engraved on its divided circumference.

Let the figures thus seen be the series of natural numbers,[3] 1, 2, 3, 4, 5, &c., each of which exceeds its immediate antecedent by unity.

Now, reader, let me ask how long you will have counted before you are firmly convinced that the engine, supposing its adjustments to remain unaltered, will continue whilst its motion is maintained, to produce the same series of natural numbers? Some minds perhaps are so constituted, that after passing the first hundred terms, they will be satisfied that they are acquainted with the law. After seeing five hundred terms, few will doubt; and after the fifty-thousandth term the propen-

[2] Babbage appended an account of his engine, or "calculating machine," which is reprinted at the end of this selection.
[3] The "natural numbers" are the positive integers.

sity to believe that the succeeding term will be fifty thousand and one, will be almost irresistible. That term *will* be fifty thousand and one: the same regular succession will continue; the five-millionth and the fifty-millionth term will still appear in their expected order; and one unbroken chain of natural numbers will pass before your eyes, from *one* up to *one hundred million*.

True to the vast induction which has thus been made, the next succeeding term will be one hundred million and one; but after that the next number presented by the rim of the wheel, instead of being one hundred million and two, is one hundred million *ten thousand* and two. The whole series from the commencement being thus: —

1

2

3

4

5

. . .

. . .

. . . . . .

. . . . . .

99,999,999

100,000,000

regularly as far as   100,000,001

100,010,002   : — the law changes

100,030,003

100,060,004

100,100,005

100,150,006

100,210,007

$$100{,}280{,}008$$
$$100{,}360{,}009$$
$$100{,}450{,}010$$
$$100{,}550{,}011$$

. . . .

. . . .

The law which *seemed* at first to govern this series fails at the hundred million and second term. That term is larger than we expected, by 10,000. The next term is larger than was anticipated, by 30,000, and the excess of each term above what we had expected forms the following table: —

$$10{,}000$$
$$30{,}000$$
$$60{,}000$$
$$100{,}000$$
$$150{,}000$$

. . . . . .

. . . . . .

being, in fact, the series of *triangular numbers,*[4] each multiplied by 10,000.

---

4 In order to explain what he meant by "triangular numbers," Babbage introduced at this point a note as follows:

The numbers 1, 3, 6, 10, 15, 21, 28, &c. are formed by adding the successive terms of the series of natural numbers thus;

$$1=1$$
$$1+2=3$$
$$1+2+3=6$$
$$1+2+3+4=10, \&c.$$

They are called triangular numbers, because a number of points corresponding to any term can always be placed in the form of a triangle, for instance: —

    1   3   6   10

If we still continue to observe the numbers presented by the wheel, we shall find, that for a hundred, or even for a thousand terms, they continue to follow the new law relating to the triangular numbers; but after watching them for 2761 terms, we find that *this* law fails in the case of the 2762d term.

If we continue to observe, we shall discover another law then coming into action, which also is dependent, but in a different manner, on triangular numbers. This will continue through about 1430 terms, when a new law is again introduced, which extends over about 950 terms; and this too, like all its predecessors, fails, and gives place to other laws, which appear at different intervals.

Now it must be remarked, that the law *that each number presented by the Engine is greater by unity than the preceding number,* which law the observer had deduced from *an induction of a hundred million instances,* was not the true law that regulated its action; and that the occurrence of the number 100,010,002 at the 100,000,002d term, was *as necessary a consequence* of the original adjustment, and might have been as fully foreknown at the commencement, as was the regular succession of any one of the intermediate numbers to its immediate antecedent. The same remark applies to the next *apparent* deviation from the new law, which was founded on an induction of 2761 terms, and to all the succeeding laws; with this limitation only — that whilst their consecutive introduction at various definite intervals is a necessary consequence of the mechanical structure of the engine, our knowledge of analysis does not yet enable us to predict the periods at which the more distant laws will be introduced.

Such are some of the facts which, by a certain adjustment

of the Calculating Engine, would be presented to the observer. Now, let him imagine another engine, offering to the eye precisely the same figures in the same order of succession; but let it be necessary for the maker of that other engine, previously to each apparent change in the law, to make some new adjustment in the structure of the engine itself, in order to accomplish the ends proposed. The first engine must be susceptible of having embodied in its mechanical structure, that more general law of which all the observed laws were but isolated portions, — a law so complicated, that analysis itself, in its present state, can scarcely grasp the whole question. The second engine might be of far simpler contrivance; it must be capable of receiving the laws impressed upon it from without, but is incapable, by its own intrinsic structure, of changing, at definite periods, and in unlimited succession, those laws by which it acts. Which of these two engines would, in the reader's opinion, give the higher proof of skill in the contriver? He cannot for a moment hesitate in pronouncing that that for which, after its original adjustment, no superintendence is required, displays far greater ingenuity than that which demands, at every change in its law, the direct intervention of its contriver.

The engine we have been considering is but a very small portion (about fifteen figures) of a much larger one, which was preparing, and is partly executed; it was intended, when completed, that it should have presented at once to the eye about one hundred and thirty figures. In that more extended form which recent simplifications have enabled me to give to machinery constructed for the purpose of making calculations, it will be possible, by certain adjustments, to set the engine so that it shall produce the series of natural numbers in regular order, from unity up to a number expressed by more than a thousand places of figures. At the end of that term, another and a different law shall regulate the succeeding terms; this law shall continue in operation perhaps for a number of terms, expressed perhaps by unity, followed by a thousand zeros, or 10^{1000}; at which period a third law shall be introduced, and, like its predecessors, govern the figures produced by the engine during a third of those enormous periods. This change of laws might continue without limit; each individual law being destined to govern for millions of ages the calculations of the engine, and then give way to its successor to pursue a like career.[5]

Thus a series of laws, each simple in itself, successively spring into existence, at distances almost too great for human conception. The full expression of that wider law, which comprehends within it this unlimited sequence of minor consequences, may indeed be beyond the utmost reach of mathematical analysis: but of one remarkable fact, however, we are certain — that the mechanism brought into action for the purpose of changing the nature of the calculation from the production of the merest elementary operations into those highly complicated ones of which we speak, is itself of the simplest kind.

In contemplating the operations of laws so uniform during such immense periods, and then changing so completely their apparent nature, whilst the alterations are in fact only the

---

[5] At this point Babbage added the following comment:
"It has been supposed that ten turns of the handle of the calculating engine might be made in a minute, or about five hundred and twenty six millions in a century. As in this case, each turn would make a calculation, after the lapse of a million of centuries, only the fifteenth place of figures would have been reached."

necessary consequences of some far higher law, we can scarcely avoid remarking the analogy which they bear to several of the phenomena of nature.

The laws of animal life which regulate the caterpillar, seem totally distinct from those which, in the subsequent stage of its existence, govern the butterfly. The difference is still more remarkable in the transformations undergone by that class of animals which spend the first portion of their life beneath the surface of the waters, and the latter part as inhabitants of air. It is true that the periods during which these laws continue to act are not, to our senses, enormous, like the mechanical ones above mentioned; but it cannot be doubted that, immeasurably more complex as they are, they were equally foreknown by their Author: and that the first creation of the egg of the moth, or the libellula, involved within its contrivance, as a necessary consequence, the whole of the subsequent transformations of every individual of their respective races.

In turning our views from these simple results of the juxta-position of a few wheels, it is impossible not to perceive the parallel reasoning, which may be applied to the mighty and far more complex phenomena of nature. To call into existence all the variety of vegetable forms, as they become fitted to exist, by the successive adaptations of their parent earth, is undoubtedly a high exertion of creative power. When a rich vegetation has covered the globe, to create animals adapted to that clothing, which, deriving nourishment from its luxuriance, shall gladden the face of nature, is not only a high but a benevolent exertion of creative power. To change, from time to time, after lengthened periods, the races which exist, as altered physical circumstances may render their abode more or less congenial to their habits, by allowing the natural extinction of some races, and supplying by a new creation others more fitted to occupy the place previously abandoned, is still but the exercise of the same benevolent power. To cause an alteration in those physical circumstances, — to add to the comforts of the newly-created animals, — all these acts imply power of the same order, a perpetual and benevolent superintendence, to take advantage of altered circumstances, for the purpose of producing additional happiness.

But, to have *foreseen,* at the creation of matter and of mind, that a period would arrive when matter, assuming its prearranged combinations, would become susceptible of the support of vegetable forms; that these should in due time themselves supply the pabulum of animal existence; that successive races of giant forms or of microscopic beings should at appointed periods necessarily rise into existence, and as inevitably yield to decay; and that decay and death — the lot of each individual existence — should also act with equal power on the races which they constitute; that the extinction of every race should be as certain as the death of each individual, and the advent of new genera be as inevitable as the destruction of their predecessors; — to have foreseen all these changes, and to have provided, by one comprehensive law, for all that should ever occur, either to the races themselves, to the individuals of which they are composed, or to the globe which they inhabit, manifests a degree of power and of knowledge of a far higher order.

The vast cycles in the geological changes that have taken place in the earth's surface, of which we have ample evidence, offer another analogy in nature to those mechanical changes of law from which we have endeavoured to extract a *unit* sufficiently large to serve as an imperfect measure for some of the simplest works of the Creator.

The gradual advance of Geology, during the last twenty years, to the dignity of a science, has arisen from the laborious and extensive collection of facts, and from the enlightened spirit in which the inductions founded on those facts have been deduced and discussed. To those who are unacquainted with this science, or indeed to any person not deeply versed in the history of this and kindred subjects, it is impossible to convey a just impression of the nature of that evidence by which a multitude of its conclusions are supported: — evidence in many cases so irresistible, that the records of the past ages, to which it refers, are traced in language more imperishable than that of the historian of any human transactions; the relics of those beings, entombed in the strata which myriads of centuries have heaped upon their graves, giving a present evidence of their past existence, with which no human testimony can compete.

It is found that each additional step, in the grouping together of the facts of geology, confirms the view that the changes of our planet, since it has been the abode of man, is but as a page in the massive volumes of its history, every leaf of which, written in the same character, conveys to the decypherer the idea of a succession of the same causes acting with varying intensity, through unequal but enormous periods, each period apparently distinguished by the coming in or going out of new subsidiary laws, yet all submitted to some still higher condition, which has stamped the mark of unity on the series, and points to the conclusion that the minutest changes, as well as those transitions apparently the most abrupt, have been throughout all time the necessary, the inevitable consequences of some more comprehensive law impressed on matter at the dawn of its existence.

* * * *

If all the combinations and modifications of matter can be supposed to be traced up to one general and comprehensive law, from which every visible form, both in the organic and inorganic world flows, as the necessary consequence of the first impression of that law upon matter, it might seem to follow that Fate or Necessity governs all things, and that the world around us may not be the result of a contriving mind working for a benevolent purpose.

Such, possibly, may be the first impression of this view of the subject; but it is an erroneous view, — one of those, perhaps, through which it is necessary to pass, in order to arrive at truth. Let us, in order to obtain more correct views upon this point, briefly review the labour which the human race has expended, in attaining the limited knowledge we possess. For about six thousand years man has claimed the earth as his heritage, and asserted his dominion over all other beings endued with life; yet, during a large portion of that period, how small comparatively has been his mental improvement! Until the invention of printing, the mass of mankind were in many respects almost the creatures of instinct. It is true, the knowledge possessed by each generation, instead of being the gift of Nature, was derived from the instruction of their predecessors; but, how little were those lessons improved by repeated communication! Transmitted most frequently by unenlightened instructors, they might lose, but could rarely gain in value.

Before the invention of printing, accidental position determined the opinions and the knowledge of the great mass of mankind. Oral information being almost the only kind accessible, each man shared the opinions of his kindred and neighbours; and truth, which is ever most quickly and most surely elicited by discussion, lost all those advantages which diversity of opinion always produces for it. The minds of individual men, however powerful, could address themselves only to a very small portion of their fellow men; their influence was limited by space and restricted by time; their highest powers were not stimulated into action by the knowledge that their reasonings could have effect where their voices were unheard, by the conviction that the truths which they arrived at, and the discoveries they made, would extend beyond their country and survive their age.

But, since the invention of printing, how different has been the position of mankind! the nature of the instruction no longer depends entirely on the knowledge of the personal instructor. The village schoolmaster communicates to his pupils the power of using an instrument by which not merely the best of their living countrymen, but the greatest and wisest men of all countries and all times, may become their instructors. Even the elementary writings through which this art is taught, give to the pupil, not the sentiments of the teacher, but those which the public opinion of his countrymen esteems most fit for the beginner in knowledge. Thus the united opinions of multitudes of human minds are brought to bear even upon seemingly unimportant points.

If such is the effect of the invention of printing upon ordinary minds, its influence over those more highly endowed is far greater. To them the discussion of the conflicting opinions of different countries and distant ages, and the establishment of new truths, present a field of boundless and exalted ambition.

Advancing beyond the knowledge of their neighbours and countrymen, they may be exposed to those prejudices which result from opinions long stationary; but encouraged by the approbation of the greatest of other nations, and the more enlightened of their own, — knowing that time alone is wanting to complete the triumph of truth, they may accelerate the approaching dawn of that day which shall pour a flood of light over the darkened intellects of their thankless countrymen — content themselves to exchange the hatred they experience from the honest and the dishonest intolerance of their contemporaries, for the higher homage, alike independent of space and of time, which their memory will for ever receive from the good and the gifted of all countries and all after ages.

Until printing was very generally spread, civilisation scarcely advanced by slow and languid steps; since this art has become cheap, its advances have been unparalleled, and its rate of progress vastly accelerated.

It has been stated that the civilisation of the Western World has resulted from its being the seat of the Christian religion: but however much the mild tenor of its doctrines is calculated to assist in producing such an effect, that religion cannot but be injured by an unfounded statement. It is to the easy and cheap methods of communicating thought from man to man, which enable a country to sift, as it were, its whole people, and to produce, in its science, its literature, and its arts, not the brightest efforts of a limited class, but the highest exertions of the most powerful minds among a whole community; — it is this which has given birth to the wide-spreading civilisation of the present day, and which promises a futurity yet more prolific. Whoever is acquainted with the present state of science and the mechanical arts, and looks back over the inventions and civilisation which the fourteen centuries subsequent to the introduction of Christianity have produced, and compares them with the advances made during the succeeding four centuries following the invention of printing, will have no doubt as to the effective cause.

It is during these last three or four centuries, that man, considered as a species, has commenced the development of his intellectual faculties — that he has emerged from a position in which he was almost the creature of instinct, to a state in which every step in advance facilitates the progress of his successors. During the first period, arts were discovered by individuals, and lost to the race; in the latter, the diffusion of thought has enabled the reasoning of one class to unite with the observations of another, and the most advanced point of one generation to become the starting post of the next.

It is during this portion of our history that man has become acquainted with his real position in the universe — that he has measured the distance from that which is to us the great fountain of light and heat — that he has traced the orbits of earth's sister spheres, and calculated the paths of all their dependent worlds — that he has arrived at the knowledge of a law which appears to govern all matter, and whose remotest consequences, if first traced by his telescope, are found to have been written in his theory; or, if first predicted by his theory, are verified by his observations.

Simple as the law of gravity now appears, and beautifully in accordance with all the observations of past and of present times, consider what it has cost of intellectual study. Copernicus, Galileo, Kepler, Euler, Lagrange, Laplace,[6] all the great names which have exalted the character of man, by carrying out trains of reasoning unparalleled in every other science; these, and a host of others, each of whom might have been the Newton of another field, have all laboured to work out, the consequences which resulted from that single law which *he* discovered. All that the human mind has produced — the brightest in genius, the most persevering in application, has been lavished on the details of the law of gravity.

Had that law been other than it is — had it been, for example, the inverse cube of the distance, it would still have required an equal expense of genius and of labour to have worked out its details. But, between the laws represented by the inverse square,[7] and the inverse cube of the distance, there are interposed an infinite number of other laws, each of which might have been the basis of a system requiring the most extensive knowledge to trace out its consequences. Again, between

6 Here Babbage lists the names of six astronomers worthy of being coupled with Newton: Nicolaus Copernicus, who in 1543 proposed a sun-centered system of the world to replace the traditional earth-centered view; Galileo Galilei, who first used the telescope to show that the planets resemble the earth so that the Copernican system was a reasonable one, and whose studies of force and motion paved the way for the work of Isaac Newton; Johannes Kepler, who discovered the laws of planetary motion; Leonhard Euler, who gave the science of dynamics its modern form; Joseph Louis Lagrange, who established dynamics on an analytic basis, divorcing it from geometry; and finally, Pierre Simon de Laplace, astronomer and mathematician, who explained the stability of the solar system and set forth the famous nebular hypothesis about the formation of the solar system.

7 The law of the "inverse square" states that the force decreases according to the square of the distance. Thus at twice a given distance, the force is not one half, but one quarter; and at three times a given distance the force is not one third but one ninth. Similarly the law of the "inverse cube" means that the force decreases inversely as the cube of the distance. In this case at twice a given distance, the force would be one eighth, and at three times a given distance, the force would be one twenty-seventh.

every law which can be expressed by whole numbers, whether it be direct or inverse, an infinity of others can still be interposed. All these might be combined by two, by three, or in any other groups, and new systems might be imagined,[8] submitted to such combinations. Thus, another infinity of laws, of a far higher order — in fact, of an *infinitely* higher order — might again be added to the list. And this might still be increased by all the other combinations, of which such laws admit, besides that by addition, to which we have already alluded, thus forming an infinity itself of so high an order, that it is difficult to conceive. Man has, as yet, no proof of the impossibility of the existence of any of these laws. Each might, for any reason we can assign, be the basis of a creation different from our own.

It is at this point that skill and knowledge re-enter the argument, and banish for ever the dominion of chance. The Being who called into existence this creation, of which we are parts, must have *chosen* the present form, the present laws, in preference to the infinitely infinite variety which he might have willed into existence. He must have known and foreseen all, even the remotest consequences of *every one* of those laws, to have penetrated but a little way into *one* of which has *exhausted* the intellect of our whole species.

If such is the view we must take of the knowledge of the Creator, when contemplating the laws of inanimate matter — laws into whose consequences it has cost us such accumulated labour to penetrate — what language can we speak, when we consider that the laws which connect matter with animal life

---

8 At this point Babbage added the following note:
"Even beyond this, every law so imagined might be made to agree, for any period, with laws of simpler form, and yet deviate, in one single, or in a certain limited number of cases, and then agree with it for ever."

may be as infinitely varied as those which regulate material existence? The little we know, might, perhaps, lead us to infer a far more unlimited field of choice. The chemist has reduced all the materials of the earth with which we are acquainted, to about fifty simple bodies;[9] but the zoologist can make no such reductions in his science. He claims for one scarcely noticed class — that of intestinal parasites — about thirty thousand species; and, not to mention the larger classes of animals, who shall number the species of infusoria in living waters, still less those which are extinct, and whose scarcely visible relics are contained within the earth, in almost mountain masses.

In absolute ignorance of any — even the smallest link of those chains which bind life to matter, or that still more miraculous one, which connects mind with both, we can pursue our path only by the feeble light of analogy, and humbly hope that the Being, whose power and benevolence are unbounded, may enable us, in some further stage of our existence, to read another page in the history of his mighty works.

Enough, however, and more than enough, may be gathered even from our imperfect acquaintance with matter, and some few of its laws, to prove the unbounded knowledge which must have preceded their organization.

* * * *

In the present chapter it is proposed to prove, that —

It is more probable that any law, at the knowledge of which we have arrived by observation, shall be subject to one of those

9 "Simple bodies" are chemical elements.

violations which, according to Hume's definition,[10] *constitutes a miracle, than that it should not be so subjected.*

To show this, we may be allowed again to revert to the Calculating Engine: and to assume that it is possible to set the machine, so that it shall calculate *any algebraic law whatsoever:* and also possible so to arrange it, that at any periods, *however remote,* the first law shall be interrupted for one or more times, and be superseded by *any other law;* after which the original law shall again be produced, and no other deviation shall ever take place.

Now, as all laws, which appear to us regular and uniform in their course, and to be subject to no exception, can be calculated by the engine: and as each of these laws may also be calculated by the same machine, subject to any assigned interruption, at distinct and definite periods; each simple law may be interrupted at any point by the temporary action of a portion of any one of all the other simple laws: it follows, that *the class of laws subject to interruption is far more extensive than that of laws which are uninterrupted.* It is, in fact, infinitely more numerous. Therefore, the probability of any law with which we have become acquainted by observation being part of a much more extensive law, and of its having, to use mathe-

10 In two separate passages the Scottish philosopher David Hume defined a miracle as follows: "A miracle is a violation of the laws of nature; and as a firm and unalterable experience has established these laws, the proof against a miracle, from the very nature of the fact, is as entire as any argument from experience can possibly be imagined." And again: "A miracle may be accurately defined, *a transgression of a law of nature by a particular volition of the Deity, or by the interposition of some invisible agent.* A miracle may either be discovered by men or not." See "Of Miracles," section 10 of *An Inquiry Concerning Human Understanding,* in *Philosophical Works* (Edinburgh: Black and Tait, 1826), IV, 133; 134, note x.

matical language, singular points or discontinuous functions contained within it, is very large.

Perhaps it may be objected, that the laws calculated by such an engine as I have referred to are not laws of nature; and that any deviation from laws produced by human mechanism does not come within Hume's definition of miracles. To this it may be answered, that a law of nature has been defined by Hume to rest upon experience, or repeated observation, just as the truth of testimony does. Now, the law produced by the engine may be arrived at by precisely the same means — namely, repeated observation.

It may, however, be desirable to explain further the nature of the evidence, on which the fact, that the engine possesses those powers, rests.

When the Calculating Engine has been set to compute the successive terms of any given law, which the observer is told will have an apparent exception (at, for example, the ten million and twenty-third term,) the observer is directed to note down the commencement of its computations; and, by comparing these results with his own independent calculations of the same law, he may verify the accuracy of the engine as far as he chooses. It may then be demonstrated to him, by the very structure of the machine, that if its motion were continued, it would, *necessarily,* at the end of a very long time, arrive at the ten-millionth term of the law assigned to it; and that, by an equal *necessity,* it would have passed through all the intermediate terms. The inquirer is now desired to turn on the wheels with his own hand, until they are precisely in the same situation as they would have been had the engine itself gone on continuously, to the ten-millionth term. The machine is again put in motion, and the observer again finds that each successive term it calculates fulfils the original law. But, after passing twenty-two terms, he now observes *one* term which does not fulfil the original law, but which does coincide with the predicted exception.

The continued movement now again produces terms according with the first law, and the observer may continue to verify them as long as he wishes. It may then be demonstrated to him, by the very structure of the machine, that, if its motion were continued, it would be *impossible* that any other deviation from the apparent law could ever occur at any future time.

Such is the evidence to the observer; and, if the superintendent of the engine were, at his request, to make it calculate a great variety of different laws, each interrupted by special and remote exceptions, he would have ample ground to believe in the assertion of its director, that he could so arrange the engine that any law, however complicated, might be calculated to any assigned extent, and then there should arise one apparent exception; after which the original law should continue uninterrupted for ever.

Let us now consider the miracle alluded to by Hume — the restoration of a dead man to life.[11] According to the definition of that author, our belief that such a fact is contrary to the laws of nature, arises from our uniform experience against it. Our personal experience is small: we must therefore have recourse to testimony; and from that we learn, that the dead are *never* restored to life; and, consequently, we have the uniform experience of all mankind since the creation, against one assigned instance of a dead man being so restored. Let us now find the

[11] The reference seems to be to the raising of Lazarus from the dead.

numerical amount of this evidence. Assuming the origin of the human race to have been about six thousand years ago, and taking thirty years as the duration of a generation, we have —

$$\frac{6000}{30} = 200 \text{ generations.}$$

And allowing that the average population of the earth has been a thousand millions, we find that there have been born and have died since the creation,

$$200 \times 1,000,000,000$$
$$= 200,000,000,000 \text{ individuals.}$$

Such, then, according to Hume, are the odds against the truth of the miracle: that is to say, it is found from experience, that it is about two hundred thousand millions to one against a dead man having been restored to life.

Let us now compare this with a parallel case in the calculations of the engine; let us suppose the number above stated to be a hundred million times as great, or that the truth of the miracles is opposed by a number of instances, expressed by twenty places of figures.

The engine may be set to count the natural numbers — 1, 2, 3, 4, &c.; and it shall continue to fulfil that law, not merely for the number of times just mentioned, for that number is quite insignificant among the vast periods it involves; but the natural numbers shall follow in continual succession, until they have reached an amount which requires for its expression above a hundred million places of figures. If every letter in the volume now before the reader's eyes were changed into a figure, and if all the figures contained in a thousand such volumes were arranged in order, the whole together would yet fall far short of the vast induction the observer would then have had in favour of the truth of the law of natural numbers. The widest range of all the cycles of astronomy and geology combined, sink into insignificance before such a period. Yet, shall the engine, true to the prediction of its director, after the lapse of myriads of ages, fulfil its task, and give that one, the *first* and *only* exception to that time-sanctioned law. What would have been the chances against the appearance of the excepted case, immediately prior to its occurrence? It would have had, according to Hume, the evidence of all experience against it, with a force myriads of times more strong than that against any miracle.

Now, let the reader, who has fully entered into the nature of the argument, ask himself this question: — Does he believe that such an engine has really been contrived, and what reasonable grounds has he for that belief?

The testimony of any single witness is small against such odds; besides, the witness may deceive himself. Whether he speaks truly, will be estimated by his moral character — whether he deceives himself, will be estimated by his intellectual character. The probability that such an engine has been contrived, will, however, receive great addition, when it is remarked, that mathematical — and, especially, geometrical evidence is, of all others, that in which the fewest mistakes arise, and in which they are most readily discovered; and when it is added, that the fact of the invention of such an engine rests on precisely the same species of evidence as the propositions of Euclid, and may be deduced from the drawings with all the force of demonstration. Whether such an engine could be actually made in the present state of mechanical art, is a question of quite a different order: it must rest upon the opinions of those who have had extensive experience in that art. The author has not the slightest hesitation in stating his opinion to be, that it is fully within those limits.

This, however, is a question foreign to the nature of the argument, which might have been stated in a more abstract manner, without any reference to such an engine. As, however, the argument really arose from that machine, and as visible forms make a much deeper impression on the mind than any abstract reasonings, it has been stated in conjunction with that subject.

NOTE ON THE CALCULATING ENGINE.

The nature of the arguments advanced in this volume having obliged me to refer, more frequently than I should have chosen, to the Calculating Engine, it becomes necessary to give the reader some brief account of its progress and present state.

About the year 1821, I undertook to superintend, for the Government, the construction of an engine for calculating and printing mathematical and astronomical tables. Early in the year 1833, a small portion of the machine was put together, and was found to perform its work with all the precision which had been anticipated. At that period circumstances, which I could not control, caused what I then considered a temporary suspension of its progress; and the Government, on whose decision the continuance or discontinuance of the work depended, have not yet communicated to me their wishes on the question. The first illustration . . . I have employed is derived from the calculations made by this engine.

About October, 1834, I commenced the design of another, and far more powerful engine. Many of the contrivances necessary for its performance have since been discussed and drawn according to various principles; and all of them have been invented in more than one form. I consider them, even in their present state, as susceptible of practical execution; but time, thought, and expense, will probably improve them. As the remaining illustrations are all drawn from the powers of this new engine, it may be right to state, that it will calculate the numerical value of any algebraical function — that, at any period previously fixed upon, or contingent on certain events, it will cease to tabulate that algebraic function, and commence the calculation of a different one, and that these changes may be repeated to any extent.

The former engine could employ about 120 figures in its calculations; the present machine is intended to compute with about 4,000.

Here I should willingly have left the subject; but the public having erroneously imagined, that the sums of money paid to the workmen for the construction of the engine, were the remuneration of my own services, for inventing and directing its progress; and a Committee of the House of Commons having incidentally led the public to believe that a sum of money was voted to me for that purpose, — I think it right to give to that report the most direct and unequivocal contradiction.

II

Astronomy

THOMAS CHALMERS

The Christian Revelation Viewed in Connexion with the Modern Astronomy*

Thomas Chalmers (1780–1847) was educated at St. Andrews, where he developed a love of science and divinity, becoming Minister of Kilmeny in Fife while giving courses of lectures on chemistry at St. Andrews. Before he was twenty-five he was proposed both for the chair of natural philosophy or physics at St. Andrews and for that of mathematics at Edinburgh. In his thirties Chalmers became more and more evangelical, and his fame caused him to be nominated minister of the Tron parish of Glasgow. There he delivered on weekdays two famous sets of discourses, one astronomical and the other commercial. The latter were designed to introduce the spirit of the gospel into the lives of businessmen, while the former sought to achieve a harmony of science and Christianity chiefly through the device of displaying the insignificance of the earth in the whole frame of the universe. Chalmers became professor of moral philosophy at St. Andrews, and then was appointed to the chair of theology at Edinburgh. Eventually, he left the Established Church and became the first Moderator of the Free Protesting Church of Scotland. A prolific author, all of his writings are characterized by a vigorous style. The following selections are taken from Chalmers's Glasgow discourse on Christianity and astronomy.

W E HAVE something more than the mere magnitude of the planets to allege, in favour of the idea that they are inhabited. — We know that this earth turns round upon itself; and we observe that all those celestial bodies, which are acces-

* From *A Series of Discourses on the Christian Revelation, Viewed in Connexion with the Modern Astronomy* (1817).

sible to such an observation, have the same movement. We know that the earth performs a yearly revolution round the sun; and we can detect in all the planets which compose our system, a revolution of the same kind, and under the same circumstances. They have the same succession of day and night. They have the same agreeable vicissitude of the seasons. To them, light and darkness succeed each other; and the gaiety of summer is followed by the dreariness of winter. To each of them the heavens present as varied and magnificent a spectacle; and this earth, the encompassing of which would require the labour of years from one of its puny inhabitants, is but one of the lesser lights which sparkle in their firmament. To them, as well as to us, has God divided the light from the darkness, and he has called the light day, and the darkness he has called night. He has said, let there be lights in the firmament of their heaven, to divide the day from the night; and let them be for signs, and for seasons, and for days, and for years; and let them be for lights in the firmament of heaven, to give lights upon their earth; and it was so. And God has also made to them great lights. To all of them he has given the sun to rule the day; and to many of them has he given moons to rule the night. To them he has made the stars also. And God has set them in the firmament of heaven, to give light unto their earth; and to rule over the day, and over the night, and to divide the light from the darkness; and God has seen that it was good.

In all these greater arrangements of divine wisdom, we can see that God has done the same things for the accommodation of the planets that he has done for the earth which we inhabit. And shall we say, that the resemblance stops here, because we are not in a situation to observe it? Shall we say, that this scene of magnificence has been called into being merely for the amusement of a few astronomers? Shall we measure the counsels of heaven by the narrow impotence of the human faculties? or conceive, that silence and solitude reign throughout the mighty empire of nature; that the greater part of creation is an empty parade; and that not a worshipper of the Divinity is to be found through the wide extent of yon vast and immeasurable regions?

It lends a delightful confirmation to the argument, when, from the growing perfection of our instruments, we can discover a new point of resemblance between our earth and the other bodies of the planetary system.[1] It is now ascertained, not merely that all of them have their day and night, and that all of them have their vicissitudes of seasons, and that some of them have their moons to rule their night and alleviate the darkness of it. We can see of one, that its surface rises into inequalities, that it swells into mountains and stretches into valleys; of another, that it is surrounded by an atmosphere which may support the respiration of animals; of a third, that clouds are formed and suspended over it, which may minister to it all the bloom and luxuriance of vegetation; and of a fourth, that

[1] It was one of the achievements of Galileo and his successors, using the newly invented astronomical telescope, to find similarities among the earth, moon, and the planets. (This point is discussed in the selection from Herschel below; see footnote 3 on page 107). Chalmers draws attention to discoveries concerning the surfaces of the planets made possible by the improvement of telescopes. Thus it was discovered that there were systems of moons around Mars, Jupiter, and Saturn, while surface studies of these planets revealed further similarities with the earth. The bands or belts across Jupiter were interpreted as evidence that the planet is enveloped in dense masses of cloud. A polar cap was seen to form during the winter season on Mars. It was suspected that an atmosphere existed on Saturn and that Venus showed mountains, but this result was strongly doubted, and became the subject of debate in the *Philosophical Transactions*, the official publication of the Royal Society in the 1790's.

a white colour spreads over its northern regions, as its winter advances, and that on the approach of summer this whiteness is dissipated — giving room to suppose, that the element of water abounds in it, that it rises by evaporation into its atmosphere, that it freezes upon the application of cold, that it is precipitated in the form of snow, that it covers the ground with a fleecy mantle, which melts away from the heat of a more vertical sun; and that other worlds bear a resemblance to our own, in the same yearly round of beneficent and interesting changes.

Who shall assign a limit to the discoveries of future ages? Who can prescribe to science her boundaries, or restrain the active and insatiable curiosity of man within the circle of his present acquirements? We may guess with plausibility what we cannot anticipate with confidence. The day may yet be coming, when our instruments of observation shall be inconceivably more powerful. They may ascertain still more decisive points of resemblance. They may resolve the same question by the evidence of sense which is now so abundantly convincing by the evidence of analogy. They may lay open to us the unquestionable vestiges of art, and industry, and intelligence. We may see summer throwing its green mantle over these mighty tracts, and we may see them left naked and colourless after the flush of vegetation has disappeared. In the progress of years, or of centuries, we may trace the hand of cultivation spreading a new aspect over some portion of a planetary surface. Perhaps some large city, the metropolis of a mighty empire, may expand into a visible spot by the powers of some future telescope. Perhaps the glass of some observer, in a distant age, may enable him to construct the map of another world, and lay down the surface of it in all its minute and topical varieties. But there is no end of conjecture, and to the men of other times we leave the full assurance of what we can assert with the highest probability, that yon planetary orbs are so many worlds, that they teem with life, and that the mighty Being who presides in high authority over this scene of grandeur and astonishment, has there planted the worshippers of his glory.

Did the discoveries of science stop here, we have enough to justify the exclamation of the Psalmist, "What is man that thou art mindful of him, or the son of man that thou shouldest deign to visit him?"[2] They widen the empire of creation far beyond the limits which were formerly assigned to it. They give us to see that yon sun, throned in the centre of his planetary system, gives light, and warmth, and the vicissitude of seasons, to an extent of surface, several hundreds of times greater than that of the earth which we inhabit. They lay open to us a number of worlds, rolling in their respective circles around this vast luminary — and prove, that the ball which we tread upon, with all its mighty burden of oceans and continents, instead of being distinguished from the others, is among the least of them; and, from some of the more distant planets, would not occupy a visible point in the concave of their firmament. They let us know, that though this mighty earth, with all its myriads of people, were to sink into annihilation, there are some worlds where an event so awful to us would be unnoticed and unknown, and others where it would be nothing more than the disappearance of a little star which had ceased from its twinkling. We should feel a sentiment of modesty at this just but humiliating representation. We should learn not to look on our

2 Psalms 8:4.

[83]

earth as the universe of God, but one paltry and insignificant portion of it; that it is only one of the many mansions which the Supreme Being has created for the accommodation of his worshippers, and only one of the many worlds rolling in that flood of light which the sun pours around him to the outer limits of the planetary system.

But is there nothing beyond these limits? The planetary system has its boundary, but space has none; and if we wing our fancy there, do we only travel through dark and unoccupied regions? There are only five, or at most six, of the planetary orbs visible to the naked eye. What then, is that multitude of other lights which sparkle in our firmament, and fill the whole concave of heaven with innumerable splendours? The planets are all attached to the sun; and, in circling around him, they do homage to that influence which binds them to perpetual attendance on this great luminary. But the other stars do not own his dominion. They do not circle around him. To all common observation, they remain immovable; and each, like the independent sovereign of his own territory, appears to occupy the same inflexible position in the regions of immensity. What can we make of them? Shall we take our adventurous flight to explore these dark and untraveled dominions? What mean these innumerable fires lighted up in distant parts of the universe? Are they only made to shed a feeble glimmering over this little spot in the kingdom of nature? or do they serve a purpose worthier of themselves, to light up other worlds, and give animation to other systems.

The first thing which strikes a scientific observer of the fixed stars, is their immeasurable distance. If the whole planetary system were lighted up into a globe of fire, it would exceed, by many millions of times, the magnitude of this world, and yet only appear a small lucid point from the nearest of them. If a body were projected from the sun with the velocity of a cannon ball, it would take hundreds of thousands of years before it described that mighty interval which separates the nearest of the fixed stars from our sun and from our system. If this earth, which moves at more than the inconceivable velocity of a million and a half miles a day,[3] were to be hurried from its orbit, and to take the same rapid flight over this immense tract, it would not have arrived at the termination of its journey, after taking all the time which has elapsed since the creation of the world. These are great numbers, and great calculations, and the mind feels its own impotency in attempting to grasp them. We can state them in words. We can exhibit them in figures. We can demonstrate them by the powers of a most rigid and infallible geometry. But no human fancy can summon up a lively or an adequate conception — can roam in its ideal flight over this immeasurable largeness — can take in this mighty space in all its grandeur, and in all its immensity — can sweep the outer boundaries of such a creation — or lift itself up to the majesty of that great and invisible arm, on which all is suspended.

But what can those stars be which are seated so far beyond the limits of our planetary system? They must be masses of immense magnitude, or they could not be seen at the distance of place which they occupy. The light which they give must pro-

[3] Since the mean distance from the earth to the sun is known to be approximately 93,000,000 miles it is easy to compute that during a single year the earth must move along the circumference of a circle having a radius of this size, or through a distance of 2π x 93,000,000 miles. Since it requires 365¼ days for the earth to revolve about the sun, the daily speed of the earth may be computed by dividing the circumference by 365¼ days. This does indeed give the result of a velocity of a bit more than a million and a half miles per day.

ceed from themselves, for the feeble reflection of light from some other quarter, would not carry through such mighty tracts to the eye of an observer. A body may be visible in two ways. It may be visible from its own light, as the flame of a candle, or the brightness of a fire, or the brilliancy of yonder glorious sun, which lightens all below, and is the lamp of the world. Or it may be visible from the light which falls upon it, as the body which receives its light from the taper that falls upon it — or the whole assemblage of objects on the surface of the earth, which appear only when the light of day rests upon them or the moon, which, in that part of it which is towards the sun, gives out a silvery whiteness to the eye of the observer, while the other part forms a black and invisible space in the firmament — or as the planets, which shine only because the sun shines upon them, and which, each of them, present the appearance of a dark spot on the side that is turned away from it. Now apply this question to the fixed stars. Are they luminous of themselves, or do they derive their light from the sun, like the bodies of our planetary system? Think of their immense distance, and the solution of this question becomes evident. The sun, like any other body, must dwindle into a less apparent magnitude as you retire from it. At the prodigious distance even of the very nearest of the fixed stars, it must have shrunk into a small indivisible point. In short it must have become a star itself, and could shed no more light than a single individual of those glimmering myriads, the whole assemblage of which cannot dissipate, and can scarcely alleviate the midnight darkness of our world. These stars are visible to us, not because the sun shines upon them, but because they shine of themselves, because they are so many luminous bodies scattered over the tracts of immensity

— in a word, because they are so many suns, each throned in the centre of his own dominions, and pouring a flood of light over his own portion of these unlimitable regions.

At such an immense distance for observation, it is not to be supposed, that we can collect many points of resemblance between the fixed stars, and the solar star which forms the centre of our planetary system. There is one point of resemblance however, which has not escaped the penetration of our astronomers. We know that our sun turns round upon himself, in a regular period of time. We also know, that there are dark spots scattered over his surface, which, though invisible to the naked eye, are perfectly noticeable by our instruments. If these spots existed in greater quantity upon one side than upon another, it would have the general effect of making that side darker, and the revolution of the sun must, in such a case, give us a brighter and a fainter side, by regular alternations. Now, there are some of the fixed stars which present this appearance. They present us with periodical variations of light. From the splendour of a star of the first or second magnitude, they fade away into some of the inferior magnitudes — and one, by becoming invisible might give reason to apprehend that we had lost him altogether — but we can still recognise him by the telescope, till at length he re-appears in his own place, and, after a regular lapse of so many days and hours, recovers his original brightness. Now, the fair inference from this is, that the fixed stars, as they resemble our sun in being so many luminous masses of immense magnitude, they resemble him in this also, that each of them turns round upon his own axis; so that if any of them should have an inequality in the brightness of their sides, this revolution is rendered evident, by the regular variations in the degree of light which it undergoes.

Shall we say, then, of these vast luminaries, that they were created in vain? Were they called into existence for no other purpose than to throw a tide of useless splendour over the solitudes of immensity? Our sun is only one of these luminaries, and we know that he has worlds in his train. Why should we strip the rest of this princely attendance? Why may not each of them be the centre of his own system, and give light to his own worlds? It is true that we see them not, but could the eye of man take its flight into those distant regions, it should lose sight of our little world, before it reached the outer limits of our system — the greater planets should disappear in their turn — before it had described a small portion of that abyss which separates us from the fixed stars the sun should decline into a little spot, and all its splendid retinue of worlds be lost in the obscurity of distance — he should, at last, shrink into a small indivisible atom, and all that could be seen of this magnificent system, should be reduced to the glimmering of a little star. Why resist any longer the grand and interesting conclusion? Each of these stars may be the token of a system as vast and as splendid as the one which we inhabit. Worlds roll in these distant regions; and these worlds must be the mansions of life and intelligence. In yon gilded canopy of heaven we see the broad aspect of the universe, where each shining point presents us with a sun, and each sun with a system of worlds — where the Divinity reigns in all the grandeur of his attributes — where he peoples immensity with his wonders; and travels in the greatness of his strength through the dominions of one vast and unlimited monarchy.

The contemplation has no limits. If we ask the number of suns and of systems, the unassisted eye of man can take in a thousand, and the best telescope which the genius of man has constructed can take in eighty millions. But why subject the dominions of the universe to the eye of man or to the powers of his genius? Fancy may take its flight far beyond the ken of eye or of telescope. It may expiate in the outer regions of all that is visible — and shall we have the boldness to say, that there is nothing there? That the wonders of the Almighty are at an end, because we can no longer trace his footsteps? that his omnipotence is exhausted, because human art can no longer follow him? that the creative energy of God has sunk into repose, because the imagination is enfeebled by the magnitude of its efforts, and can keep no longer on the wing through those mighty tracts, which shoot far beyond what eye hath seen, or the heart of man hath conceived — which sweep endlessly along, and merge into an awful and mysterious infinity?

But thirdly, it was the telescope, that, by piercing the obscurity which lies between us and distant worlds, put infidelity in possession of the argument, against which we are now contending. But, about the time of its invention, another instrument was formed, which laid open a scene no less wonderful, and rewarded the inquisitive spirit of man with a discovery, which serves to neutralize the whole of this argument. This was the microscope. The one led me to see a system in every star. The other leads me to see a world in every atom. The one taught me, that this mighty globe, with the whole burden of its people, and of its countries, is but a grain of sand on the high field of immensity. The other teaches me, that every grain of sand may harbour within it the tribes and the families of a busy population. The one told me of the insignificance of the world I tread upon. The other redeems it from all its insignificance; for it tells me that in the leaves of every forest, and in the flowers of every garden, and in the waters of every rivulet, there are worlds teeming with life, and numberless as are the glories of the firmament. The one has suggested to me, that beyond and above all that is visible to man, there may lie fields of creation which sweep immeasurably along, and carry the impress of the Almighty's hand to the remotest scenes of the universe. The other suggests to me, that within and beneath all that minuteness which the aided eye of man has been able to explore, there may be a region of invisibles; and that could we draw aside the mysterious curtain which shrouds it from our senses, we might there see a theatre of as many wonders as astronomy has unfolded, a universe within the compass of a point so small, as to elude all the powers of the microscope, but where the wonderworking God finds room for the exercise of all his attributes, where he can raise another mechanism of worlds, and fill and animate them all with the evidences of his glory.

Now, mark how all this may be made to meet the argument of our infidel astronomers. By the telescope they have discovered, that no magnitude, however vast, is beyond the grasp of the Divinity. But by the microscope, we have also discovered, that no minuteness, however shrunk from the notice of the human eye, is beneath the condescension of his regard. Every addition to the powers of the one instrument, extends the limit of his visible dominions. But, by every addition to the powers of the other instrument, we see each part of them more crowded than before, with the wonders of his unwearying hand. The one is constantly widening the circle of his territory. The other is as constantly filling up its separate portions, with all that is rich, and various, and exquisite. In a word, by the one I am told that the Almighty is now at work in regions more distant than geometry has ever measured, and among worlds more manifold than numbers have ever reached. But, by the other, I am also told, that, with a mind to comprehend the whole, in the vast compass of its generality, he has also a mind to concentrate a close and a separate attention on each and on all of its particulars; and that the same God, who sends forth an upholding influence among the orbs and the movements of astronomy, can fill the recesses of every single atom with the intimacy of his presence, and travel, in all the greatness of his unimpaired attributes, upon every one spot and corner of the universe he has formed.

They, therefore, who think that God will not put forth such a power, and such a goodness, and such a condescension, in behalf of this world, as are ascribed to him in the New Testament, because he has so many other worlds to attend to, think of him as a man. They confine their view to the informations of the telescope, and forget altogether the informations of the other instrument. They only find room in their minds for his one attribute of a large and general superintendence, and keep out of their remembrance the equally impressive proofs we have for his other attribute of a minute and multiplied attention to all that diversity of operations, where it is he that worketh all in all. And then I think, that, as one of the instruments of philosophy has heightened our every impression of the first of these attributes, so another instrument has no less heightened our impression of the second of them — then I can no longer resist the conclusion, that it would be a transgression of sound argument, as well as a daring of impiety to draw a limit around the doings of this unsearchable God — and, should a professed revelation from heaven, tell me of an act of condescension, in behalf of some separate world, so wonderful that angels desired to look into it, and the Eternal Son had to move from his seat of glory to carry it into accomplishment all I ask is the evidence of such a revelation; for let it tell me as much as it may of God letting himself down for the benefit of one single province of his dominions, this is no more than what I see lying scattered, in numberless examples, before me; and running through the whole line of my recollections; and meeting me in every walk of observation to which I can betake myself; and, now that the microscope has unveiled the wonders of another region, I see strewed around me with a profusion which baffles my every attempt to comprehend it, the evidence that there is no one portion of the universe of God too minute for his notice, nor too humble for the visitations of his care.

As the end of all these illustrations, let me bestow a single paragraph on what I conceive to be the precise state of this argument.

It is a wonderful thing that God should be so unincumbered by the concerns of a whole universe, that he can give a constant attention to every moment of every individual in this world's population. But wonderful as it is, you do not hesitate to admit it as true, on the evidence of your own recollections. It is a wonderful thing that he whose eye is at every instant on so many worlds, should have peopled the world we inhabit with all the traces of the varied design and benevolence which abound in it. But, great as the wonder is, you do not allow so much as the shadow of improbability to darken it, for its reality is what you actually witness, and you never think of questioning the evidence of observation. It is wonderful, it is passing wonderful, that the same God, whose presence is diffused through immensity, and who spreads the ample canopy of his administration over all its dwelling places, should, with an energy as fresh and as unexpended as if he had only begun the work of creation, turn him to the neighbourhood around us, and lavish on its every hand-breadth, all the exuberance of his goodness, and crowd it with the many thousand varieties of conscious existence. But, be the wonder incomprehensible as it may, you do not suffer in your mind the burden of a single doubt to lie upon it, because you do not question the report of the microscope. You do not refuse its information, nor turn away from it as an incompetent channel of evidence. But to bring it still nearer to the point at issue, there are many who never look through a microscope, but who rest an implicit faith in all its revelation; and upon what evidence, I would ask? Upon the evidence of testimony — upon the credit they give to the authors of the books they have read, and the belief they put in the record of their observations. Now, at this point I make my stand. It is wonderful that God should be so interested in the redemption of a single world, as to send forth his well-beloved Son upon the errand, and he, to accomplish it, should, mighty to save, put forth all his strength, and travail in the greatness of it. But such wonders as these have already multiplied upon you; and when evidence is given of their truth, you have resigned your every judgment of the unsearchable God, and rested in the faith of them. I demand, in the name of sound and consistent philosophy, that you do the same in the matter before us — and take it up as a question of evidence — and examine that medium of testimony through which the miracles and informations of the Gospel have come to your door — and go not to admit as argument here, what would not be admitted as argument in any of the analogies of nature and observation — and take along with you in this field of inquiry, a lesson which you should have learned upon other fields — even the depth of the riches both of the wisdom and the knowledge of God, that his judgments are unsearchable, and his ways are past finding out.

Now what is true of a scene on earth, is also true of that wider and more elevated scene which stretches over the immensity around it, into a dark and a distant unknown. Who does not feel an aggrandisement of thought and of faculty, when he looks abroad over the amplitudes of creation — when placed on a telescopic eminence, his aided eye can find a pathway to innumerable worlds — when that wondrous field, over which there had hung for many ages the mantle of so deep an obscurity, is laid open to him, and instead of a dreary and unpeopled solitude, he can see over the whole face of it such an extended garniture of rich and goodly habitations! Even the Atheist, who tells us that the universe is self-existent and indestructible — even he, who instead of seeing the traces of a manifold wisdom in its manifold varieties, sees nothing in them all but the exquisite structures and the lofty dimensions of materialism — even he, who would despoil creation of its God, cannot look upon its golden suns, and their accompanying systems, without the solemn impression of a magnificence that fixes and overpowers him. Now, conceive such a belief of God as you all profess, to dawn upon his understanding. Let him become as one of yourselves — and so be put into the condition of rising from the sublime of matter to the sublime of mind. Let him now learn to subordinate the whole of this mechanism to the design and authority of a great presiding intelligence: and re-assembling all the members of the universe, however distant, into one family, let him mingle with his former conceptions of the grandeur which belonged to it, the conception of that eternal Spirit who sits enthroned on the immensity of his own wonders, and embraces all that he has made, within the ample scope of one great administration. Then will the images and the impressions of sublimity come in upon him from a new quarter. Then will another avenue be opened, through which a sense of grandeur may find its way into his soul, and have a mightier influence than ever to fill, and to elevate, and to expand it. Then will be established a new and a noble association, by the aid of which all that he formerly looked upon as fair, becomes more lovely; and all that he formerly looked upon as great, becomes more magnificent. But will you believe me, that even with this accession to his mind of ideas gathered from the contemplation of the Divinity; even with that pleasurable glow which steals over his imagination, when he now thinks him of the majesty of God; even with as much of what you would call piety, as I fear is enough to soothe and to satisfy many of yourselves, and which stirs and kindles within you when you hear the goings forth of the Supreme set before you in the terms of a lofty representation; even with all this, I say there may be as wide a distance from the habit and the character of godliness, as if God was still atheistically disowned by him. Take the conduct of his life and the currency of his affections; and you may see as little upon them of the stamp of loyalty to God, or of reverence for any one of his authenticated proclamations, as

[95]

you may see in him who offers his poetic incense to the genii, or weeps enraptured over the visions of a beauteous mythology. The sublime of Deity has wrought up his soul to a pitch of conscious and pleasing elevation — and yet this no more argues the will of Deity to have a practical authority over him, than does that tone of elevation which is caught by looking at the sublime of a naked materialism. The one and the other have their little hour of ascendency over him; and when he turns him to the rude and ordinary world, both vanish alike from his sensibilities, as does the loveliness of a song.

JOHN HERSCHEL

Outlines of Astronomy *

Sir John Herschel (1792–1871), an astronomer, was the only child of Sir
William Herschel, also an astronomer, famous for being the first man in
recorded history to discover a new planet. A man of many talents,
Herschel devoted himself to mathematics after receiving his M.A. at
Cambridge, then studied the law, and even tried to be a chemist. Finally
adopting his father's profession, he rapidly rose to fame as the most
famous astronomer of his age, becoming one of the founders of the Royal
Astronomical Society, and winning many prizes. He was noted chiefly for
his astronomical work on variable and double stars and nebulae. His
most famous single publication was *Results of Astronomical Observations Made during the Years 1834–1838 at the Cape of Good Hope.* Long
a lover of poetry, he published English verse translations of Schiller,
Homer, and Dante. His *Preliminary Discourse on the Study of Natural
Philosophy,* published in 1830, quickly became a classic and was translated
into French, German and Italian. The *Treatise on Astronomy,* from the
introduction to which the following extract is taken, was published in
1833 and was enlarged in 1849 into the *Outlines of Astronomy.* By 1873
this work had appeared in twelve editions in English, and had been
translated into many languages, including Russian, Chinese and Arabic.
Described as "perhaps the most completely satisfactory general exposition
of a science ever penned," this book remains to our day a model of scientific exposition that may at once satisfy the specialist and the general
reader.

E VERY student who enters upon a scientific pursuit, especially if at a somewhat advanced period of life, will find not
only that he has much to learn, but much also to unlearn. Fa-

* From *Outlines of Astronomy* (1849).

miliar objects and events are far from presenting themselves to our senses in that aspect and with those connections under which science requires them to be viewed, and which constitute their rational explanation. There is, therefore, every reason to expect that those objects and relations which, taken together, constitute the subject he is about to enter upon will have been previously apprehended by him, at least imperfectly, because much has hitherto escaped his notice which is essential to its right understanding: and not only so, but too often also erroneously, owing to mistaken analogies, and the general prevalence of vulgar errors. As a first preparation, therefore, for the course he is about to commence, he must loosen his hold on all crude and hastily adopted notions, and must strengthen himself, by something of an effort and a resolve, for the unprejudiced admission of any conclusion which shall appear to be supported by careful observation and logical argument, even should it prove of a nature adverse to notions he may have previously formed for himself, or taken up, without examination, on the credit of others. Such an effort is, in fact, a commencement of that intellectual discipline which forms one of the most important ends of all science. It is the first movement of approach towards that state of mental purity which alone can fit us for a full and steady perception of moral beauty as well as physical adaptation. It is the "euphrasy and rue"[1] with which we must "purge our sight" before we can receive and contemplate as they are the lineaments of truth and nature.

[1] The reference is to Milton's *Paradise Lost,* XI:414: "Michael . . . purg'd with Euphrasie and Rue/The Visual Nerve." The plant *Euphrasia Officinalis* in early days was held to have medicinal virtues in the treatment of diseases of the eye and, used as a remedy for weak eyes, was popularly called "Eyebright." Rue is the common name for a perennial evergreen shrub known as *Ruta graveolens,* also used in earlier days for medicinal purposes.

There is no science which, more than astronomy, stands in need of such a preparation, or draws more largely on that intellectual liberality which is ready to adopt whatever is demonstrated, or concede whatever is rendered highly probable, however new and uncommon the points of view may be in which objects the most familiar may thereby become placed. Almost all its conclusions stand in open and striking contradiction with those of superficial and vulgar observation, and with what appears to every one, until he has understood and weighed the proofs to the contrary, the most positive evidence of his senses. Thus, the earth on which he stands, and which has served for ages as the unshaken foundation of the firmest structures, either of art or nature, is divested by the astronomer of its attribute of fixity, and conceived by him as turning swiftly on its centre, and at the same time moving onwards through space with great rapidity. The sun and the moon, which appear to untaught eyes round bodies of no very considerable size, become enlarged in his imagination into vast globes, — the one approaching in magnitude to the earth itself, the other immensely surpassing it. The planets, which appear only as stars somewhat brighter than the rest, are to him spacious, elaborate, and habitable worlds; several of them much greater and far more curiously furnished than the earth he inhabits, as there are also others less so; and the stars themselves, properly so called, which to ordinary apprehension present only lucid sparks or brilliant atoms, are to him suns of various and transcendent glory — effulgent centres of life and light to myriads of unseen worlds. So that when, after dilating his thoughts to comprehend the grandeur of those ideas his calculations have called up, and exhausting his imagination and the powers of his language to devise similes and

[99]

metaphors illustrative of the immensity of the scale on which his universe is constructed, he shrinks back to his native sphere, he finds it, in comparison, a mere point; so lost — even in the minute system to which it belongs — as to be invisible and unsuspected from some of its principal and remoter members.

There is hardly any thing which sets in a stronger light the inherent power of truth over the mind of man, when opposed by no motives of interest or passion, than the perfect readiness with which all these conclusions are assented to as soon as their evidence is clearly apprehended, and the tenacious hold they acquire over our belief when once admitted. In the conduct, therefore, of this volume, I shall take it for granted that the reader is more desirous to learn the system which it is its object to teach, as it now stands, than to raise or revive objections against it; and that, in short, he comes to the task with a willing mind; an assumption which will not only save the trouble of piling argument on argument to convince the sceptical, but will greatly facilitate his actual progress; inasmuch as he will find it at once easier and more satisfactory to pursue from the outset a straight and definite path, than to be constantly stepping aside, involving himself in perplexities and circuits, which, after all, can only terminate in finding himself compelled to adopt the same road.

The method, therefore, we propose to follow in this work is neither strictly the analytic nor the synthetic, but rather such a combination of both, with a leaning to the latter, as may best suit with a *didactic* composition. Its object is not to convince or refute opponents, nor to inquire, under the semblance of an assumed ignorance, for principles of which we are all the time in full possession — but simply to *teach* what is *known*. The moderate limit of a single volume, to which it will be confined, and the necessity of being on every point, within that limit, rather diffuse and copious in explanation, as well as the eminently matured and ascertained character of the science itself, render this course both practicable and eligible. Practicable, because there is now no danger of any revolution in astronomy, like those which are daily changing the features of the less advanced sciences, supervening, to destroy all our hypotheses, and throw our statements into confusion. Eligible, because the space to be bestowed, either in combating refuted systems, or in leading the reader forward by slow and measured steps from the known to the unknown, may be more advantageously devoted to such explanatory illustrations as will impress on him a familiar and, as it were, a practical sense of the sequence of phenomena, and the manner in which they are produced. We shall not, then, reject the analytic course where it leads more easily and directly to our objects, or in any way fetter ourselves by a rigid adherence to method. Writing only to be understood, and to communicate as much information in as little space as possible, consistently with its *distinct* and *effectual* communication, no sacrifice can be afforded to system, to form, or to affectation.

We shall take for granted, from the outset, the Copernican system of the world; relying on the easy, obvious, and natural explanation it affords of all the phenomena as they come to be described, to impress the student with a sense of its truth, without either the formality of demonstration or the superfluous tedium of eulogy, calling to mind that important remark of Bacon: — "Theoriarum vires, areta et quasi se mutuo sustinente partium adaptatione, quâ quasi in orbem cohærent, firmantur;"[2] not failing, however, to point out to the reader, as occasion offers, the contrast which its superior simplicity offers to the complication of other hypotheses.

The preliminary knowledge which it is desirable that the student should possess, in order for the more advantageous perusal of the following pages, consists in the familiar practice of decimal and sexagesimal arithmetic, some moderate acquaintance with geometry and trigonometry, both plane and spherical; the elementary principles of mechanics; and enough of optics to understand the construction and use of the telescope, and some other of the simpler instruments. Of course, the more of such knowledge he brings to the perusal, the easier will be his progress, and the more complete the information gained; but we shall endeavour in every case, as far as it can be done without a sacrifice of clearness, and of that useful brevity which consists in the absence of prolixity and episode, to render what we have to say as independent of other books as possible.

After all, I must distinctly caution such of my readers as may commence and terminate their astronomical studies with the present work (though of such, — at least in the latter predicament, — I trust the number will be few), that its utmost pretension is to place them on the threshold of this particular wing of the temple of Science, or rather on an eminence exterior to it, whence they may obtain something like a general notion of its structure; or, at most, to give those who may wish to enter

2 In the original edition, a footnote gave a translation into English of this quotation from Bacon, as follows: "The confirmation of theories relies on the compact adaption of their parts, by which, like those of an arch or dome, they mutually sustain each other, and form a coherent whole." The author added to this translation the comment that "this is what Dr. Whewell expressively terms the *consilience* of inductions." A selection from Whewell will be found elsewhere in this book.

a ground-plan of its accesses, and put them in possession of the pass-word. Admission to its sanctuary, and to the privileges and feelings of a votary, is only to be gained by one means, — *sound and sufficient knowledge of mathematics, the great instrument of all exact inquiry, without which no man can ever make such advances in this or any other of the higher departments of science as can entitle him to form an independent opinion on any subject of discussion within their range.* It is not without an effort that those who possess this knowledge can communicate on such subjects with those who do not, and adapt their language and their illustrations to the necessities of such an intercourse. Propositions which to the one are almost identical, are theorems of import and difficulty to the other; nor is their evidence presented in the same way to the mind of each. In teaching such propositions, under such circumstances, the appeal has to be made, not to the pure and abstract reason, but to the sense of analogy — to practice and experience: principles and modes of action have to be established not by direct argument from acknowledged axioms, but by continually recurring to the sources from which the axioms themselves have been drawn; viz. examples; that is to say, by bringing forward and dwelling on simple and familiar instances in which the same principles and the same or similar modes of action take place: thus erecting, as it were, in each particular case, a separate induction, and constructing at each step a little body of science to meet its exigencies. The difference is that of pioneering a road through an untraversed country and advancing at ease along a broad and beaten highway; that is to say, if we are determined to make ourselves distinctly understood, and will appeal to reason at all. As for the method of *assertion,* or a direct demand on the *faith* of the student (though in some complex cases indispensable, where illustrative explanation would defeat its own end by becoming tedious and burdensome to both parties), it is one which I shall neither willingly adopt nor would recommend to others.

On the other hand, although it is something new to abandon the road of mathematical demonstration in the treatment of subjects susceptible of it, and to teach any considerable branch of science entirely or chiefly by the way of illustration and familiar parallels, it is yet not impossible that those who are already well acquainted with our subject, and whose knowledge has been acquired by that confessedly higher practice which is incompatible with the avowed objects of the present work, may yet find their account in its perusal, — for this reason, that it is always of advantage to present any given body of knowledge to the mind in as great a variety of different lights as possible. It is a property of illustrations of this kind to strike no two minds in the same manner, or with the same force; because no two minds are stored with the same images, or have acquired their notions of them by similar habits. Accordingly, it may very well happen, that a proposition, even to one best acquainted with it, may be placed not merely in a new and uncommon, but in a more impressive and satisfactory light by such a course — some obscurity may be dissipated, some inward misgivings cleared up, or even some links supplied which may lead to the perception of connections and deductions altogether unknown before. And the probability of this is increased when, as in the present instance, the illustrations chosen have not been studiously selected from books, but are such as have presented themselves freely to the author's mind as being most in harmony with his own views; by which, of course, he means to lay no claim to originality in all or any of them beyond what they may really possess.

Besides, there are cases in the application of mechanical principles with which the mathematical student is but too familiar, where, when the data are before him, and the numerical and geometrical relations of his problems all clear to his conception, — when his forces are estimated and his lines measured, — nay, when even he has followed up the application of his technical processes, and fairly arrived at his conclusion, — there is still something wanting in his mind — not in the evidence, for he has examined each link, and finds the chain complete — not in the principles, for those he well knows are too firmly established to be shaken — but precisely in the *mode of action.* He has followed out a train of reasoning by logical and technical rules, but the signs he has employed are not pictures of nature, or have lost their original meaning as such to his mind: he has not seen, as it were, the process of nature passing under his eye in an instant of time, and presented as a consecutive whole to his imagination. A familiar parallel, or an illustration drawn from some artificial or natural process, of which he has that direct and individual impression which gives it a reality and associates it with a name, will, in almost every such case, supply in a moment this deficient feature, will convert all his symbols into real pictures, and infuse an animated meaning into what was before a lifeless succession of words and signs. I cannot, indeed, always promise myself to attain this degree of vividness of illustration, nor are the points to be elucidated themselves always capable of being so *paraphrased* (if I may use the expression) by any single instance adducible in the ordinary course of experience; but the object will at least be kept in view; and, as I am very conscious of having, in making such attempts, gained for myself much clearer views of several of the more concealed effects of planetary perturbation than I had acquired by their mathematical investigation in detail, it may reasonably be hoped that the endeavour will not always be unattended with a similar success in others.

From what has been said, it will be evident that our aim is not to offer to the public a technical treatise, in which the student of practical or theoretical astronomy shall find consigned the minute description of methods of observation, or the formulæ he requires prepared to his hand, or their demonstrations drawn out in detail. In all these the present work will be found meagre, and quite inadequate to his wants. Its aim is entirely different; being to present to him in each case the mere ultimate *rationale* of facts, arguments, and processes; and, in all cases of mathematical application, avoiding whatever would tend to encumber its pages with algebraic or geometrical symbols, to place under his inspection that central thread of common sense on which the pearls of analytical research are invariably strung; but which, by the attention the latter claim for themselves, is often concealed from the eye of the gazer, and not always disposed in the straightest and most convenient form to follow by those who string them. This is no fault of those who have conducted the inquiries to which we allude. The contention of mind for which they call is enormous; and it may, perhaps, be owing to their experience of *how little* can be accomplished in carrying such processes on to their conclusion, by mere ordinary *clearness of head;* and how necessary it often is to pay more attention to the purely mathematical conditions which ensure success, — the hooks-and-eyes of their equations and series, — than to those which enchain causes with their effects, and both with the human reason, — that we must attribute something of that indistinctness of view which is often complained of as a grievance by the earnest student, and still more commonly ascribed ironically to the native cloudliness of an atmosphere too sublime for vulgar comprehension. We think we shall render good service to both classes of readers, by dissipating, so far as lies in our power, that accidental obscurity, and by showing ordinary untutored comprehension clearly what it *can*, and what it *cannot*, hope to attain.

To the reader who now for the first time takes up a book on astronomy, it will no doubt seem strange to class the earth with the heavenly bodies, and to assume any community of nature among things apparently so different. For what, in fact, can be more apparently different than the vast and seemingly immeasurable extent of the earth, and the stars, which appear but as points, and seem to have no size at all? The earth is dark and opaque, while the celestial bodies are brilliant. We perceive in it no motion, while in them we observe a continual change of place, as we view them at different hours of the day or night, or at different seasons of the year. The ancients,[3] accordingly, one

3 In the Aristotelean cosmology, which in major part was at the basis of most scientific belief until the seventeenth century, a distinction was made between heavenly objects and terrestrial objects. The former were supposed to be made of the fifth element, ether, and were not subject to change, while earthly objects were made of the four elements air, earth, fire, water, and were subject to change. The earth itself and everything within its immediate surrounding sphere were therefore subject to a special set of laws of nature that differed from those laws which held good in the outer regions of space where celestial objects may be found. The moon, at the dividing point between the terrestrial and celestial realms, to some degree partook of both. This system received a shattering blow when Galileo, quickly followed by others, began in 1609 to observe the heavens with a telescope, to discover that the moon and the planets,

or two of the more enlightened of them only excepted, admitted no such community of nature; and, by thus placing the heavenly bodies and their movements without the pale of analogy and experience, effectually intercepted the progress of all reasoning from what passes here below, to what is going on in the regions where they exist and move. Under such conventions, astronomy, as a science of cause and effect, could not exist, but must be limited to a mere registry of appearances, unconnected with any attempt to account for them on reasonable principles, however successful to a certain extent might be the attempt to follow out their order of sequence, and to establish empirical laws expressive of this order. To get rid of this prejudice, therefore, is the first step towards acquiring a knowledge of what is really the case; and the student has made his first effort towards the acquisition of sound knowledge, when he has learnt to familiarize himself with the idea that the earth, after all, *may* be nothing but a great star. How correct such an idea may be, and with what limitations and modifications it is to be admitted, we shall see presently.

It is evident, that, to form any just notions of the arrangement, in space, of a number of objects which we cannot approach and examine, but of which all the information we can gain is by sitting still and watching their evolutions, it must be very important for us to know, in the first instance, whether what we call sitting still is *really* such: whether the station from which we view them, with ourselves, and all objects which immediately surround us, be not itself in motion, unperceived by

far from being different from the earth, greatly resembled the earth and hence reasonably might be considered subject to the same physical laws. This point is discussed at some length by Chalmers, in the selection from him printed elsewhere in this volume.

us; and if so, of what nature that motion is. The apparent places of a number of objects, and their apparent arrangement with respect to each other, will of course be materially dependent on the situation of the spectator among them; and if this situation be liable to change, unknown to the spectator himself, an appearance of change in the respective situations of the objects will arise, without the reality. If, then, such be actually the case, it will follow that *all* the movements we think we perceive among the stars will not be real movements, but that some part, at least, of whatever changes of relative place we perceive among them must be merely apparent, the results of the shifting of our own point of view; and that, if we would ever arrive at a knowledge of their real motions, it can only be by first investigating our own, and making due allowance for its effects. Thus, the question whether the earth is in motion or at rest, and if in motion, what that motion is, is no idle inquiry, but one on which depends our only chance of arriving at true conclusions respecting the constitution of the universe.

Nor let it be thought strange that we should speak of a motion existing in the earth, unperceived by its inhabitants: we must remember that it is of the earth *as a whole,* with all that it holds within its substance, or sustains on its surface, that we are speaking; of a motion common to the solid mass beneath, to the ocean which flows around it, the air that rests upon it, and the clouds which float above it in the air. Such a motion, which should displace no terrestrial object from its relative situation among others, interfere with no natural processes, and produce no sensations of shocks or jerks, might, it is very evident, subsist undetected by us. There is no peculiar sensation which advertises us that we are *in motion.* We perceive *jerks,* or *shocks,* it is true, because these are sudden *changes* of motion, produced, as the laws of mechanics teach us, by sudden and powerful forces acting during short times; and these forces, applied to our bodies, are what we *feel*. When, for example, we are carried along in a carriage with the blinds down, or with our eyes closed (to keep us from seeing external objects), we perceive a tremor arising from inequalities in the road, over which the carriage is successively lifted and let fall, but we have no sense of *progress*. As the road is smoother, our sense of motion is diminished, though our rate of travelling is accelerated. Railway travelling, especially by night or in a tunnel, has familiarized every one with this remark. Those who have made aeronautic voyages testify that with closed eyes, and under the influence of a steady breeze communicating no oscillatory or revolving motion to the car, the *sensation* is that of perfect rest, however rapid the transfer from place to place.

But it is on shipboard, where a great system is maintained in motion, and where we are surrounded with a multitude of objects which participate with ourselves and each other in the common progress of the whole mass, that we feel most satisfactorily the identity of sensation between a state of motion and one of rest. In the cabin of a large and heavy vessel, going smoothly before the wind in still water, or drawn along a canal, not the smallest indication acquaints us with the way it is making. We read, sit, walk, and perform every customary action as if we were on land. If we throw a ball into the air, it falls back into our hand; or if we drop it, it alights at our feet. Insects buzz around us as in the free air; and smoke ascends in the same manner as it would do in an apartment on shore. If, indeed, we come on deck, the case is, in some respects, different;

the air, not being carried along with us, drifts away smoke and other light bodies — such as feathers abandoned to it — apparently, in the opposite direction to that of the ship's progress; but, in reality, *they* remain at rest, and we leave them behind in the air. Still, the illusion, so far as massive objects and our own movements are concerned, remains complete; and when we look at the shore, we then perceive the effect of our own motion transferred, in a contrary direction, to external objects — *external, that is, to the system of which we form a part.*

"Provehimur portu, terræque urbesque recedunt."[4]

In order, however, to conceive the earth as in motion, we must form to ourselves a conception of its shape and size. Now, an object cannot have shape and size unless it is *limited* on all sides by some definite outline, so as to admit of our imagining it, at least, disconnected from other bodies, and existing insulated in space. The first rude notion we form of the earth is that of a flat surface, of indefinite extent in all directions from the spot where we stand, *above* which are *the air* and *sky;* below, to an indefinite profundity, solid matter. This is a prejudice to be got rid of, like that of the earth's immobility; — but it is one much easier to rid ourselves of, inasmuch as it originates only in our own mental inactivity, in not questioning ourselves *where* we will place a limit to a thing we have been accustomed from infancy to regard as immensely large; and does not, like that, originate in the testimony of our senses unduly interpreted. On the contrary, the direct testimony of our senses

---

[4] The line of Latin poetry is from Virgil, *Aeneid,* III:71, and means: We left the harbor, and the land and the city disappeared. This same line from Virgil was quoted by Copernicus in his "On the Revolutions of the Celestial Spheres" in 1543 to illustrate the principle of relativity of motion.

lies the other way. When we see the sun set in the evening in the west, and rise again in the east, as we cannot doubt that it is the *same* sun we see after a temporary absence, we must do violence to all our notions of solid matter, to suppose it to have made its way *through* the substance of the earth. It must, therefore, have gone *under* it, and that not by a mere subterraneous *channel;* for if we notice the points where it sets and rises for many successive days, or for a whole year, we shall find them constantly shifting, round a very large extent of the horizon; and, besides, the moon and stars also set and rise again in *all* points of the visible horizon. The conclusion is plain: the earth cannot extend indefinitely in depth downwards, nor indefinitely in surface laterally; it must have not only bounds in a horizontal direction, but also an *under side* round which the sun, moon, and stars can pass; and that side must, at least, be so far like what we see, that it must have a sky and sunshine, and a day when it is night to us, and *vice versâ;* where, in short,

— "redit a nobis Aurora, diemque reducit.
Nosque ubi primus equis oriens afflavit anhelis,
Illic sera rubens accendit lumina Vesper." *Georg.*[5]

As soon as we have familiarized ourselves with the conception of an earth without *foundations* or fixed supports — existing insulated in space from contact of every thing external, it becomes easy to imagine it in motion — or, rather, difficult to

[5] The lines of Latin poetry are from Virgil, *Georgics*, I:249–251, and mean: Aurora retires from our sky and brings morning back to them [on the other side of the world]; and when the horses of the sun make us here feel their burning breath, there Vesper, kindling, lights their stars.

imagine it otherwise; for, since there is nothing to *retain* it in one place, should any causes of motion exist, or any *forces* act upon it, it must obey their impulse. Let us next see what obvious circumstances there are to help us to a knowledge of the *shape* of the earth.

Let us first examine what we can actually *see* of its shape. Now, it is not on land (unless, indeed, on uncommonly level and extensive plains), that we can see any thing of the *general* figure of the earth; — the hills, trees, and other objects which roughen its surface, and break and elevate the line of the horizon, though obviously bearing a most minute proportion to the *whole* earth, are yet too considerable with respect to our-selves and to that small portion of it which we can see at a single view, to allow of our forming any judgment of the form of the whole, from that of a part so disfigured. But with the surface of the sea or any vastly extended level plain, the case is other-wise. If we sail out of sight of land, whether we stand on the deck of the ship or climb the mast, we see the surface of the sea — not losing itself in distance and mist, but terminated by a sharp, clear, well-defined line or *offing* as it is called, which runs all round us in a circle, having our station for its centre. That this line is really a circle, we conclude, first, from the perfect apparent similarity of all its parts; and, secondly, from the fact of all its parts appearing at the same distance from us, and that, evidently, a moderate one; and thirdly, from this, that its ap-parent *diameter*, measured with an instrument called the *dip sector*, is the same (except under some singular atmospheric circumstances, which produce a temporary distortion of the outline), in whatever direction the measure is taken, — prop-erties which belong only to the circle among geometrical figures.

If we ascend a high eminence on a plain (for instance, one of the Egyptian pyramids), the same holds good.

Masts of ships, however, and the edifices erected by man, are trifling eminences compared to what nature itself affords; Ætna,[6] Teneriffe, Mowna Roa, are eminences from which no contemptible *aliquot* part of the whole earth's surface can be seen; but from these again — in those few and rare occasions when the transparency of the air will permit the real boundary of the horizon, the true sea-line, to be seen — the very same appearances are witnessed, but with this remarkable addition, viz. that the angular *diameter* of the visible area, as measured by the dip sector, is materially *less* than at a lower level; or, in other words, that the *apparent size* of the earth has sensibly diminished as we have receded from its surface, while yet the *absolute quantity* of it seen at once has been increased.

The same appearances are observed universally, in every part of the earth's surface visited by man. Now, the figure of a body which, however seen, appears always *circular*, can be no other than a sphere or globe.

From the foregoing explanations it appears, 1st, That the general figure of the earth (so far as it can be gathered from this kind of observation) is that of a sphere or globe. In this we also include that of the sea, which, wherever it extends, covers and fills in those inequalities and local irregularities which exist on land, but which can of course only be regarded as trifling deviations from the general outline of the whole mass, as we consider an orange not the less round for the roughness on its

6 Mount Aetna or Etna is a volcano in N.E. Sicily; Teneriffe is the largest of the Canary Islands and contains a volcano sometimes known as the Peak of Tenerife, while "Mowna Roa" is apparently Mauna Loa, a volcano on Hawaii Island.

rind. 2dly, That the appearance of a *visible* horizon, or sea-offing, is a consequence of the curvature of the surface, and does not arise from the inability of the eye to follow objects to a greater distance, or from atmospheric indistinctness. It will be worth while to pursue the general notion thus acquired into some of its consequences, by which its consistency with observations of a different kind, and on a larger scale, will be put to the test, and a clear conception be formed of the manner in which the parts of the earth are related to each other, and held together as a whole.

In the first place, then, every one who has passed a little while at the sea side is aware that objects may be seen perfectly well beyond the *offing* or visible horizon — but not the *whole* of them. We only see their upper parts. Their bases where they rest on, or rise out of the water, are hid from view by the spherical surface of the sea, which protrudes between them and ourselves. Suppose a ship, for instance, to sail directly away from our station; — at first, when the distance of the ship is small, a spectator, S, situated at some certain height above the sea, sees the whole of the ship, even to the *water line* where it rests on the sea, as at A. As it recedes it diminishes, it is true, in apparent size, but still the *whole* is seen down to the water line, till it reaches the *visible* horizon at B. But as soon as it has passed this distance, not only does the visible portion still continue to diminish in apparent *size,* but the hull begins to disappear bodily, as if sunk below the surface. When it has reached a certain distance, as at C, its hull has entirely vanished, but the masts and sails remain, presenting the appearance c. But if, in this state of things, the spectator quickly ascends to a higher station, T, whose visible horizon is at D, the hull comes again

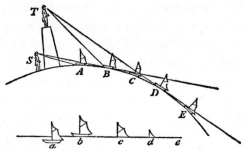

in sight; and, when he descends again, he loses it. The ship still receding, the lower sails seem to sink below the water, as at d, and at length the whole disappears: while yet the distinctness with which the last portion of the sail d is seen is such as to satisfy us that were it not for the interposed segment of the sea, A B C D E, the distance T E is not so great as to have prevented an equally perfect view of the whole.

The history of aëronautic adventure affords a curious illustration of the same principle. The late Mr. Sadler,[7] the celebrated aëronaut, ascended on one occasion in a balloon from Dublin, and was wafted across the Irish Channel, when, on his approach to the Welsh coast, the balloon descended nearly to the surface of the sea. By this time the sun was set, and the shades of evening began to close in. He threw out nearly all his ballast, and suddenly sprang upwards to a great height, and by so doing brought his horizon to *dip* below the sun, producing the whole phenomenon of a western sunrise. M. Charles[8] in his memorable

[7] Windham William Sadler, an aeronaut educated as an engineer, is known for his crossing by balloon from Dublin to Holyhead across St. George's Channel in 1817. Sadler died in 1824 of injuries sustained in a balloon accident.

[8] The French physicist J.-A.-C. Charles devised a balloon inflated with hydrogen gas or inflammable air, in rivalry of the balloon invented by the brothers Montgolfier which used heated air. The first hydrogen balloon, employing Charles's principle, ascended from Paris on August 27, 1783.

ascent from Paris in 1783 witnessed the same phenomenon.

After what has been said of the small extent of the atmosphere in comparison with the mass of the earth, we shall have little hesitation in admitting those luminaries which people and adorn the the sky, and which, while they obviously form no part of the earth, and receive no support from it, are yet not borne along at random like clouds upon the air, nor drifted by the winds, to be external to our atmosphere. As such we have considered them while speaking of their refractions — as existing in the immensity of space beyond, and situated, perhaps, for any thing we can perceive to the contrary, at enormous distances from us and from each other.

Could a spectator exist unsustained by the earth, or any solid support, he would see around him at one view the whole contents of space — the visible constituents of the universe: and, in the absence of any means of judging of their distances from him, would refer them, in the directions in which they were seen from his station, to the concave surface of an imaginary sphere, having his eye for a centre, and its surface at some vast indeterminate distance. Perhaps he might judge those which appear to him large and bright, to be nearer to him than the smaller and less brilliant; but, independent of other means of judging, he would have no warrant for this opinion, any more than for the idea that all were equidistant from him, and *really* arranged on such a spherical surface. Nevertheless, there would be no impropriety in his referring their places, geometrically speaking, to those points of such a purely imaginary sphere, which their respective visual rays intersect; and there would be much advantage in so doing, as by that means their appearance and relative situation could be accurately measured, recorded, and mapped down. The objects in a landscape are at every variety of distance from the eye, yet we lay them all down in a picture on one plane, and at one distance, in their actual *apparent proportions,* and the likeness is not taxed with incorrectness, though a man in the foreground should be represented larger than a mountain in the distance. So it is to a spectator of the heavenly bodies pictured, *projected,* or mapped down on that imaginary sphere we call the *sky* or *heaven.* Thus, we may easily conceive that the moon, which appears to us as large as the sun, though less bright, *may* owe that apparent equality to its greater proximity, and *may* be really much less; while both the moon and sun may only appear larger and brighter than the stars, on account of the remoteness of the latter.

A spectator on the earth's surface is prevented, by the great mass on which he stands, from seeing into all that portion of space which is below him, or to see which he must look in any degree downwards. It is true that, if his place of observation be at a great elevation, the dip of the horizon will bring within the scope of vision a little more than a hemisphere, and refraction, wherever he may be situated, will enable him to look, as it were, a little round the corner; but the zone thus added to his visual range can hardly ever, unless in very extraordinary circumstances, exceed a couple of degrees in breadth, and is always ill seen on account of the vapours near the horizon. Unless, then, by a change of his geographical situation, he should shift his horizon (which is always a plane passing through his eye, and touching the spherical convexity of the earth); or unless, by some movements proper to the heavenly bodies, they should of themselves come above his horizon; or, lastly, unless, by some rotation of the earth itself on its centre, the point of its surface

which he occupies should be carried round, and presented towards a different region of space; he would never obtain a sight
of almost one half the objects external to our atmosphere. But
if any of these cases be supposed, more, or all, may come into
view according to the circumstances.

A traveller, for example, shifting his locality on our globe,
will obtain a view of celestial objects invisible from his original
station, in a way which may be not inaptly illustrated by comparing him to a person standing in a park close to a large tree.
The massive obstacle presented by its trunk cuts off his view of
all those parts of the landscape which it occupies as an object;
but by walking round it a complete successive view of the whole
panorama may be obtained. Just in the same way, if we set off
from any station, as London, and travel southwards, we shall not
fail to notice that many celestial objects which are never seen
from London come successively into view, as if rising up above
the horizon, night after night, from the south, although it is in
reality our horizon, which, travelling with us southwards round
the sphere, sinks in succession beneath them. The novelty and

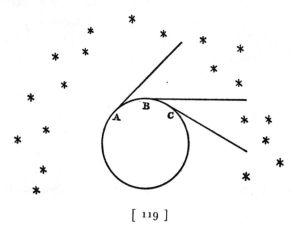

splendour of fresh constellations thus gradually brought into
view in the clear calm nights of tropical climates, in long
voyages to the south, is dwelt upon by all who have enjoyed
this spectacle, and never fails to impress itself on the recollection
among the most delightful and interesting of the associations
connected with extensive travel. A glance at the accompanying
figure, exhibiting three successive stations of a traveller, A, B, C,
with the horizon corresponding to each, will place this process
in clearer evidence than any description.

Again: suppose the earth itself to have a motion of rotation
on its centre. It is evident that a spectator at rest (as it appears
to him) on any part of it will, unperceived by himself, be
carried round with it: unperceived, we say, because his horizon
will constantly contain, and be limited by, the same terrestial
objects. He will have the same landscape constantly before his
eyes, in which all the familiar objects in it, which serve him for
landmarks and directions, retain, with respect to himself or to
each other, the same invariable situations. The perfect smooth-
ness and equality of the motion of so vast a mass, in which every
object he sees around him participates alike, will prevent his
entertaining any suspicion of his actual change of place. Yet,
with respect to external objects, — that is to say, all celestial
ones which do not participate in the supposed rotation of the
earth, — his horizon will have been all the while shifting in
its relation to them, precisely as in the case of our traveller
in the foregoing article. Recurring to the figure of that article,
it is evidently the same thing, so far as their visibility is concerned, whether he has been carried by the earth's rotation
successively into the situations A, B, C; or whether, the earth
remaining at rest, he has transferred himself personally along

its surface to those stations. Our spectator in the park will obtain precisely the same view of the landscape, whether he walk round the tree, or whether we suppose it sawed off, and made to turn on an upright pivot, while he stands on a projecting step attached to it, and allows himself to be carried round by its motion. The only difference will be in his view of the tree itself, of which, in the former case, he will see every part, but, in the latter, only that portion of it which remains constantly opposite to him, and immediately under his eye.

III

The Physical Sciences

JOHN DALTON

On the Constitution of Bodies*

A Quaker from the Midlands of England, John Dalton (1766–1844) was a wholly self-trained scientist. His contemporary John Davy left the following description of him: "Mr. Dalton's aspect and manner were repulsive. There was no gracefulness belonging to him. His voice was harsh and brawling; his gait stiff and awkward; his style of writing and conversation dry and almost crass. . . . Independence and simplicity of manner and originality were his best qualities." In his *New System of Chemical Philosophy,* Dalton laid the basis for chemical combination. His atomic theory assumes a difference in the relative weights of the basic particles of different kinds of matter. His graphic representation of atoms in combination (as shown in the accompanying plate) provided the foundation for a new scheme of chemical notation.

ON THE CONSTITUTION OF BODIES.

THERE are three distinctions in the kinds of bodies, or three states, which have more especially claimed the attention of philosophical chemists; namely, those which are marked by the terms *elastic fluids, liquids, and solids.* A very familiar instance is exhibited to us in water, of a body, which, in certain circumstances, is capable of assuming all the three states. In steam we recognise a perfectly elastic fluid, in water, a perfect liquid, and in ice a complete solid. These observations have tacitly led to the conclusion which seems universally adopted, that all

* From *A New System of Chemical Philosophy* (1808).

bodies of sensible magnitude, whether liquid or solid, are constituted of a vast number of extremely small particles, or atoms of matter bound together by a force of attraction, which is more or less powerful according to circumstances, and which as it endeavours to prevent their separation, is very properly called in that view, *attraction of cohesion;* but as it collects them from a dispersed state (as from steam into water) it is called, *attraction of aggregation,* or more simply, *affinity.* Whatever names it may go by, they still signify one and the same power. It is not my design to call in question this conclusion, which appears completely satisfactory; but to shew that we have hitherto made no use of it, and that the consequence of the neglect, has been a very obscure view of chemical agency, which is daily growing more so in proportion to the new lights attempted to be thrown upon it.

The opinions I more particularly allude to, are those of Berthollet on the Laws of chemical affinity;[1] such as that chemical agency is proportional to the mass, and that in all chemical unions, there exist insensible gradations in the proportions of the constituent principles. The inconsistence of these opinions, both with reason and observation, cannot, I think, fail to strike every one who takes a proper view of the phenomena.

Whether the ultimate particles of a body, such as water, are all alike, that is, of the same figure, weight, &c. is a question of some importance. From what is known, we have no reason to apprehend a diversity in these particulars: if it does exist in

[1] Claude Louis Berthollet (1748–1822) believed that chemical affinity involved a force similar to gravity and that the type of combination brought about between substances was dependent upon this force. These views led him to propose a theory of combinations in variable rather than constant proportions. Dalton is rightly critical of the latter idea.

water, it must equally exist in the elements constituting water, namely, hydrogen and oxygen. Now it is scarcely possible to conceive how the aggregates of dissimilar particles should be so uniformly the same. If some of the particles of water were heavier than others, if a parcel of the liquid on any occasion were constituted principally of these heavier particles, it must be supposed to affect the specific gravity of the mass, a circumstance not known. Similar observations may be made on other substances. Therefore we may conclude that *the ultimate particles of all homogeneous bodies are perfectly alike in weight, figure, &c.* In other words, every particle of water is like every other particle of water; every particle of hydrogen is like every other particle of hydrogen, &c.

Besides the force of attraction, which, in one character or another, belongs universally to ponderable bodies, we find another force that is likewise universal, or acts upon all matter which comes under our cognisance, namely, a force of repulsion. This is now generally, and I think properly, ascribed to the agency of heat. An atmosphere of this subtile fluid constantly surrounds the atoms of all bodies, and prevents them from being drawn into actual contact. This appears to be satisfactorily proved by the observation, that the bulk of a body may be diminished by abstracting some of its heat: But from what has been stated in the last section, it should seem that enlargement and diminution of bulk depend perhaps more on the arrangement, than on the size of the ultimate particles. Be this as it may, we cannot avoid inferring from the preceding doctrine on heat, and particularly from the section on the natural zero of temperature, that solid bodies, such as ice, contain a large

[127]

portion, perhaps ⅘ of the heat which the same are found to
contain in an elastic state, as steam.

ON THE CONSTITUTION OF PURE ELASTIC FLUIDS.

A pure elastic fluid is one, the constituent particles of which
are all alike, or in no way distinguishable. Steam, or aqueous
vapour, hydrogenous gas, oxygenous gas, azotic gas,[2] and several
others are of this kind. These fluids are constituted of particles
possessing very diffuse atmospheres of heat, the capacity or bulk
of the atmosphere being often one or two thousand times that
of the particle in a liquid or solid form. Whatever therefore
may be the shape or figure of the solid atom abstractedly, when
surrounded by such an atmosphere it must be globular; but as
all the globules in any small given volume are subject to the
same pressure, they must be equal in bulk, and will therefore
be arranged in horizontal strata, like a pile of shot. A volume of
elastic fluid is found to expand whenever the pressure is taken
off. This proves that the repulsion exceeds the attraction in
such case. The absolute attraction and repulsion of the particles
of an elastic fluid, we have no means of estimating, though we
can have little doubt but that the cotemporary energy of both is
great; but the excess of the repulsive energy above the attractive
can be estimated, and the law of increase and diminution be
ascertained in many cases. Thus in steam, the density may be
taken at $\frac{1}{1728}$ that of water; consequently each particle of steam
has 12 times the diameter that one of water has, and must press
upon 144 particles of a watery surface; but the pressure upon
each is equivalent to that of a column of water of 34 feet; there-

2 The early term for nitrogen.

fore the excess of the elastic force in a particle of steam is equal
to the weight of a column of particles of water, whose height is
$34 \times 144 = 4896$ feet. And further, this elastic force decreases
as the distance of the particles increases. With respect to steam
and other elastic fluids then, the force of cohesion is entirely
counteracted by that of repulsion, and the only force which is
efficacious to move the particles is the excess of the repulsion
above the attraction. Thus, if the attraction be as 10 and the
repulsion as 12, the effective repulsive force is as 2. It appears
then, that an elastic fluid, so far from requiring any force to
separate its particles, it always requires a force to retain them in
their situation, or to prevent their separation.

A vessel full of any pure elastic fluid presents to the imagination a picture like one full of small shot. The globules are all
of the same size; but the particles of the fluid differ from those
of the shot, in that they are constituted of an exceedingly small
central atom of solid matter, which is surrounded by an atmosphere of heat, of great density next the atom, but gradually
growing rarer according to some power of the distance; whereas
those of the shot are globules, uniformly hard throughout, and
surrounded with atmospheres of heat of no comparative magnitude.

It is known from experience, that the force of a mass of
elastic fluid is directly as the density. Whence is derived the
law already mentioned, that the repulsive power of each particle
is inversely as its diameter. That is, the *apparent* repulsive
power, if we may so speak; for the real or absolute force of repulsion is not known, as long as we remain ignorant of the
attractive force. When we expand any volume of elastic fluid,
its particles are enlarged, without any material change in the

quantity of their heat; it follows then, that the density of the atmospheres of heat must fluctuate with the pressure. Thus, suppose a measure of air were expanded into 8 measures; then, because the diameters of the elastic particles are as the cube root of the space, the distances of the particles would be twice as great as before, and the elastic atmospheres would occupy nearly 8 times the space they did before, with nearly the same quantity of heat: whence we see that these atmospheres must be diminished in density in nearly the same ratio as the mass of elastic fluid.

Some elastic fluids, as hydrogen, oxygen, &c. resist any pressure that has yet been applied to them. In such then it is evident the repulsive force of heat is more than a match for the affinity of the particles, and the external pressure united. To what extent this would continue we cannot say; but from analogy we might apprehend that a still greater pressure would succeed in giving the attractive force the superiority, when the elastic fluid would become a liquid or solid. In other elastic fluids, as steam, upon the application of compression to a certain degree, the elasticity apparently ceases altogether, and the particles collect in small drops of liquid, and fall down. This phenomenon requires explanation.

From the very abrupt transition of steam from a volume of 1700 to that of 1, without any material increase of pressure, one would be inclined to think that the condensation of it was owing to the *breaking* of a spring, rather than to the *curbing* of one. The last however I believe is the fact. The condensation arises from the action of affinity becoming superior to that of heat, by which the latter is overruled, but not weakened. As the approximation of the particles takes place, their repulsion in-

creases from the condensation of the heat, but their affinity increases, it should seem, in a still greater ratio, till the approximation has attained a certain degree, when an equilibrium between
those two powers takes place, and the liquid, water, is the result.
That this is the true explanation we may learn from what has been
stated [in a previous chapter]; wherein it is shewn that the heat
given off by the condensation of steam, is in all probability no
more than would be given off by any permanently elastic fluid,
could it be mechanically condensed into the like volume, and
is moreover a small portion of the whole heat previously in combination. As far then as the heat is concerned in this phenomenon, the circumstances would be the same, whether the approximation of the particles was the effect of affinity, or of external
mechanical force.

The constitution of a liquid, as water, must then be conceived to be that of an aggregate of particles, exercising in a
most powerful manner the forces of attraction and repulsion,
but nearly in an equal degree. — Of this more in the sequel.

ON THE CONSTITUTION OF MIXED ELASTIC FLUIDS.

When two or more elastic fluids, whose particles do not unite
chemically upon mixture, are brought together, one measure
of each, they occupy the space of two measures, but become uniformly diffused through each other, and remain so, whatever
may be their specific gravities. The fact admits of no doubt; but
explanations have been given in various ways, and none of them
completely satisfactory. As the subject is one of primary importance in forming a system of chemical principles, we must
enter somewhat more fully into the discussion.

Dr. Priestley[3] was one of the earliest to notice the fact: it naturally struck him with surprise, that two elastic fluids, having apparently no affinity for each other, should not arrange themselves according to their specific gravities, as liquids do in like circumstances. Though he found this was not the case after the elastic fluids had once been thoroughly mixed, yet he suggests it as probable, that if two of such fluids could be exposed to each other without agitation, the one specifically heavier would retain its lower situation. He does not so much as hint at such gases being retained in a mixed state by affinity. With regard to his suggestion of two gases being carefully exposed to each other without agitation, I made a series of experiments expressly to determine the question, the results of which are given in the Manch. Memoirs, Vol. 1. *new series*. From these it seems to be decided that gases always intermingle and gradually diffuse themselves amongst each other, if exposed ever so carefully; but it requires a considerable time to produce a complete intermixture, when the surface of communication is small. This time may vary from a minute, to a day or more, according to the quantity of the gases and the freedom of communication.

When or by whom the notion of mixed gases being held together by chemical affinity was first propagated, I do not know; but it seems probable that the notion of water being dissolved in air, led to that of air being dissolved in air. — Philosophers found that water gradually disappeared or evaporated in air, and increased its elasticity; but steam at a low temperature was known to be unable to overcome the resistance of the air, therefore the agency of affinity was necessary to account for the

[3] Joseph Priestley (1733–1804) was one of the most important English chemists of the eighteenth century.

effect. In the permanently elastic fluids indeed, this agency did not seem to be so much wanted, as they are all able to support themselves; but the diffusion through each other was a circumstance which did not admit of an easy solution any other way. In regard to the solution of water in air, it was natural to suppose, nay, one might almost have been satisfied without the aid of experiment, that the different gases would have had different affinities for water, and that the quantities of water dissolved in like circumstances, would have varied according to the nature of the gas. Saussure[4] found however that there was no difference in this respect in the solvent powers of carbonic acid, hydrogen gas, and common air. — It might be expected that at least the *density* of the gas would have some influence upon its solvent powers, that air of half density would take half the water, or the quantity of water would diminish in some proportion to the density; but even here again we are disappointed; whatever be the rarefaction, if water be present, the vapour produces the same elasticity, and the hygrometer finally settles at extreme moisture, as in air of common density in like circumstances. These facts are sufficient to create extreme difficulty in the conception how any principle of affinity or *cohesion* between air and water can be the agent. It is truly astonishing that the same quantity of vapour should cohere to *one* particle of air in a given space, as to *one thousand* in the same space. But the wonder does not cease here; a torricellian vacuum dissolves water; and in this instance we have vapour existing independently of air at all temperatures; what makes it still more remarkable is, the vapour in such vacuum is precisely the same in quantity

4 The chemist Nicolas de Saussure (1709–1790).

and force as in the like volume of any kind of air of extreme moisture.

These and other considerations which occurred to me some years ago, were sufficient to make me altogether abandon the hypothesis of air dissolving water, and to explain the phenomena some other way, or to acknowledge they were inexplicable. In the autumn of 1801, I hit upon an idea which seemed to be exactly calculated to explain the phenomena of vapour; it gave rise to a great variety of experiments upon which a series of essays were founded, which were read before the Literary and Philosophical Society of Manchester, and published in the 5th Vol. of their memoirs, 1802.

The distinguishing feature of the new theory was, that the particles of one gas are not elastic or repulsive in regard to the particles of another gas, but only to the particles of their own kind. Consequently when a vessel contains a mixture of two such elastic fluids, each acts independently upon the vessel, with its proper elasticity, just as if the other were absent, whilst no mutual action between the fluids themselves is observed. This position most effectually provided for the existence of vapour of any temperature in the atmosphere, because it could have nothing but its own weight to support; and it was perfectly obvious why neither more nor less vapour could exist in air of extreme moisture, than in a vacuum of the same temperature. So far then the great object of the theory was attained. The law of the condensation of vapour in the atmosphere by cold, was evidently the same on this scheme, as that of the condensation of pure steam, and experience was found to confirm the conclusion at all temperatures. The only thing now wanting to completely establish the independent existence of aqueous vapour in the atmosphere, was the conformity of other liquids to water, in regard to the diffusion and condensation of their vapour. This was found to take place in several liquids, and particularly in sulphuric ether, one which was most likely to shew any anomaly to advantage if it existed, on account of the great change of expansibility in its vapour at ordinary temperatures. The existence of vapour in the atmosphere and its occasional condensation were thus accounted for; but another question remained, how does it rise from a surface of water subject to the pressure of the atmosphere? The consideration of this made no part of the essays above mentioned, it being apprehended, that if the other two points could be obtained by any theory, this third too, would, in the sequel, be accomplished.

ON CHEMICAL SYNTHESIS.

When any body exists in the elastic state, its ultimate particles are separated from each other to a much greater distance than in any other state; each particle occupies the centre of a comparatively large sphere, and supports its dignity by keeping all the rest, which by their gravity, or otherwise are disposed to encroach up it, at a respectful distance. When we attempt to conceive the *number* of particles in an atmosphere, it is somewhat like attempting to conceive the number of stars in the universe; we are confounded with the thought. But if we limit the subject, by taking a given volume of any gas, we seem persuaded that, let the divisions be ever so minute, the number of particles must be finite; just as in a given space of the universe, the number of stars and planets cannot be infinite.

Chemical analysis and synthesis go no farther than to the separation of particles one from another, and to their reunion. No new creation or destruction of matter is within the reach of chemical agency. We might as well attempt to introduce a new

[135]

planet into the solar system, or to annihilate one already in existence, as to create or destroy a particle of hydrogen. All the changes we can produce, consist in separating particles that are in a state of cohesion or combination, and joining those that were previously at a distance.

In all chemical investigations, it has justly been considered an important object to ascertain the relative *weights* of the simples which constitute a compound. But unfortunately the enquiry has terminated here; whereas from the relative weights in the mass, the relative weights of the ultimate particles or atoms of the bodies might have been inferred, from which their number and weight in various other compounds would appear, in order to assist and to guide future investigations, and to correct their results. Now it is one great object of this work, to shew the importance and advantage of ascertaining *the relative weights of the ultimate particles, both of simple and compound bodies, the number of simple elementary particles which constitute one compound particle, and the number of less compound particles which enter into the formation of one more compound particle.*

If there are two bodies, A and B, which are disposed to combine, the following is the order in which the combinations may take place, beginning with the most simple: namely,

1 atom of A + 1 atom of B = 1 atom of C, binary.
1 atom of A + 2 atoms of B = 1 atom of D, ternary.
2 atoms of A + 1 atom of B = 1 atom of E, ternary.
1 atom of A + 3 atoms of B = 1 atom of F, quaternary.
3 atoms of A + 1 atom of B = 1 atom of G, quaternary.

&c. &c.

[136]

The following general rules may be adopted as guides in all our investigations respecting chemical synthesis.

1ST. When only one combination of two bodies can be obtained, it must be presumed to be a *binary* one, unless some cause appear to the contrary.

2D. When two combinations are observed, they must be presumed to be a *binary* and a *ternary*.

3D. When three combinations are obtained, we may expect one to be a *binary*, and the other two *ternary*.

4TH. When four combinations are observed, we should expect one *binary*, two *ternary*, and one *quaternary*, &c.

5TH. A *binary* compound should always be specifically heavier than the mere mixture of its two ingredients.

6TH. A *ternary* compound should be specifically heavier than the mixture of a binary and a simple, which would, if combined, constitute it; &c.

7TH. The above rules and observations equally apply, when two bodies, such as C and D, D and E, &c. are combined.

From the application of these rules, to the chemical facts already well ascertained, we deduce the following conclusions; 1st. That water is a binary compound of hydrogen and oxygen, and the relative weights of the two elementary atoms are as 1:7, nearly; 2d. That ammonia is a binary compound of hydrogen and azote, and the relative weights of the two atoms are as 1:5, nearly; 3d. That nitrous gas is a binary compound of azote and oxygen, the atoms of which weigh 5 and 7 respectively; that nitric acid is a binary or ternary compound according as it is derived, and consists of one atom of azote and two of oxygen, together weighing 19; that nitrous oxide is a compound similar to nitric acid, and consists of one atom of oxygen and two of azote, weighing 17; that nitrous acid is a binary compound of nitric acid and nitrous gas, weighing 31; that oxynitric acid is a binary compound of nitric acid and oxygen, weighing 26; 4th. That carbonic oxide is a binary compound, consisting of one atom of charcoal, and one of oxygen, together weighing nearly 12; that carbonic acid is a ternary compound, (but sometimes binary) consisting of one atom of charcoal, and two of oxygen, weighing 19; &c. &c. In all these cases the weights are expressed in atoms of hydrogen, each of which is denoted by unity.

In the sequel, the facts and experiments from which these conclusions are derived, will be detailed; as well as a great variety of others from which are inferred the constitution and weight of the ultimate particles of the principal acids, the alkalis, the earths, the metals, the metallic oxides and sulphurets, the long train of neutral salts, and in short, all the chemical compounds which have hitherto obtained a tolerably good analysis. Several of the conclusions will be supported by original experiments.

From the novelty as well as importance of the ideas suggested in this chapter, it is deemed expedient to give plates, exhibiting the mode of combination in some of the more simple cases. A specimen of these accompanies this first part. The elements or atoms of such bodies as are conceived at present to be simple, are denoted by a small circle, with some distinctive mark; and the combinations consist in the juxta-position of two or more of these; when three or more particles of elastic fluids are combined together in one, it is to be supposed that the particles of the same kind repel each other, and therefore take their stations accordingly.

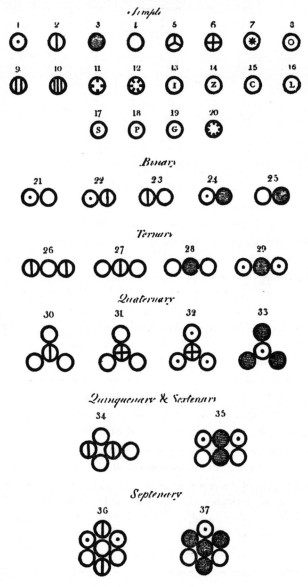

ELEMENTS

Simple

Binary

Ternary

Quaternary

Quinquenary & Sextenary

Septenary

[139]

EXPLANATION OF THE PLATE

This plate contains the arbitrary marks or signs chosen to represent the several chemical elements or ultimate particles.

Fig.			Fig.	
1. Hydrog. its rel. weight	1		11. Strontites - - - - - - -	46
2. Azote - - - - - - - - -	5		12. Barytes - - - - - - - -	68
3. Carbone or charcoal - -	5		13. Iron - - - - - - - - - - -	38
4. Oxygen - - - - - - - -	7		14. Zinc - - - - - - - - - - -	56
5. Phosphorus - - - - - -	9		15. Copper - - - - - - - - -	56
6. Sulphur - - - - - - - -	13		16. Lead - - - - - - - - -	95
7. Magnesia - - - - - - -	20		17. Silver - - - - - - - - -	100
8. Lime - - - - - - - - - -	23		18. Platina - - - - - - - -	100
9. Soda - - - - - - - - - -	28		19. Gold - - - - - - - - -	140
10. Potash - - - - - - - - -	42		20. Mercury - - - - - - - -	167

21. An atom of water or steam, composed of 1 of oxygen and 1 of hydogen, retained in physical contact by a strong affinity, and supposed to be surrounded by a common atmosphere of heat; its relative weight = - - - - - - - -   8
22. An atom of ammonia, composed of 1 of azote and 1 of hydrogen -   6
23. An atom of nitrous gas, composed of 1 of azote and 1 of oxygen -   12
24. An atom of olefiant gas, composed of 1 of carbone and 1 of hydrogen -   6
25. An atom of carbonic oxide composed of 1 of carbone and 1 of oxygen -   12
26. An atom of nitrous oxide, 2 azote + 1 oxygen - - - - - -   17
27. An atom of nitric acid, 1 azote + 2 oxygen - - - - - - -   19
28. An atom of carbonic acid, 1 carbone + 2 oxygen - - - - -   19
29. An atom of carburetted hydrogen, 1 carbone + 2 hydrogen -   7

30. An atom of oxynitric acid, 1 azote + 3 oxygen   - - - - -   26
31. An atom of sulphuric acid, 1 sulphur + 3 oxygen - - - -   34
32. An atom of sulphuretted hydrogen, 1 sulphur + 3 hydrogen -   16
33. An atom of alcohol, 3 carbone + 1 hydrogen - - - - - - -   16
34. An atom of nitrous acid, 1 nitric acid + 1 nitrous gas - -   31
35. An atom of acetous acid, 2 carbone + 2 water - - - - - -   26
36. An atom of nitrate of ammonia, 1 nitric acid + 1 ammonia + 1 water - - - - - - - - - - - - - - - - - -   33
37. An atom of sugar, 1 alcohol + 1 carbonic acid - - - - - -   35

Enough has been given to shew the method; it will be quite unnecessary to devise characters and combinations of them to exhibit to view in this way all the subjects that come under investigation; nor is it necessary to insist upon the accuracy of all these compounds, both in number and weight; the priciple will be entered into more particularly hereafter, as far as respects the individual results. It is not to be understood that all those articles marked as simple substances, are necessarily such by the theory; they are only necessarily of such weights. Soda and Potash, such as they are found in combination with acids, are 28 and 42 respectively in weight; but according to Mr. Davy's very important discoveries, they are metallic oxides; the former then must be considered as composed of an atom of metal, 21, and one of oxygen, 7; and the latter, of an atom of metal, 35, and one of oxygen, 7. Or, soda contains 75 per cent. metal and 25 oxygen; potash, 83.3 metal and 16.7 oxygen. It is particularly remarkable, that according to the above-mentioned gentleman's essay on the Decomposition and Composition of the fixed alkalies, in the Philosophical Transactions (a copy of which essay he has just favoured me with) it appears that "the largest quantity of oxygen indicated by these experiments was, for potash 17, and for soda, 26 parts in 100, and the smallest 13 and 19."

HUMPHRY DAVY

On Some New Phenomena of Chemical Changes Produced by Electricity*

Starting his scientific training as an apprentice to an apothecary, Humphry Davy (1778–1829) intended to enter the medical profession. He was brought by Dr. Thomas Beddoes to the Pneumatic Institution of Bristol in 1795, where he assisted in a series of investigations of the medicinal effects of the newly discovered gases of the atmosphere. After moving to the newly established Royal Institution in London in 1801, Davy commenced his important studies, utilizing voltaic batteries for the decomposition and recomposition of the fixed alkalies. Through experimentation in other areas of chemistry Davy showed the elemented nature of chlorine and also identified iodine. Perhaps best known to the layman were Davy's investigations of the nature of flame, from which he developed the miner's safety lamp. Through his researches and lectures at the Royal Institution, Davy became a major figure in English science and succeeded to the presidency of the Royal Society in 1820.

I N THE Bakerian Lecture which I had the honour of presenting to the Royal Society last year, I described a number of decompositions and chemical changes produced in substances of known composition by electricity, and I ventured to conclude from the general principles on which the phenomena were

* From "The Bakerian Lecture, On Some New Phenomena of Chemical Changes Produced by Electricity, Particularly the Decomposition of Fixed Alkalies, and the Exhibition of the New Substances which Constitute their Bases; and on the General Nature of Alkaline Bodies," *Philosophical Transactions of the Royal Society* (1808).

capable of being explained, that the new methods of investigation promised to lead to a more intimate knowledge than had hitherto been obtained, concerning the true elements of bodies.

This conjecture, then sanctioned only by strong analogies, I am now happy to be able to support by some conclusive facts. In the course of a laborious experimental application of the powers of electro-chemical analysis, to bodies which have appeared simple when examined by common chemical agents, or which at least have never been decomposed, it has been my good fortune to obtain new and singular results.

Such of the series of experiments as are in a tolerably mature state, and capable of being arranged in a connected order, I shall detail in the following sections, particularly those which demonstrate the decomposition and composition of the fixed alkalies, and the production of the new and extraordinary bodies which constitute their bases.

In speaking of novel methods of investigation, I shall not fear to be minute. When the common means of chemical research have been employed, I shall mention only results. A historical detail of the progress of the investigation, of all the difficulties that occurred, and of the manner in which they were overcome, and of all the manipulations employed, would far exceed the limits assigned to this Lecture. It is proper to state, however, that when general facts are mentioned, they are such only as have been deduced from processes carefully performed and often repeated.

The researches I had made on the decomposition of acids, and of alkaline and earthy neutral compounds, proved that the powers of electrical decomposition were proportional to the strength of the opposite electricities in the circuit, and to the conducting power and degree of concentration of the materials employed.

In the first attempts that I made on the decomposition of the fixed alkalies, I acted upon aqueous solutions of potash and soda, saturated at common temperatures, by the highest electrical power I could command, and which was produced by a combination of Voltaic batteries belonging to the Royal Institution, containing 24 plates of copper and zinc of 12 inches square, 100 plates of 6 inches, and 150 of 4 inches square, charged with solutions of alum and nitrous acid; but in these cases, though there was a high intensity of action, the water of the solutions alone was affected, and hydrogen and oxygen disengaged with the production of much heat and violent effervescence.

The presence of water appearing thus to prevent any decomposition, I used potash in igneous fusion. By means of a stream of oxygen gas from a gasometer applied to the flame of a spirit lamp, which was thrown on a platina[1] spoon containing potash, this alkali was kept for some minutes in a strong red heat, and in a state of perfect fluidity. The spoon was preserved in communication with the positive side of the battery of the power of 100 of 6 inches, highly charged; and the connection from the negative side was made by a platina wire.

By this arrangement some brilliant phenomena were produced. The potash appeared a conductor in a high degree, and as long as the communication was preserved, a most intense light was exhibited at the negative wire, and a column of flame, which seemed to be owing to the developement of combustible matter, arose from the point of contact.

[1] Platina is platinum, the precious metal often used in the laboratory because it is resistant to most chemicals and has a high melting point.

When the order was changed, so that the platina spoon was made negative, a vivid and constant light appeared at the opposite point: there was no effect of inflammation round it; but aëriform globules, which inflamed in the atmosphere, rose through the potash.

The platina, as might have been expected, was considerably acted upon; and in the cases when it had been negative, in the highest degree.

The alkali was apparently dry in this experiment; and it seemed probable that the inflammable matter arose from its decomposition. The residual potash was unaltered; it contained indeed a number of dark grey metallic particles, but these proved to be derived from the platina.

I tried several experiments on the electrization of potash rendered fluid by heat, with the hopes of being able to collect the combustible matter, but without success; and I only attained my object, by employing electricity as the common agent for fusion and decomposition.

Though potash, perfectly dried by ignition, is a non-conductor, yet it is rendered a conductor, by a very slight addition of moisture, which does not perceptibly destroy its aggregation; and in this state it readily fuses and decomposes by strong electrical powers.

A small piece of pure potash, which had been exposed for a few seconds to the atmosphere, so as to give conducting power to the surface, was placed upon an insulated disc of platina, connected with the negative side of the battery of the power of 250 of 6 and 4, in a state of intense activity; and a platina wire, communicating with the positive side, was brought in contact with the upper surface of the alkali.[2] The whole apparatus was in the open atmosphere.

Under these circumstances a vivid action was soon observed to take place. The potash began to fuse at both its points of electrization. There was a violent effervescence at the upper surface; at the lower, or negative surface, there was no liberation of elastic fluid; but small globules having a high metallic lustre, and being precisely similar in visible characters to quick-silver, appeared, some of which burnt with explosion and bright flame, as soon as they were formed, and others remained, and were merely tarnished, and finally covered by a white film which formed on their surfaces.*

These globules, numerous experiments soon shewed to be the substance I was in search of, and a peculiar inflammable principle the basis of potash. I found that the platina was in no way connected with the result, except as the medium for exhibiting the electrical powers of decomposition; and a substance of the same kind was produced when pieces of copper, silver, gold, plumbago, or even charcoal were employed for completing the circuit.

The phenomenon was independent of the presence of air; I found that it took place when the alkali was in the vacuum of an exhausted receiver.

The substance was likewise produced from potash fused by means of a lamp, in glass tubes confined by mercury, and furnished with hermetically inserted platina wires by which the

2 The battery would have contained 250 plates, 6 inches square and 4 inches square, as described in an earlier paragraph.

* [In a Manuscript Lecture it is stated by the author, that he discovered Potassium on the 6th October 1807, and Sodium a few days after as reported in Vol. I., p. 109, of the *Collected Works of Sir Humphry Davy*.]

electrical action was transmitted. But this operation could not be carried on for any considerable time; the glass was rapidly dissolved by the action of the alkali, and this substance soon penetrated through the body of the tube.

Soda, when acted upon in the same manner as potash, exhibited an analogous result: but the decomposition demanded greater intensity of action in the batteries, or the alkali was required to be in much thinner and smaller pieces. With the battery of 100 of 6 inches in full activity I obtained good results from pieces of potash weighing from 40 to 70 grains, and of a thickness which made the distance of the electrified metallic surfaces nearly a quarter of an inch; but with a similar power it was impossible to produce the effects of decomposition on pieces of soda of more than 15 or 20 grains in weight, and that only when the distance between the wires was about ⅛ or ⅒ of an inch.

The substance produced from potash remained fluid at the temperature of the atmosphere at the time of its production; that from soda, which was fluid in the degree of heat of the alkali during its formation, became solid on cooling, and appeared having the lustre of silver.

When the power of 250 was used, with a very high charge for the decomposition of soda, the globules often burnt at the moment of their formation, and sometimes violently exploded and separated into smaller globules, which flew with great velocity through the air in a state of vivid combustion, producing a beautiful effect of continued jets of fire.*

* [Recently some able writers on the subject of the progress of science, in noticing the decomposition of the fixed alkalies by Voltaic electricity, have attributed the success of the author to the supposed very powerful batteries of the Laboratory of the Royal Institution—confounding, as I apprehend they have

As in all decompositions of compound substances which I
had previously examined, at the same time that combustible
bases were developed at the negative surface in the electrical
circuit, oxygen was produced, and evolved or carried into com-

done, the really very powerful apparatus, [that of 2000 double plates described
in the Elements of Chemical Philosophy, page 110,]³ constructed subsequently
to the discoveries alluded to, with the means at his disposal, as stated in the
text; and which, from his manner of using them—bringing together to produce
a joint effect, instruments of different sizes, indicates clearly, that he could not
depend on the power of any one battery to effect that separation of elements on
which he calculated, according to the principles of electro-chemical decomposition, established by his former researches. Neither at the time, nor till recently, was the merit of the discovery considered as diminished by the favourable
circumstances under which it was made, and which he himself, in the spirit of
the Baconian philosophy, amply acknowledged, when remarking, in relation to
the discoveries effected by electro-chemical decomposition, in the introduction
to his Elements of Chemical Philosophy, "that the native intellectual powers of
men in different times, are not so much the causes of the different success of
their labours, as the peculiar nature of the means and artificial resources in
their possession." An acknowledgment which the able critic in the Quarterly
Review⁴ for 1812, before alluded to, notices as an example of laudable modesty;
observing as justly as liberally, "It must be remembered, that almost every other
discovery of importance, which has been made in science, has been facilitated
by some previous steps, which have rendered practicable what might otherwise
have presented insuperable obstacles to human ingenuity; nor has such a preparation ever been allowed to detract from the just applause bestowed on those
who have been distinguished from their contemporaries by a more successful
exertion of talent." Unless men of science are actuated by this feeling of justice,
in the bestowing of honour, when deserved, in full and free measure, they
should not find fault with the neglect of science on the part of government.
Flattery is not applicable to the dead; but admiration of their deeds may stimulate the living. He is not to be envied, who would detract from the merit of
the elder Herschel,⁵ because he did not invent the telescope, or from that of
the majority of the distinguished men of this, and of former periods, who have
employed in their researches, means previously existing.]

³ Elements of Chemical Philosophy, Part I, vol. 1, London (J. Johnson & Co.),
1812. The note is by John Davy.

⁴ The Quarterly Review, a general review which was politically conservative,
High Church in religion, and "highbrow" in attitude.

⁵ Friedrich Wilhelm Herschel (1738–1822), a German-born astronomer, spent
most of his life in England; father of an equally prominent scientist son, John
F. W. Herschel.

bination at the positive surface, it was reasonable to conclude that this substance was generated in a similar manner by the electrical action upon the alkalies; and a number of experiments made above mercury, with the apparatus for excluding external air, proved that this was the case.

When solid potash, or soda in its conducting state, was included in glass tubes furnished with electrified platina wires, the new substances were generated at the negative surfaces; the gas given out at the other surface proved by the most delicate examination to be pure oxygen; and unless an excess of water was present, no gas was evolved from the negative surface.

In the synthetical experiments, a perfect coincidence likewise will be found.

I mentioned that the metallic lustre of the substance from potash immediately became destroyed in the atmosphere, and that a white crust formed upon it. This crust I soon found to be pure potash, which immediately deliquesced, and new quantities were formed, which in their turn attracted moisture from the atmosphere till the whole globule disappeared, and assumed the form of a saturated solution of potash.*

When globules were placed in appropriate tubes containing common air or oxygen gas confined by mercury, an absorption of oxygen took place; a crust of alkali instantly formed upon the globule; but from the want of moisture for its solution, the

* Water likewise is decomposed in the process. We shall hereafter see that the bases of the fixed alkalies act upon this substance with greater energy than any other known bodies. The minute theory of the oxidation of the bases of the alkalies in the free air, is this:—oxygen gas is first attracted by them, and alkali formed. This alkali speedily absorbs water. This water is again decomposed. Hence, during the conversion of a globule into alkaline solution, there is a constant and rapid disengagement of small quantities of gas.

process stopped, the interior being defended from the action of the gas.

With the substance from soda, the appearances and effects were analogous.

When the substances were strongly heated, confined in given portions of oxygen, a rapid combustion with a brilliant white flame was produced, and the metallic globules were found converted into a white and solid mass, which in the case of the substance from potash was found to be potash, and in the case of that from soda, soda.

Oxygen gas was absorbed in this operation, and nothing emitted which affected the purity of the residual air.

The alkalies produced were apparently dry, or at least contained no more moisture than might well be conceived to exist in the oxygen gas absorbed; and their weights considerably exceeded those of the combustible matters consumed.

The processes on which these conclusions are founded will be fully described hereafter, when the minute details which are necessary will be explained, and the proportions of oxygen, and of the respective inflammable substances which enter into union to form the fixed alkalies, will be given.

It appears then, that in these facts there is the same evidence for the decomposition of potash and soda into oxygen and two peculiar substances, as there is for the decomposition of sulphuric and phosphoric acids and the metallic oxides into oxygen and their respective combustible bases.

In the analytical experiments, no substances capable of decomposition are present but the alkalies and a minute portion of moisture; which seems in no other way essential to the result, than in rendering them conductors at the surface: for the new substances are not generated till the interior, which is dry, begins to be fused; they explode when in rising through the fused alkali they come in contact with the heated moistened surface; they cannot be produced from crystallized alkalies, which contain much water; and the effect produced by the electrization of ignited potash, which contains no sensible quantity of water, confirms the opinion of their formation independently of the presence of this substance.

The combustible bases of the fixed alkalies seem to be repelled as other combustible substances, by positively electrified surfaces, and attracted by negatively electrified surfaces, and the oxygen follows the contrary order; or the oxygen being naturally possessed of the negative energy, and the bases of the positive, do not remain in combination when either of them is brought into an electrical state opposite to its natural one. In the synthesis, on the contrary, the natural energies or attractions come in equilibrium with each other; and when these are in a low state at common temperatures, a slow combination is effected; but when they are exalted by heat, a rapid union is the result; and, as in other like cases, with the production of fire. — A number of circumstances relating to the agencies of the bases of the alkalies will be immediately stated, and will be found to offer confirmations of these general conclusions.

MICHAEL FARADAY

On the Chemical History of a Candle*

Michael Faraday (1791–1867), one of the most remarkable men of science in the nineteenth century, was a self-educated scientist. Apprenticed to a bookbinder at the age of thirteen, he eventually found employment at the Royal Institution (which had been founded by Benjamin, Count Rumford) as assistant to Sir Humphry Davy, the famous chemist. Eventually Faraday became Davy's successor and established his own reputation by a series of brilliant discoveries in chemistry and physics, including studies of the liquefaction of gases, the discovery of benzene, and, above all, fundamental contributions to the new sciences of electrochemistry and electromagnetism. Equally renowned as lecturer and discoverer, Faraday gave many courses of lectures at the Royal Institution, designed primarily for juvenile audiences and delivered during the Christmas season. Of these the most famous is the set dealing with the chemical history of a candle, delivered during the Christmas holiday season of 1860–1861 (and also given earlier, in 1848–1849 and 1854–1855). The first chapter of the book in which these lectures were eventually published is given below.

I PURPOSE, in return for the honor you do us by coming to see what are our proceedings here, to bring before you, in the course of these lectures, the Chemical History of a Candle. I have taken this subject on a former occasion, and, were it left to my own will, I should prefer to repeat it almost every year, so abundant is the interest that attaches itself to the subject, so wonderful are the varieties of outlet which if offers into the various departments of philosophy. There is not a law

* From *A Course of Six Lectures on the Chemical History of a Candle* (1861).

under which any part of this universe is governed which does not come into play and is touched upon in these phenomena. There is no better, there is no more open door by which you can enter into the study of natural philosophy than by considering the physical phenomena of a candle. I trust, therefore, I shall not disappoint you in choosing this for my subject rather than any newer topic, which could not be better, were it even so good.

And, before proceeding, let me say this also: that, though our subject be so great, and our intention that of treating it honestly, seriously, and philosophically, yet I mean to pass away from all those who are seniors[1] among us. I claim the privilege of speaking to juveniles as a juvenile myself. I have done so on former occasions, and, if you please, I shall do so again. And, though I stand here with the knowledge of having the words I utter given to the world, yet that shall not deter me from speaking in the same familiar way to those whom I esteem nearest to me on this occasion.

And now, my boys and girls, I must first tell you of what candles are made. Some are great curiosities. I have here some bits of timber, branches of trees particularly famous for their burning. And here you see a piece of that very curious substance, taken out of some of the bogs in Ireland, called *candle-wood;* a hard, strong, excellent wood, evidently fitted for good work as a register for force, and yet, withal, burning so well that where it is found they make splinters of it, and torches, since it burns like a candle, and gives a very good light indeed. And in

[1] The word "seniors" does not refer to students at any particular stage, but rather to grown-ups who had accompanied the boys and girls composing this juvenile audience.

this wood we have one of the most beautiful illustrations of the general nature of a candle that I can possibly give. The fuel provided, the means of bringing that fuel to the place of chemical action, the regular and gradual supply of air to that place of action—heat and light—all produced by a little piece of wood of this kind, forming, in fact, a natural candle.

But we must speak of candles as they are in commerce. Here are a couple of candles commonly called dips. They are made of lengths of cotton cut off, hung up by a loop, dipped into melted tallow, taken out again and cooled, then redipped, until there is an accumulation of tallow round the cotton. In order that you may have an idea of the various characters of these candles, you see these which I hold in my hand — they are very small and very curious. They are, or were, the candles used by the miners in coal mines. In olden times the miner had to find his own candles, and it was supposed that a small candle would not so soon set fire to the fire-damp in the coal mines as a large one; and for that reason, as well as for economy's sake, he had candles made of this sort — 20, 30, 40, or 60 to the pound. They have been replaced since then by the steel-mill, and then by the Davy lamp,[2] and other safety-lamps of various kinds. I have here a candle that was taken out of the *Royal George*,[3] it is

[2] The Davy lamp, invented by Sir Humphry Davy in 1815, was constructed with a window of wire gauze to prevent the flame of the lamp from igniting the explosive mixture of gases found in mines. Davy, Faraday's predecessor as professor at the Royal Institution, made many important scientific discoveries, but it was said that his greatest was Faraday.

[3] In the original edition, the editor, William Crookes, added a footnote as follows: "The Royal George sunk at Spithead on the 29th August, 1782. Colonel [Sir Charles William] Pasley commenced operations for the removal of the wreck by the explosion of gunpowder, in August, 1839. The candle which Professor Faraday exhibited must therefore have been exposed to the action of salt water for upwards of fifty-seven years."

said, by Colonel Pasley. It has been sunk in the sea for many years, subject to the action of salt water. It shows you how well candles may be preserved; for, though it is cracked about and broken a good deal, yet when lighted it goes on burning regularly, and the tallow resumes its natural condition as soon as it is fused.

Mr. Field,[4] of Lambeth, has supplied me abundantly with beautiful illustrations of the candle and its materials; I shall therefore now refer to them. And, first, there is the suet — the fat of the ox — Russian tallow, I believe, employed in the manufacture of these dips, which Gay-Lussac,[5] or some one who intrusted him with his knowledge, converted into that beautiful substance, stearin, which you see lying beside it. A candle, you know, is not now a greasy thing like an ordinary tallow candle, but a clean thing, and you may almost scrape off and pulverize the drops which fall from it without soiling any thing. This is the process he adopted: The fat or tallow is first boiled with quick-lime, and made into a soap, and then the soap is decomposed by sulphuric acid, which takes away the lime, and leaves the fat rearranged as stearic acid, while a quantity of glycerin is produced at the same time. Glycerin — absolutely a sugar, or a substance similar to sugar — comes out of the tallow in this chemical change. The oil is then pressed out of it; and you see here this series of pressed cakes, showing how beautifully

4 Joshua Field, Civil Engineer and partner in the firm of Maudslay, Sons & Field which constructed in 1838 steam engines capable of propelling a vessel across the Atlantic. He was one of the founders of the Institute of Civil Engineers (1817).

5 Joseph-Louis Gay-Lussac, a French chemist known today chiefly for the law which states that whenever two or more gasses combine to form a gaseous product, the volumes — referred to the same temperature and pressure — are in the ratio of simple whole numbers.

the impurities are carried out by the oily part as the pressure goes on increasing, and at last you have left that substance, which is melted, and cast into candles as here represented. The candle I have in my hand is a stearin candle, made of stearin from tallow in the way I have told you. Then here is a sperm candle, which comes from the purified oil of the spermaceti whale. Here, also, are yellow bees'-wax and refined bees'-wax, from which candles are made. Here, too, is that curious substance called paraffine, and some paraffine candles, made of paraffine obtained from the bogs of Ireland. I have here also a substance brought from Japan since we have forced an entrance into that out-of-the-way place[6] — a sort of wax which a kind friend has sent me, and which forms a new material for the manufacture of candles.

And how are these candles made? I have told you about dips, and I will show you how moulds are made. Let us imagine any of these candles to be made of materials which can be cast. "Cast!" you say. "Why, a candle is a thing that melts, and surely if you can melt it you can cast it." Not so. It is wonderful, in the progress of manufacture, and in the consideration of the means best fitted to produce the required result, how things turn up which one would not expect beforehand. Candles can not always be cast. A wax candle can never be cast. It is made by a particular process which I can illustrate in a minute or two, but I must not spend much time on it. Wax is a thing which, burning so well, and melting so easily in a candle, can not be

6 Reference is made to the entrance into Japan by Westerners, not necessarily the British, dating from the activities of Commodore Matthew Calbraith Perry, sent to Japan in November 1852. Perry obtained a treaty in March, 1854, establishing certain trading rights which marked the beginning of modern contacts between Japan and the West.

cast. However, let us take a material that can be cast. Here is a frame, with a number of moulds fastened in it. The first thing to be done is to put a wick through them. Here is one — a plaited wick, which does not require snuffing — supported by a little wire. It goes to the bottom, where it is pegged in; the little peg holding the cotton tight, and stopping the aperture so that nothing fluid shall run out. At the upper part there is a little bar placed across, which stretches the cotton and holds it in the mould. The tallow is then melted, and the moulds are filled. After a certain time, when the moulds are cool, the excess of tallow is poured off at one corner, and then cleaned off altogether, and the ends of the wick cut away. The candles alone then remain in the mould, and you have only to upset them, as I am doing, when out they tumble, for the candles are made in the form of cones, being narrower at the top than at the bottom; so that, what with their form and their own shrinking, they only need a little shaking and out they fall. In the same way are made these candles of stearin and of paraffine. It is a curious thing to see how wax candles are made. A lot of cottons[7] are hung upon frames, as you see here, and covered with metal tags at the ends to keep the wax from covering the cotton in those places. These are carried to a heater, where the wax is melted. As you see, the frames can turn round; and, as they turn, a man takes a vessel of wax and pours it first down one, and then the next, and the next, and so on. When he has gone once round, if it is sufficiently cool, he gives the first a second coat, and so on until they are all of the required thickness. When they have been thus clothed, or fed, or made up to that thickness, they are taken off and placed elsewhere. I

7 The cottons are cotton threads or wicks.

have here, by the kindness of Mr. Field, several specimens of these candles. Here is one only half finished. They are then taken down and well rolled upon a fine stone slab, and the conical top is moulded by properly shaped tubes, and the bottoms cut off and trimmed. This is done so beautifully that they can make candles in this way weighing exactly four or six to the pound, or any number they please.

We must not, however, take up more time about the mere manufacture, but go a little farther into the matter. I have not yet referred you to luxuries in candles (for there is such a thing as luxury in candles). See how beautifully these are colored; you see here mauve, Magenta,[8] and all the chemical colors recently introduced, applied to candles. You observe, also, different forms employed. Here is a fluted pillar most beautifully shaped; and I have also here some candles sent me by Mr. Pearsall, which are ornamented with designs upon them, so that, as they burn, you have, as it were, a glowing sun above, and a bouquet of flowers beneath. All, however, that is fine and beautiful is not useful. These fluted candles, pretty as they are, are bad candles; they are bad because of their external shape. Nevertheless, I show you these specimens, sent to me from kind friends on all sides, that you may see what is done and what may be done in this or that direction; although, as I have said, when we come to these refinements, we are obliged to sacrifice a little in utility.

Now as to the light of the candle. We will light one or two, and set them at work in the performance of their proper func-

[8] Both mauve and Magenta were new colors, produced synthetically in Faraday's day from coal tar. Magenta was capitalized because it had been named after a city in Italy where a battle occurred about the time the new dye was discovered.

tions. You observe a candle is a very different thing from a lamp. With a lamp you take a little oil, fill your vessel, put in a little moss or some cotton prepared by artificial means, and then light the top of the wick. When the flame runs down the cotton to the oil, it gets extinguished, but it goes on burning in the part above. Now I have no doubt you will ask how it is that the oil which will not burn of itself gets up to the top of the cotton, where it will burn. We shall presently examine that; but there is a much more wonderful thing about the burning of a candle than this. You have here a solid substance with no vessel to contain it; and how is it that this solid substance can get up to the place where the flame is? How is it that this solid gets there, it not being a fluid? or, when it is made a fluid, then how is it that it keeps together? This is a wonderful thing about a candle.

We have here a good deal of wind, which will help us in some of our illustrations, but tease us in others; for the sake, therefore, of a little regularity, and to simplify the matter, I shall make a quiet flame, for who can study a subject when there are difficulties in the way not belonging to it? Here is a clever invention of some costermonger[9] or street-stander in the market-place for the shading of their candles on Saturday nights, when they are selling their greens, or potatoes, or fish. I have very often admired it. They put a lamp-glass round the candle, supported on a kind of gallery,[10] which clasps it, and it can be slipped up and down as required. By the use of this lamp-glass, employed in the same way, you have a steady flame, which you

[9] A costermonger is one who sells fruit or vegetables from a street stand, barrow, or cart.
[10] A gallery is a ring with perforated sides into which the glass chimney is set.

can look at, and carefully examine, as I hope you will do, at home.

You see then, in the first instance, that a beautiful cup is formed. As the air comes to the candle, it moves upward by the force of the current which the heat of the candle produces, and it so cools all the sides of the wax, tallow, or fuel as to keep the edge much cooler than the part within; the part within melts by the flame that runs down the wick as far as it can go before it is extinguished, but the part on the outside does not melt. If I made a current in one direction, my cup would be lop-sided, and the fluid would consequently run over; for the same force of gravity which holds worlds together holds this fluid in a horizontal position, and if the cup be not horizontal, of course the fluid will run away in guttering. You see, therefore, that the cup is formed by this beautifully regular ascending current of air playing upon all sides, which keeps the exterior of the candle cool. No fuel would serve for a candle which has not the property of giving this cup, except such fuel as the Irish bog-wood, where the material itself is like a sponge and holds its own fuel. You see now why you would have had such a bad result if you were to burn these beautiful candles that I have shown you, which are irregular, intermittent in their shape, and can not, therefore, have that nicely-formed edge to the cup which is the great beauty in a candle. I hope you will now see that the perfection of a process — that is, its utility — is the better point of beauty about it. It is not the best looking thing, but the best acting thing, which is the most advantageous to us. This good-looking candle is a bad-burning one. There will be a guttering round about it because of the irregularity of the stream of air and the badness of the cup which is formed thereby. You may see some pretty examples (and I trust you will notice these instances) of the action of the ascending current when you have a little gutter run down the side of a candle, making it thicker there than it is elsewhere. As the candle goes on burning, that keeps its place and forms a little pillar sticking up by the side, because, as it rises higher above the rest of the wax or fuel, the air gets better round it, and it is more cooled and better able to resist the action of the heat at a little distance. Now the greatest mistakes and faults with regard to candles, as in many other things, often bring with them instruction which we should not receive if they had not occurred. We come here to be philosophers,[11] and I hope you will always remember that whenever a result happens, especially if it be new, you should say, "What is the cause? Why does it occur?" and you will, in the course of time, find out the reason.

Then there is another point about these candles which will answer a question — that is, as to the way in which this fluid gets out of the cup, up the wick, and into the place of combustion. You know that the flames on these burning wicks in candles made of bees'-wax, stearin, or spermaceti, do not run down to the wax or other matter, and melt it all away, but keep to their own right place. They are fenced off from the fluid below, and do not encroach on the cup at the sides. I can not imagine a more beautiful example than the condition of adjustment under which a candle makes one part subserve to the other to the very end of its action. A combustible thing like that, burning away gradually, never being intruded upon

11 Faraday used the word *philosophers* in its older signification of natural philosopher, or physical scientist. Faraday, throughout his life, refused to apply to himself the new term, invented in the nineteenth century, of *physicist*, but always insisted on referring to himself as a natural philosopher.

by the flame, is a very beautiful sight, especially when you come to learn what a vigorous thing flame is — what power it has of destroying the wax itself when it gets hold of it, and of disturbing its proper form if it come only too near.

But how does the flame get hold of the fuel? There is a beautiful point about that — *capillary attraction.* "Capillary attraction!" you say — "the attraction of hairs." Well, never mind the name; it was given in old times, before we had a good understanding of what the real power was. It is by what is called capillary attraction that the fuel is conveyed to the part where combustion goes on, and is deposited there, not in a careless way, but very beautifully in the very midst of the centre of action, which takes place around it. Now I am going to give you one or two instances of capillary attraction. It is that kind of action or attraction which makes two things that do not dissolve in each other still hold together. When you wash your hands, you wet them thoroughly; you take a little soap to make the adhesion better, and you find your hand remains wet. This is by that kind of attraction of which I am about to speak. And, what is more, if your hands are not soiled (as they almost always are by the usages of life), if you put your finger into a little warm water, the water will creep a little way up the finger, though you may not stop to examine it. I have here a substance which is rather porous — a column of salt — and I will pour into the plate at the bottom, not water, as it appears, but a saturated solution of salt which can not absorb more, so that the action which you see will not be due to its dissolving any thing. We may consider the plate to be the candle, and the salt the wick, and this solution the melted tallow. (I have colored the fluid, that you may see the action better.) You observe that, now I pour

[163]

in the fluid, it rises and gradually creeps up the salt higher and higher; and provided the column does not tumble over, it will go to the top. If this blue solution were combustible, and we were to place a wick at the top of the salt, it would burn as it entered into the wick. It is a most curious thing to see this kind of action taking place, and to observe how singular some of the circumstances are about it. When you wash your hands, you take a towel to wipe off the water; and it is by that kind of wetting, or that kind of attraction which makes the towel become wet with water, that the wick is made wet with the tallow. I have known some careless boys and girls (indeed, I have known it happen to careful people as well) who, having washed their hands and wiped them with a towel, have thrown the towel over the side of the basin, and before long it has drawn all the water out of the basin and conveyed it to the floor, because it happened to be thrown over the side in such a way as to serve the purpose of a siphon. That you may the better see the way in which the substances act one upon another, I have here a vessel made of wire gauze filled with water, and you may compare it in its action to the cotton in one respect, or to a piece of calico in the other. In fact, wicks are sometimes made of a kind of wire gauze. You will observe that this vessel is a porous thing; for if I pour a little water on to the top, it will run out at the bottom. You would be puzzled for a good while if I asked you what the state of this vessel is, what is inside it, and why is it there? The vessel is full of water, and yet you see the water goes in and runs out as if it were empty. In order to prove this to you I have only to empty it. The reason is this: the wire, being once wetted, remains wet; the meshes are so small that the fluid is attracted so strongly from the one side to the other as to remain in the vessel, although it is porous. In like manner, the particles of melted tallow ascend the cotton and get to the top; other particles then follow by their mutual attraction for each other, and as they reach the flame they are gradually burned.

Here is another application of the same principle. You see this bit of cane. I have seen boys about the streets, who are very anxious to appear like men, take a piece of cane, and light it, and smoke it, as an imitation of a cigar. They are enabled to do so by the permeability of the cane in one direction, and by its capillarity. If I place this piece of cane on a plate containing some camphene (which is very much like paraffine in its general character), exactly in the same manner as the blue fluid rose through the salt will this fluid rise through the piece of cane. There being no pores at the side, the fluid can not go in that direction, but must pass through its length. Already the fluid is at the top of the cane; now I can light it and make it serve as a candle. The fluid has risen by the capillary attraction of the piece of cane, just as it does through the cotton in the candle.

Now the only reason why the candle does not burn all down the side of the wick is that the melted tallow extinguishes the flame. You know that a candle, if turned upside down, so as to allow the fuel to run upon the wick, will be put out. The reason is, that the flame has not had time to make the fuel hot enough to burn, as it does above, where it is carried in small quantities into the wick, and has all the effect of the heat exercised upon it.

There is another condition which you must learn as regards the candle, without which you would not be able fully to understand the philosophy of it, and that is the vaporous condition of the fuel. In order that you may understand that, let me show you a very pretty but very commonplace experiment. If you blow a candle out cleverly, you will see the vapor rise from it. You have, I know, often smelt the vapor of a blown-out candle, and a very bad smell it is; but if you blow it out cleverly, you will be able to see pretty well the vapor into which this solid matter is transformed. I will blow out one of these candles in such a way as not to disturb the air around it by the continuing action of my breath; and now, if I hold a lighted taper two or three inches from the wick, you will observe a train of fire going through the air till it reaches the candle. I am obliged to be quick and ready, because if I allow the vapor time to cool, it becomes condensed into a liquid or solid, or the stream of combustible matter gets disturbed.

Now as to the shape or form of the flame. It concerns us much to know about the condition which the matter of the candle finally assumes at the top of the wick, where you have such beauty and brightness as nothing but combustion or flame can produce. You have the glittering beauty of gold and silver, and the still higher lustre of jewels like the ruby and diamond; but none of these rival the brilliancy and beauty of flame. What diamond can shine like flame? It owes its lustre at night-time to the very flame shining upon it. The flame shines in darkness, but the light which the diamond has is as nothing until the flame shines upon it, when it is brilliant again. The candle alone shines by itself and for itself, or for those who have arranged the materials. Now let us look a little at the form of the flame as you see it under the glass shade. It is steady and equal, and its general form is that which is represented in the diagram, varying with atmospheric disturbances, and also varying according to the size of the candle. It is a bright oblong, brighter at the top than toward the bottom, with the wick in the middle, and, besides the wick in the middle, certain darker parts toward the bottom, where the ignition is not so perfect as in the part above. I have a drawing here, sketched many years ago by Hooker [sic],[12] when he made his investigations. It is the drawing of the flame of a lamp, but it will apply to the flame of a candle. The cup of the candle is the vessel or lamp; the melted spermaceti is the oil; and the wick is common to both. Upon that he sets this little flame, and then he represents what is true, a certain quantity of matter rising about it which you do not see, and which, if you have not been here before, or are not familiar with the subject, you will not know of. He has here represented the parts of the surrounding atmosphere that are very essential to the flame, and that are always present with it. There is a current formed, which draws the flame out; for the flame which you see is really drawn out by the current, and drawn upward to a great height, just as Hooker has here shown you by that prolongation of the current in the diagram. You may see this by taking a lighted candle, and putting it in the sun so as to get its shadow thrown on a piece of paper. How remarkable it is that that thing which is light enough to produce shadows of other objects can be made to throw its own shadow on a piece of white paper or card, so that you can actually see streaming round the flame something which is not part of the flame, but is ascending and drawing the flame upward. Now I am going to imitate the sunlight by applying the voltaic battery to the electric lamp. You now see our sun and

[12] Faraday is clearly referring to Robert Hooke whose description of a candle flame is found in his *Lampas,* 1677.

[167]

its great luminosity; and by placing a candle between it and the screen, we get the shadow of the flame. You observe the shadow of the candle and of the wick; then there is a darkish part, as represented in the diagram, and then a part which is more distinct. Curiously enough, however, what we see in the shadow as the darkest part of the flame is, in reality, the brightest part; and here you see streaming upward the ascending current of hot air, as shown by Hooker, which draws out the flame, supplies it with air, and cools the sides of the cup of melted fuel.

I can give you here a little farther illustration, for the purpose of showing you how flame goes up or down according to the current. I have here a flame — it is not a candle flame — but you can, no doubt, by this time generalize enough to be able to compare one thing with another: what I am about to do is to change the ascending current that takes the flame upward into a descending current. This I can easily do by the little apparatus you see before me. The flame, as I have said, is not a candle flame, but it is produced by alcohol, so that it shall not smoke too much. I will also color the flame with another substance, so that you may trace its course; for, with the spirit alone, you could hardly see well enough to have the opportunity of tracing its direction. By lighting this spirit of wine[13] we have then a flame produced, and you observe that when held in the air it naturally goes upward. You understand now, easily enough, why flames go up under ordinary circumstances: it is because of the draught of air by which the combustion is formed. But now, by blowing the flame down, you see I am enabled to make it go downward into this little chimney, the direction of the cur-

[13] "Spirit of wine" denotes alcohol, the "spirit" distilled from wine.

rent being changed. Before we have concluded this course of lectures we shall show you a lamp in which the flame goes up and the smoke goes down, or the flame goes down and the smoke goes up. You see, then, that we have the power in this way of varying the flame in different directions.

There are now some other points that I must bring before you. Many of the flames you see here vary very much in their shape by the currents of air blowing around them in different directions; but we can, if we like, make flames so that they will look like fixtures, and we can photograph them — indeed, we have to photograph them — so that they become fixed to us, if we wish to find out every thing concerning them. That, however, is not the only thing I wish to mention. If I take a flame sufficiently large, it does not keep that homogeneous, that uniform condition of shape, but it breaks out with a power of life which is quite wonderful. I am about to use another kind of fuel, but one which is truly and fairly a representative of the wax or tallow of a candle. I have here a large ball of cotton, which will serve as a wick. And, now that I have immersed it in spirit and applied a light to it, in what way does it differ from an ordinary candle? Why, it differs very much in one respect, that we have a vivacity and power about it, a beauty and a life entirely different from the light presented by a candle. You see those fine tongues of flame rising up. You have the same general disposition of the mass of the flame from below upward, but, in addition to that, you have this remarkable breaking out into tongues which you do not perceive in the case of a candle. Now, why is this? I must explain it to you, because, when you understand that perfectly, you will be able to follow me better in what I have to say hereafter. I suppose some here will have made

[169]

for themselves the experiment I am going to show you. Am I right in supposing that any body here has played at snapdragon? I do not know a more beautiful illustration of the philosophy of flame, as to a certain part of its history, than the game of snapdragon. First, here is the dish; and let me say, that when you play snapdragon properly you ought to have the dish well warmed; you ought also to have warm plums, and warm brandy, which, however, I have not got. When you have put the spirit into the dish, you have the cup and the fuel; and are not the raisins acting like the wicks? I now throw the plums into the dish, and light the spirit, and you see those beautiful tongues of flame that I refer to. You have the air creeping in over the edge of the dish forming these tongues. Why? Because, through the force of the current and the irregularity of the action of the flame, it can not flow in one uniform stream. The air flows in so irregularly that you have what would otherwise be a single image broken up into a variety of forms, and each of these little tongues has an independent existence of its own. Indeed, I might say, you have here a multitude of independent candles. You must not imagine, because you see these tongues all at once, that the flame is of this particular shape. A flame of that shape is never so at any one time. Never is a body of flame, like that which you just saw rising from the ball, of the shape it appears to you. It consists of a multitude of different shapes, succeeding each other so fast that the eye is only able to take cognizance of them all at once. In former times I purposely analyzed a flame of that general character, and the diagram shows you the different parts of which it is composed. They do not occur all at once; it is only because we see these shapes in such rapid succession that they seem to us to exist all at one time.

It is too bad that we have not got farther than my game of snapdragon; but we must not, under any circumstances, keep you beyond your time. It will be a lesson to me in future to hold you more strictly to the philosophy of the thing than to take up your time so much with these illustrations.

JAMES PRESCOTT JOULE

On Matter, Living Force and Heat*

James Prescott Joule (1818–1889) received his initiation into science under John Dalton, at the time president of the Manchester Literary and
Philosophical Society. Of independent means, Joule was a private re-
searcher without academic connections, whose laboratory was located
in his home. Librarian, honorary secretary, vice-president and finally
president of the Manchester Literary and Philosophical Society, Joule
typifies the rise in nineteenth-century England of the provincial indus-
trial city as scientific center. A careful experimenter, Joule is known for
many discoveries, such as the change in the length of an iron bar on
being magnetized. Two important physical laws are named after him,
one relating the rate at which heat is evolved in a metallic conductor to
the resistance of the conductor multiplied by the square of the current;
the other, known as the third law of thermodynamics, stating the general
equivalence of heat and all forms of energy. In the selection printed below, a lecture given at St. Ann's Church Reading Room in 1847, Joule
describes his work leading up to the principle generally known today as
the law of conservation of energy.

IN OUR notion of matter two ideas are generally included,
namely, those of *impenetrability* and *extension*. By the extension of matter we mean the space which it occupies; by its
impenetrability we mean that two bodies cannot exist at the
same time in the same place. Impenetrability and extension
cannot with much propriety be reckoned among the *properties*
of matter, but deserve rather to be called its *definitions*, be-

* From "On Matter, Living Force and Heat," A Lecture at St. Ann's Church
Reading Room (1847).

cause nothing that does not possess the two qualities bears the name of matter. If we conceive of impenetrability and extension we have the idea of matter, and of matter only.

Matter is endowed with an exceedingly great variety of wonderful properties, some of which are common to all matter, while others are present variously, so as to constitute a difference between one body and another. Of the first of these classes, the attraction of gravitation is one of the most important. We observe its presence readily in all solid bodies, the component parts of which are, in the opinion of Majocchi,[1] held together by this force. If we break the body in pieces, and remove the separate pieces to a distance from each other, they will still be found to attract each other, though in a very slight degree, owing to the force being one which diminishes very rapidly as the bodies are removed further from one another. The larger the bodies are the more powerful is the force of attraction subsisting between them. Hence, although the force of attraction between small bodies can only be appreciated by the most delicate apparatus except in the case of contact, that which is occasioned by a body of immense magnitude, such as the earth, becomes very considerable. This attraction of bodies towards the earth constitutes what is called their *weight* or *gravity,* and is always exactly proportional to the quantity of matter. Hence, if any body be found to weigh 2 lb., while another only weighs 1 lb., the former will contain exactly twice as much matter as the latter; and this is the case, whatever the bulk of the bodies may be: 2 lb. weight of air contains exactly twice the quantity of matter that 1 lb. of lead does.

[1] Giovanni Alessandro Majocchi (d. 1854), professor of physics and mechanics at Milan, later at Turin.

Matter is sometimes endowed with other kinds of attraction besides the attraction of gravitation; sometimes also it possesses the faculty of *repulsion,* by which force the particles tend to separate further from each other. Wherever these forces exist, they do not supersede the attraction of gravitation. Thus the weight of a piece of iron or steel is in no way affected by imparting to it the magnetic virtue.

Besides the force of gravitation, there is another very remarkable property displayed in an equal degree by every kind of matter — its perseverance in any condition, whether of rest or motion, in which it may have been placed. This faculty has received the name of *inertia,* signifying passiveness, or the inability of any thing to change its own state. It is in consequence of this property that a body at rest cannot be set in motion without the application of a certain amount of force to it, and also that when once the body has been set in motion it will never stop of itself, but continue to move straight forwards with a uniform velocity until acted upon by another force, which, if applied contrary to the direction of motion, will retard it, if in the same direction will accelerate it, and if sideways will cause it to move in a curved direction. In the case in which the force is applied contrary in direction, but equal in degree to that which set the body first in motion, it will be entirely deprived of motion whatever time may have elapsed since the first impulse, and to whatever distance the body may have travelled.

From these facts it is obvious that the force expended in setting a body in motion is carried by the body itself, and exists with it and in it, throughout the whole course of its motion. This force possessed by moving bodies is termed by mechanical

philosophers *vis viva*,[2] or *living force.* The term may be deemed
by some inappropriate, inasmuch as there is no life, properly
speaking, in question; but it is *useful* in order to distinguish
the moving force from that which is stationary in its character,
as the force of gravity. When, therefore, in the subsequent parts
of this lecture I employ the term *living force,* you will understand that I simply mean the force of bodies in motion. The
living force of bodies is regulated by their weight and by the
velocity of their motion. You will readily understand that if a
body of a certain weight possess a certain quantity of living
force, twice as much living force will be possessed by a body of
twice the weight, provided both bodies move with equal velocity. But the law by which the *velocity* of a body regulates its
living force is not so obvious. At first sight one would imagine
that the living force would be simply proportional to the velocity, so that if a body moved twice as fast as another, it would
have twice the impetus or living force. Such, however, is not the
case; for if three bodies of equal weight move with the respective velocities of 1, 2, and 3 miles per hour, their living forces
will be found to be proportional to those numbers multiplied
by themselves, viz., to 1×1, 2×2, 3×3, or 1, 4, and 9, the
squares of 1, 2, and 3. This remarkable law may be proved in
several ways. A bullet fired from a gun at a certain velocity
will pierce a block of wood to only one quarter of the depth it
would if propelled at twice the velocity. Again, if a cannon-
ball were found to fly at a certain velocity when propelled by a
given charge of gunpowder, and it were required to load the
cannon so as to propel the ball with twice that velocity, it would
be found necessary to employ four times the weight of powder

2 "Living force" or "vis viva" is now denoted by kinetic energy.

previously used. Thus, also, it will be found that a railway-train going at 70 miles per hour possesses 100 times the impetus, or living force, that it does when travelling at 7 miles per hour.

A body may be endowed with living force in several ways. It may receive it by the impact of another body, Thus, if a perfectly elastic ball be made to strike another similar ball of equal weight at rest, the striking ball will communicate the whole of its living force to the ball struck, and, remaining at rest itself, will cause the other ball to move in the same direction and with the same velocity that it did itself before the collision. Here we see an instance of the facility with which living force may be transferred from one body to another. A body may also be endowed with living force by means of the action of gravitation upon it through a certain distance. If I hold a ball at a certain height and drop it, it will have acquired when it arrives at the ground a degree of living force proportional to its weight and the height from which it has fallen. We see, then, that living force may be produced by the action of gravity through a given distance or space. We may, therefore, say that the former is of equal value, or *equivalent,* to the latter. Hence, if I raise a weight of 1 lb. to the height of one foot, so that gravity may act on it through that distance, I shall communicate to it that which is of equal value or equivalent to a certain amount of living force; if I raise the weight to twice the height, I shall communicate to it the equivalent of twice the quantity of living force. Hence, also, when we compress a spring, we communicate to it the equivalent to a certain amount of living force; for in that case we produce molecular attraction between the particles of the spring through the distance they are forced asunder,

[177]

which is strictly analogous to the production of the attraction of gravitation through a certain distance.

You will at once perceive that the living force of which we have been speaking is one of the most important qualities with which matter can be endowed, and, as such, that it would be absurd to suppose that it can be destroyed, or even lessened, without producing the equivalent of attraction through a given distance of which we have been speaking. You will therefore be surprised to hear that until very recently the universal opinion has been that living force could be absolutely and irrevocably destroyed at any one's option. Thus, when a weight falls to the ground, it has been generally supposed that its living force is absolutely annihilated, and that the labour which may have been expended in raising it to the elevation from which it fell has been entirely thrown away and wasted, without the production of any permanent effect whatever. We might reason, *à priori,* that such absolute destruction of living force cannot possibly take place, because it is manifestly absurd to suppose that the powers with which God has endowed matter can be destroyed any more than that they can be created by man's agency; but we are not left with this argument alone, decisive as it must be to every unprejudiced mind. The common experience of every one teaches him that living force is not *destroyed* by the friction or collision of bodies. We have reason to believe that the manifestations of living force on our globe are, at the present time, as extensive as those which have existed at any time since its creation, or, at any rate, since the deluge — that the winds blow as strongly, and the torrents flow with equal impetuosity now, as at the remote period of 4000 or even 6000 years ago; and yet we are certain that, through that vast interval of time, the motions of the air and of the water have been incessantly obstructed and hindered by friction. We may conclude, then, with certainty, that these motions of air and water, constituting living force, are not *annihilated* by friction. We lose sight of them, indeed, for a time; but we find them again reproduced. Were it not so, it is perfectly obvious that long ere this all nature would have come to a dead standstill. What, then, may we inquire, is the cause of this apparent anomaly? How comes it to pass that, though in almost all natural phenomena we witness the arrest of motion and the apparent destruction of living force, we find that no waste or loss of living force has actually occurred? Experiment has enabled us to answer these questions in a satisfactory manner; for it has shown that, whenever living force is *apparently* destroyed, an equivalent is produced which in process of time may be reconverted into living force. This equivalent is *heat*. Experiment has shown that wherever living force is apparently destroyed or absorbed, heat is produced. The most frequent way in which living force is thus converted into heat is by means of friction. Wood rubbed against wood or against any hard body, metal rubbed against metal or against any other body — in short, all bodies, solid or even liquid, rubbed against each other are invariably heated, sometimes even so far as to become red-hot. In all these instances the quantity of heat produced is invariably in proportion to the exertion employed in rubbing the bodies together — that is to the living force absorbed. By fifteen or twenty smart and quick strokes of a hammer on the end of an iron rod of about a quarter of an inch in diameter placed upon an anvil an expert blacksmith will render that end of the iron visibly red-hot. Here heat is produced by the absorption of the living force of the descending hammer in the soft iron; which is proved to be the case from the fact that the iron cannot be heated if it be rendered hard and elastic, so as to transfer the living force of the hammer to the anvil.

The general rule, then, is, that wherever living force is *apparently* destroyed, whether by percussion, friction, or any similar means, an exact equivalent of heat is restored. The converse of this proposition is also true, namely, that heat cannot be lessened or absorbed without the production of living force, or its equivalent attraction through space. Thus, for instance, in the steam-engine it will be found that the power gained is at the expense of the heat of the fire, — that is, that the heat occasioned by the combustion of the coal would have been greater had a part of it not been absorbed in producing and maintaining the living force of the machinery. It is right, however, to observe that this has not as yet been demonstrated by experiment. But there is no room to doubt that experiment would prove the correctness of what I have said; for I have myself proved that a conversion of heat into living force takes place in the expansion of air, which is analogous to the expansion of steam in the cylinder of the steam-engine. But the most convincing proof of the conversion of heat into living force has been derived from my experiments with the electro-magnetic engine, a machine composed of magnets and bars of iron set in motion by an electrical battery. I have proved by actual experiment that, in exact proportion to the force with which this machine works, heat is abstracted from the electrical battery. You see, therefore, that living force may be converted into heat, and that heat may be converted into living force, or its equivalent attraction through space. All three, therefore — namely, heat, living force, and attraction through space (to which I might also add *light,* were it consistent with the scope of the present lecture) — are mutually convertible into one another. In these conversions nothing is ever lost. The same quantity of heat will always be converted into the same quantity of living force. We can therefore express the equivalency in definite language applicable at all times and under all circumstances. Thus the attraction of 817 lb. through the space of one foot is equivalent to, and convertible into, the living force possessed by a body of the same weight of 817 lb. when moving with the velocity of eight feet per second, and this living force is again convertible into the quantity of heat which can increase the temperature of one pound of water by one degree Fahrenheit. The knowledge of the equivalency of heat to mechanical power is of great value in solving a great number of interesting and important questions. In the case of the steam-engine, by ascertaining the quantity of heat produced by the combustion of coal, we can find out how much of it is converted into mechanical power, and thus come to a conclusion how far the steam-engine is susceptible of further improvements. Calculations made upon this principle have shown that at least ten times as much power might be produced as is now obtained by the combustion of coal. Another interesting conclusion is, that the animal frame, though destined to fulfil so many other ends, is as a machine more perfect than the best contrived steam-engine — that is, is capable of more work with the same expenditure of fuel.

Behold, then, the wonderful arrangements of creation. The earth in its rapid motion round the sun possesses a degree of living force so vast that, if turned into the equivalent of heat, its temperature would be rendered at least 1000 times greater than that of red-hot iron, and the globe on which we tread would in all probability be rendered equal in brightness to the sun itself. And it cannot be doubted that if the course of the earth were changed so that it might fall into the sun, that body, so far from being cooled down by the contact of a comparatively cold body, would actually blaze more brightly than before in consequence of the living force with which the earth struck the sun being converted into its equivalent of heat. Here we see that our existence depends upon the *maintenance* of the living force of the earth. On the other hand, our safety equally depends in some instances upon the *conversion* of living force into heat. You have, no doubt, frequently observed what are called *shooting-stars*, as they appear to emerge from the dark sky at night, pursue a short and rapid course, burst, and are dissipated in shining fragments. From the velocity with which these bodies travel, there can be little doubt that they are small planets which, in the course of their revolution round the sun, are attracted and drawn to the earth. Reflect for a moment on the consequences which would ensue, if a hard meteoric stone were to strike the roof in which we are assembled with a velocity sixty times as great as that of a cannon-ball. The dire effects of such a collision are effectually prevented by the atmosphere surrounding our globe, by which the velocity of the meteoric stone is checked and its living force converted into heat, which at last becomes so intense as to melt the body and dissipate it into fragments too small probably to be noticed in their fall to the ground. Hence it is that, although multitudes of shooting-stars appear every night, few meteoric stones have been found, those few corroborating the truth of our hypothesis by the marks of intense heat which they bear on their surfaces.

Descending from the planetary space and firmament to the surface of our earth, we find a vast variety of phenomena connected with the conversion of living force and heat into one another, which speak in language which cannot be misunderstood of the wisdom and beneficence of the Great Architect of nature. The motion of air which we call *wind* arises chiefly from the intense heat of the torrid zone compared with the temperature of the temperate and frigid zones. Here we have an instance of heat being converted into the living force of currents of air. These currents of air, in their progress across the sea, lift up its waves and propel the ships; whilst in passing across the land they shake the trees and disturb every blade of grass. The waves by their violent motion, the ships by their passage through a resisting medium, and the trees by the rubbing of their branches together and the friction of their leaves against themselves and the air, each and all of them generate heat equivalent to the diminution of the living force of the air which they occasion. The heat thus restored may again contribute to raise fresh currents of air; and thus the phenomena may be repeated in endless succession and variety.

When we consider our own animal frames, "fearfully and wonderfully made,"[3] we observe in the motion of our limbs a continual conversion of heat into living force, which may be either converted back again into heat or employed in producing an attraction through space, as when a man ascends a mountain. Indeed the phenomena of nature, whether mechanical, chemical, or vital, consist almost entirely in a continual conversion of attraction through space, living force, and heat into one another. Thus it is that order is maintained in the universe —

[3] "Fearfully and wonderfully made." See Psalms 139:14.

[183]

nothing is deranged, nothing ever lost, but the entire machinery, complicated as it is, works smoothly and harmoniously. And though, as in the awful vision of Ezekiel, "wheel may be in the middle of wheel," and every thing may appear complicated and involved in the apparent confusion and intricacy of an almost endless variety of causes, effects, conversions, and arrangements, yet is the most perfect regularity preserved — the whole being governed by the sovereign will of God.

A few words may be said, in conclusion, with respect to the real nature of heat. The most prevalent opinion, until of late, has been that it is a *substance* possessing, like all other matter, impenetrability and extension. We have, however, shown that heat can be converted into living force and into attraction through space. It is perfectly clear, therefore, that unless matter can be converted into attraction through space, which is too absurd an idea to be entertained for a moment, the hypothesis of heat being a substance must fall to the ground. Heat must therefore consist of either living force or of attraction through space. In the former case we can conceive the constituent particles of heated bodies to be, either in whole or in part, in a state of motion. In the latter we may suppose the particles to be removed by the process of heating, so as to exert attraction through greater space. I am inclined to believe that both of these hypotheses will be found to hold good, — that in some instances, particularly in the case of *sensible* heat, or such as is indicated by the thermometer, heat will be found to consist in the living force of the particles of the bodies in which it is induced; whilst in others, particularly in the case of *latent* heat, the phenomena are produced by the separation of particle from particle, so as to cause them to attract one another through a greater space. We may conceive, then, that the communication of heat to a body consists, in fact, in the communication of impetus, or living force, to its particles. It will perhaps appear to some of you something strange that a body apparently quiescent should in reality be the seat of motions of great rapidity; but you will observe that the bodies themselves, considered as wholes, are not supposed to be in motion. The constituent particles, or atoms of the bodies, are supposed to be in motion, without producing a gross motion of the whole mass. These particles, or atoms, being far too small to be seen even by the help of the most powerful microscopes, it is no wonder that we cannot observe their motion. There is therefore reason to suppose that the particles of all bodies, their constituent atoms, are in a state of motion almost too rapid for us to conceive, for the phenomena cannot be otherwise explained. The velocity of the atoms of water, for instance, is at least equal to a mile per second of time. If, as there is reason to think, some particles are at rest while others are in motion, the velocity of the latter will be proportionally greater. An increase of the velocity of revolution of the particles will constitute an increase of temperature, which may be distributed among the neighbouring bodies by what is called *conduction* — that is, on the present hypothesis, by the communication of the increased motion from the particles of one body to those of another. The velocity of the particles being further increased, they will tend to fly from each other in consequence of the centrifugal force overcoming the attraction subsisting between them. This removal of the particles from each other will constitute a new condition of the body — it will enter into the state of fusion, or become melted. But, from what we have already stated, you will perceive that in order to remove the particles violently attracting one another asunder, the expenditure of a certain amount of living force or heat will be required. Hence it is that heat is always absorbed when the state of a body is changed from solid to liquid, or from liquid to gas. Take, for example, a block of ice cooled down to zero; apply heat to it, and it will gradually arrive at 32°, which is the number conventionally employed to represent the temperature at which ice begins to melt. If, when the ice has arrived at this temperature, you continue to apply heat to it, it will become melted; but its temperature will not increase beyond 32° until the whole has been converted into water. The explanation of these facts is clear on our hypothesis. Until the ice has arrived at the temperature of 32° the application of heat increases the velocity of rotation of its constituent particles; but the instant it arrives at that point, the velocity produces such an increase of the centrifugal force of the particles that they are compelled to separate from each other. It is in effecting this separation of particles strongly attracting one another that the heat applied is *then* spent; not in increasing the velocity of the particles. As soon, however, as the separation has been effected, and the fluid water produced, a further application of heat will cause a further increase of the velocity of the particles, constituting an increase of temperature, on which the thermometer will immediately rise above 32°. When the water has been raised to the temperature of 212°, or the boiling-point, a similar phenomenon will be repeated; for it will be found impossible to increase the temperature beyond that point, because the heat then applied is employed in separating the particles of water so as to form steam, and not in increasing their velocity and living force. When, again, by the application of cold we condense the steam into water, and by a further abstraction of heat we bring the water to the solid condition of ice, we witness the repetition of similar phenomena in the reverse order. The particles of steam, in assuming the condition of water, fall together through a certain space. The living force thus produced becomes converted into heat, which must be removed before any more steam can be converted into water. Hence it is always necessary to abstract a great quantity of heat in order to convert steam into water, although the temperature will all the while remain exactly at 212°; but the instant that all the steam has been condensed, the further abstraction of heat will cause a diminution of temperature, since it can only be employed in diminishing the velocity of revolution of the atoms of water. What has been said with regard to the condensation of steam will apply equally well to the congelation of water.

I might proceed to apply the theory to the phenomena of combustion, the heat of which consists in the living force occasioned by the powerful attraction through space of the combustible for the oxygen, and to a variety of other thermo-chemical phenomena; but you will doubtless be able to pursue the subject further at your leisure.

I do assure you that the principles which I have very imperfectly advocated this evening may be applied very extensively in elucidating many of the abstruse as well as the simple points of science, and that patient inquiry on these grounds can hardly fail to be amply rewarded.

IV

Geology

JOHN PLAYFAIR

Illustrations of the Huttonian Theory*

A Scottish-born, St. Andrews-educated mathematician and geologist, John
Playfair (1748–1819) was professor of mathematics and then of natural
philosophy at Edinburgh University. His *Illustrations of the Huttonian
Theory* (1802) gave popularity to this early version of the geological theory
of uniformitarianism and rescued from oblivion the work of a fellow
Scot, James Hutton. Hutton's theories had originally been presented to
the Royal Society of Edinburgh in 1785 in a paper, "Concerning the Systems of the Earth, Its Duration, and Stability." The printed version appeared in the first volume of the Society's *Transactions* (1788) as "Theory
of the Earth; or an Investigation of the Laws Observable in the Composition, Dissolution, and Restoration of Land upon the Globe." Hutton
argued, as all geological uniformitarians after him were to do, that nature
was generous of time and parsimonious of violence; that the processes now
observable in action were the processes which through time had caused
the configuration of the earth's crust. Republished in more substantial
form in 1795, Hutton's ideas were much criticized; and after his death in
1797, his friends urged his former associate John Playfair to publish
a commentary upon them. The heavy, repetitive style of Hutton was replaced by the readable exposition of Playfair.

T HE series of changes which fossil bodies are destined to
undergo, does not cease with their elevation above the level of
the sea; it assumes, however, a new direction, and from the
moment that they are raised up to the surface, is constantly exerted in reducing them again under the dominion of the ocean.
The solidity is now destroyed which was acquired in the bowels

* From *Illustrations of the Huttonian Theory of the Earth* (1802).

of the earth; and as the bottom of the sea is the great laboratory, where loose materials are mineralized and formed into stone, the atmosphere is the region where stones are decomposed, and again resolved into earth.

This decomposition of all mineral substances exposed to the air, is continual, and is brought about by a multitude of agents, both chemical and mechanical, of which some are known to us, and many, no doubt, remain to be discovered. Among the various aëriform fluids which compose our atmosphere, one is already distinguished as the grand principle of mineral decomposition; the others are not inactive, and to them we must add moisture, heat, and perhaps light; substances which, from their affinities to the elements of mineral bodies, have a power of entering into combination with them, and of thus diminishing the forces by which they are united to one another. By the action of air and moisture, the metallic particles, particularly the iron, which enters in such abundance into the composition of almost all fossils, becomes oxydated in such a degree as to lose its tenacity; so that the texture of the surface is destroyed, and a part of the body resolved into earth.

Some earths, again, such as the calcareous, are immediately dissolved by water; and though the quantity so dissolved be extremely small, the operation, by being continually renewed, produces a slow but perpetual corrosion by which the greatest rocks must in time be subdued. The action of water in destroying hard bodies into which it has obtained entrance, is much assisted by the vicissitudes of heat and cold, especially when the latter extends as far as the point of congelation; for the water, when frozen, occupies a greater space than before, and if the body is compact enough to refuse room for this expansion, its parts are torn asunder by a repulsive force acting in every direction.

Besides these causes of mineral decomposition, the action of which we can in some measure trace, there are others known to us only by their effects.

We see, for instance, the purest rock crystal affected by exposure to the weather, its lustre tarnished, and the polish of its surface impaired, but we know nothing of the power by which these operations are performed. Thus also, in the precautions which the mineralogist takes to preserve the fresh fracture of his specimens, we have a proof how indiscriminately all the productions of the fossil kingdom are exposed to the attacks of their unknown enemies, and we perceive how difficult it is to delay the beginnings of a process which no power whatever can finally counteract.

The mechanical forces employed in the disintegration of mineral substances, are more easily marked than the chemical. Here again water appears as the most active enemy of hard and solid bodies; and, in every state, from transparent vapour to solid ice, from the smallest rill to the greatest river, it attacks whatever has emerged above the level of the sea, and labours incessantly to restore it to the deep. The parts loosened and disengaged by the chemical agents, are carried down by the rains, and, in their descent, rub and grind the superficies of other bodies. Thus water, though incapable of acting on hard substances by direct attrition, is the cause of their being so acted on; and, when it descends in torrents, carrying with it sand, gravel, and fragments of rock, it may be truly said to turn the forces of the mineral kingdom against itself. Every separation which it makes is necessarily permanent, and the parts once detached can never be united, save at the bottom of the ocean.

But it would far exceed the limits of this sketch, to pursue the causes of mineral decomposition through all their forms. It is sufficient to remark, that the consequence of so many minute, but indefatigable agents, all working together, and having *gravity* in their favour, is a system of universal decay and degradation, which may be traced over the whole surface of the land, from the mountain top to the sea shore. That we may perceive the full evidence of this truth, one of the most important in the natural history of the globe, we will begin our survey from the latter of these stations, and retire gradually toward the former.

If the coast is bold and rocky, it speaks a language easy to be interpreted. Its broken and abrupt contour, the deep gulphs and salient promontories by which it is indented, and the proportion which these irregularities bear to the force of the waves, combined with the inequality of hardness in the rocks, prove, that the present line of the shore has been determined by the action of the sea. The naked and precipitous cliffs which overhang the deep, the rocks hollowed, perforated, as they are farther advanced in the sea, and at last insulated, lead to the same conclusion, and mark very clearly so many different stages of decay. It is true, we do not see the successive steps of this progress exemplified in the states of the same individual rock, but we see them clearly in different individuals; and the conviction thus produced, when the phenomena are sufficiently multiplied and varied, is as irresistible, as if we saw the changes actually effected in the moment of observation.

On such shores, the fragments of rock once detached, become instruments of further destruction, and make a part of the powerful artillery with which the ocean assails the bulwarks of the land: they are impelled against the rocks, from which they break off other fragments, and the whole are thus ground against one another; whatever be their hardness, they are reduced to gravel, the smooth surface and round figure of which, are the most certain proofs of a *detritus* which nothing can resist.

Again, where the sea-coast is flat, we have abundant evidence of the degradation of the land in the beaches of sand and small gravel; the sand banks and shoals that are continually changing; the alluvial land at the mouths of the rivers; the bars that seem to oppose their discharge into the sea, and the shallowness of the sea itself. On such coasts, the land usually seems to gain upon the sea, whereas, on shores of a bolder aspect, it is the sea that generally appears to gain upon the land. What the land acquires in extent, however, it loses in elevation; and, whether its surface increase or diminish, the depredations made on it are in both cases evinced with equal certainty.

If we proceed in our survey from the shores, inland, we meet at every step with the fullest evidence of the same truths, and particularly in the nature and economy of rivers. Every river appears to consist of a main trunk, fed from a variety of branches, each running in a valley proportioned to its size, and all of them together forming a system of vallies, communicating with one another, and having such a nice adjustment of their declivities, that none of them join the principal valley, either on too high or too low a level; a circumstance which would be infinitely improbable, if each of these vallies were not the work of the stream that flows in it.

If indeed a river consisted of a single stream, without branches, running in a straight valley, it might be supposed that some great concussion, or some powerful torrent, had opened at once the channel by which its waters are conducted to the ocean; but, when the usual form of a river is considered, the trunk divided into many branches, which rise at a great distance from one another, and these again subdivided into an infinity of smaller ramifications, it becomes strongly impressed upon the mind, that all these channels have been cut by the waters themselves; that they have been slowly dug out by the washing and erosion of the land; and that it is by the repeated touches of the same instrument, that this curious assemblage of lines has been engraved so deeply on the surface of the globe.

The changes which have taken place in the courses of rivers, are also to be traced, in many instances, by successive platforms of flat alluvial land, rising one above another, and marking the different levels on which the river has run at different periods of time. Of these, the number to be distinguished, in some instances, is not less than four, or even five; and this necessarily carries us back, like all the operations we are now treating of, to an antiquity extremely remote: for, if it be considered, that each change which the river makes in its bed, obliterates at least a part of the monuments of former changes, we shall be convinced, that only a small part of the progression can leave any distinct memorial behind it, and that there is no reason to think, that, in the part which we see, the beginning is included.

In the same manner, when a river undermines its banks, it often discovers deposites of sand and gravel, that have been made when it ran on a higher level than it does at present. In other instances, the same strata are seen on both the banks, though the bed of the river is now sunk deep between them, and perhaps holds as winding a course through the solid rock, as if it flowed along the surface; a proof that it must have begun to sink its bed, when it ran through such loose materials as opposed but a very inconsiderable resistance to its stream. A river, of which the course is both serpentine and deeply excavated in the rock, is among the phenomena, by which the slow waste of the land, and also the cause of that waste, are most directly pointed out.

It is, however, where rivers issue through narrow defiles among mountains, that the identity of the strata on both sides is most easily recognised, and remarked at the same time with the greatest wonder. On observing the Patowmack, where it penetrates the ridge of the Allegany mountains, or the Irtish, as it issues from the defiles of Altai, there is no man, however little addicted to geological specifications, who does not immediately acknowledge, that the mountain was once continued quite across the space in which the river now flows; and, if he ventures to reason concerning the cause of so wonderful a change, he ascribes it to some great convulsion of nature, which has torn the mountain asunder, and opened a passage for the waters. It is only the philosopher, who has deeply meditated on the effects which action long continued is able to produce, and on the simplicity of the means which nature employs in all her operations, who sees in this nothing but the gradual working of a stream, that once flowed as high as the top of the ridge which it now so deeply intersects, and has cut its course through the rock, in the same way, and almost with the same instrument, by which the lapidary divides a block of marble or granite.

It is highly interesting to trace up, in this manner, the action

of causes with which we are familiar, to the production of
effects, which at first seem to require the introduction of unknown and extraordinary powers; and it is no less interesting
to observe, how skilfully nature has balanced the action of all
the minute causes of waste, and rendered them conducive to
the general good. Of this we have a most remarkable instance,
in the provision made for preserving the soil, or the coat of
vegetable mould, spread out over the surface of the earth. This
coat, as it consists of loose materials, is easily washed away by
the rains, and is continually carried down by the rivers into the
sea. This effect is visible to every one; the earth is removed not
only in the form of sand and gravel, but its finer particles suspended in the waters, tinge those of some rivers continually,
and those of all occasionally, that is, when they are flooded or
swollen with rains. The quantity of earth thus carried down,
varies according to circumstances; it has been computed, in
some instances, that the water of a river in a flood, contains
earthy matter suspended in it, amounting to more than the two
hundred and fiftieth part of its own bulk.* The soil, therefore,
is continually diminished, its parts being transported from higher
to lower levels, and finally delivered into the sea. But it is a
fact, that the soil, notwithstanding, remains the same in quantity, or at least nearly the same, and must have done so, ever
since the earth was the receptacle of animal or vegetable life.
The soil, therefore, is augmented from other causes, just as

* See Lehman, Traités de Phys.&c. tom. iii, p. 359.[1]

[1] Johann Gottlob Lehmann, *Traités de Physique, d'Histoire naturelle, de
Mineralogie et de Metallurgie* (Paris, 1759), III, 359n. Lehmann (d. 1767), a
teacher of mineralogy and mining, was one of the first to recognize that the
earth's crust was built up of strata or layers in a definite order. He also made
an important contribution to the theory of the origin of mountains.

much, at an average, as it is diminished by that now mentioned; and this augmentation evidently can proceed from nothing but the constant and slow disintegration of the rocks. In the permanence, therefore, of a coat of vegetable mould on the surface of the earth, we have a demonstrative proof of the continual destruction of the rocks; and cannot but admire the skill, with which the powers of the many chemical and mechanical agents employed in this complicated work, are so adjusted, as to make the supply and the waste of the soil exactly equal to one another.

Before we take leave of the rivers and the plains, we must remark another fact, often observed in the natural history of the latter, and clearly evincing the former existence of immense bodies of strata, in situations from which they have now entirely disappeared. The fact here alluded to is, the great quantity of round and hard gravel, often to be met with in the soil, under such circumstances, as prove, that it can only have come from the decomposition of rocks, that once occupied the very ground over which this gravel is now spread. In the chalk country, for instance, about London, the quantity of flints in the soil is every where great; and, in particular situations, nothing but flinty gravel is found to a considerable depth. Now, the source from which these flints are derived is quite evident, for they are precisely the same with those contained in the chalk beds, wherever these last are found undisturbed, and from the destruction of such beds they have no doubt originated. Hence a great thickness of chalk must have been decomposed, to yield the quantity of flints now in the soil of these countries; for the flints are but thinly scattered through the native chalk, compared with their abundance in the loose earth. To afford, for example, such a body of flinty gravel as is found about Kensington, what an enormous quantity of chalk rock must have been destroyed?

This argument, which Dr. Hutton has applied particularly to the chalk countries, may be extended to many others. The great plain of Crau, near the mouth of the Rhone, is well known, and was regarded with wonder, even in ages when the natural history of the globe was not an object of much attention.[2] The immense quantity of large round gravel-stones, with which this extensive plain is entirely covered, has been supposed, by some mineralogists, to have been brought down by the Durance, and other torrents, from the Alps; but, on further examination, has been found to be of the same kind that is contained in certain horizontal layers of pudding-stone, which are the basis of the whole plain. It cannot be doubted, therefore, that the vast body of gravel spread over it, has originated from the destruction of layers of the same rock, which may perhaps have risen to a great height above what is now the surface. Indeed, from knowing the depth of the gravel that covers the plain, and the average quantity of the like gravel contained in a given thickness of rock, one might estimate how much of the latter has been actually worn away. Whether data precise enough could be found, to give any weight to such a computation, must be left for future inquiry to determine.

[2] From Playfair's Note XVII: "The plain of Crau was the *Campus Lapideus* of the ancients; and, as mythology always seeks to connect itself with the extraordinary facts in natural history, it was said to be the spot where Hercules, fighting with the sons of Neptune, and being in want of weapons, was supplied from heaven by a shower of stones: hence it was called *Campus Herculeus*."

In these instances, chalk and pudding-stone, by containing in them parts infinitely less destructible than their general mass, have, after they are worn away, left behind them very unequivocal marks of their existence. The same has happened in the case of mineral veins, where the substances least subject to dissolution have remained, and are scattered at a great distance from their native place. Thus gold, the least liable to decomposition of all the metals, is very generally diffused through the earth, and is found, in a greater or less abundance, in the sand of almost all rivers. But the native place of this mineral is the solid rock, or the veins and cavities contained in the rock, and from thence it must have made its way into the soil. This, therefore, is another proof of the vast extent to which the degradation of the land, and of the rock, which is the basis of it, has been carried; and consequently, of the great difference between the elevation and shape of the earth's surface in the present, and in former ages.

The veins of tin furnish an argument of the same kind. The ores of this metal are very indestructible, and little subject to decomposition, so that they remain very long in the ground without change. Where there are tin veins, as in Cornwall, the tin-stone or tin-ore is found in great abundance in such vallies and streams as have the same direction with the veins; and hence the *streaming*, as it is called, or wasting of the earth, to obtain the tin-stone from it. Now, if it be considered, that none of this ore can have come into the soil but from parts of a vein actually destroyed, it must appear evident that a great waste of these veins has taken place, and consequently of the schistus or granite in which they are contained.

These lessons, which the geologist is taught in flat and open countries, become more striking, by the study of those Alpine tracts, where the surface of the earth attains its greatest elevation. If we suppose him placed for the first time in the midst of such a scene, as soon as he has recovered from the impression made by the novelty and magnificence of the spectacle before him, he begins to discover the footsteps of time, and to perceive, that the works of nature, usually deemed the most permanent, are those on which the characters of vicissitude are most deeply imprinted. He sees himself in the midst of a vast ruin, where the precipices which rise on all sides with such boldness and asperity, the sharp peaks of the granite mountains, and the huge fragments that surround their bases, do but mark so many epochs in the progress of decay, and point out the energy of those destructive causes, which even the magnitude and solidity of such great bodies have been unable to resist.

The result of a more minute investigation, is in perfect unison with this general impression. Whence is it, that the elevation of mountains is so obviously connected with the hardness and indestructibility of the rocks which compose them? Why is it, that a lofty mountain of soft and secondary rock is no where to be found; and that such chains, as the Pyrenees or the Alps, never consist of any but the hardest stone, of granite for instance, or of those primary strata, which, if we are to credit the preceding theory, have been twice heated in the fires, and twice tempered in the waters, of the mineral regions? Is it not plain that this arises, not from any direct connection between the hardness of stones, and their height in the atmosphere, but from this, that the waste and *detritus* to which all things are subject, will not allow soft and weak substances to remain long in an exposed and elevated situation? Were it not for this, the secondary rocks, being in position superincumbent on the primary, ought to be the highest of the two, and should cover the primary, (as they no doubt have at one time done), in the highest as well as the lowest situations, or among the mountains as well as in the plains.

Again, wherefore is it, that among all mountains, remarkable for their ruggedness and asperity, the rock, on examination, is always found of very unequal destructibility, some parts yielding to the weather, and to the other causes of disintegration, much more slowly than the rest, and having strength sufficient to support themselves, when left alone, in slender pyramids, bold projections, and overhanging cliffs? Where, on the other hand, the rock wastes uniformly, the mountains are similar to one another; their swells and slopes are gentle, and they are bounded by a waving and continuous surface. The intermediate degrees of resistance which the rocks oppose to the causes of destruction, produce intermediate forms. It is this which gives to the mountains, of every different species of rock, a different habit and expression, and which, in particular, has imparted to those of granite that venerable and majestic character, by which they rarely fail to be distinguished.

The structure of the vallies among mountains, shews clearly to what cause their existence is to be ascribed. Here we have first a large valley, communicating directly with the plain, and winding between high ridges of mountains, while the river in the bottom of it descends over a surface, remarkable, in such a scene, for its uniform declivity. Into this, open a multitude of transverse or secondary vallies, intersecting the ridges on either side of the former, each bringing a contribution to the main stream, proportioned to its magnitude; and, except where a cataract now and then intervenes, all having that nice adjust-ment in their levels, which is the more wonderful, the greater the irregularity of the surface. These secondary vallies have others of a smaller size opening into them; and, among moun-tains of the first order, where all is laid out on the greatest scale, these ramifications are continued to a fourth, and even a fifth, each diminishing in size as it increases in elevation, and as its supply of water is less. Through them all, this law is in general observed, that where a higher valley joins a lower one, of the two angles which it makes with the latter, that which is obtuse is always on the descending side; a law that is the same with that which regulates the confluence of streams running on a surface nearly of uniform inclination. This alone is a proof that the vallies are the work of the streams; and indeed what else but the water itself, working its way through obstacles of unequal resistance, could have opened or kept up a communi-cation between the inequalities of an irregular and alpine sur-face.

Many more arguments, all leading to the same conclusion, may be deduced from the general facts, known in the natural history of mountains; and, if the Oreologist would trace back the progress of waste, till he come in sight of that original structure, of which the remains are still so vast, he perceives an immense mass of solid rock, naked and unshapely, as it first emerged from the deep, and incomparably greater than all that is now before him. The operation of rains and torrents, modified by the hardness and tenacity of the rock, has worked the whole into its present form; has hollowed out the vallies, and gradually detached the mountains from the general mass, cutting down their sides into steep precipices at one place, and smoothing them into gentle declivities at another. From this has resulted a transportation of materials, which, both for the quantity of the whole, and the magnitude of the individual fragments, must seem incredible to every one, who has not learned to calculate the effects of continued action, and to reflect, that length of time can convert accidental into steady causes. Hence fragments of rock, from the central chain, are found to have travelled into distant vallies, even where many inferior ridges intervene: hence the granite of Mount Blanc is seen in the plains of Lombardy, or on the sides of Jura; and the ruins of the Carpathian mountains lie scattered over the shores of the Baltic.

Thus, with Dr. Hutton, we shall be disposed to consider those great chains of mountains, which traverse the surface of the globe, as cut out of masses vastly greater, and more lofty than any thing that now remains. The present appearances afford no data for calculating the original magnitude of these masses, or the height to which they may have been elevated. The nearest estimate we can form is, where a chain or group of mountains, like those of Rosa in the Alps, is horizontally stratified, and where, of consequence, the undisturbed position of the mineral beds enables us to refer the whole of the present inequalities of the surface to the operation of waste or decay. These mountains, as they now stand, may not inaptly be compared to the pillars of earth which workmen leave behind them, to afford a measure of the whole quantity of earth which they have removed. As the pillars, (considering the mountains as such), are in this case of less height than they originally were, so the measure furnished by them is but a limit, which the quantity sought must necessarily exceed.

Such, according to Dr. Hutton's theory, are the changes

which the daily operations of waste have produced on the surface of the globe. These operations, inconsiderable if taken
separately, become great, by conspiring all to the same end,
never counteracting one another, but proceeding, through a
period of indefinite extent, continually in the same direction.
Thus every thing descends, nothing returns upward; the hard
and solid bodies every where dissolve, and the loose and soft no
where consolidate. The powers which tend to preserve, and
those which tend to change the condition of the earth's surface,
are never *in equilibrio;* the latter are, in all cases, the most
powerful, and, in respect of the former, are like *living* in comparison of *dead* forces. Hence the law of decay is one which
suffers no exception: The elements of all bodies were once loose
and unconnected, and to the same state nature has appointed
that they should all return.

It affords no presumption against the reality of this progress,
that, in respect of man, it is too slow to be immediately perceived: The utmost portion of it to which our experience can
extend, is evanescent, in comparison with the whole, and must
be regarded as the momentary increment of a vast progression,
circumscribed by no other limits than the duration of the
world. Time performs the office of *integrating* the infinitesimal
parts of which this progression is made up; it collects them into
one sum, and produces from them an amount greater than any
that can be assigned.

While on the surface of the earth so much is every where
going to decay, no new production of mineral substances is
found in any region accessible to man. The instances of what
are called petrifactions, or the formation of stony substances
by means of water, which we sometimes observe, whether they

be ferruginous concretions, or calcareous, or, as happens in some rare cases, siliceous stalactites, are too few in number, and too inconsiderable in extent, to be deemed material exceptions to this general rule. The bodies thus generated, also, are no sooner formed, than they become subject to waste and dissolution, like all the other hard substances in nature; so that they but retard for a while the progress by which they are all resolved in to dust, and sooner or later committed to the bosom of the deep.

We are not, however, to imagine, that there is no where any means of repairing this waste; for, on comparing the conclusion at which we are now arrived, viz. that the present continents are all going to decay, and their materials descending into the ocean, with the proposition first laid down, that these same continents are composed of materials which must have been collected from the decay of former rocks, it is impossible not to recognise two corresponding steps of the same progress; of a progress, by which mineral substances are subjected to the same series of changes, and alternately wasted away and renovated. In the same manner, as the present mineral substances derive their origin from substances similar to themselves; so, from the land now going to decay, the sand and gravel forming on the sea-shore, or in the beds of rivers; from the shells and corals which in such enormous quantities are every day accumulated in the bosom of the sea; from the drift wood, and the multitude of vegetable and animal remains continually deposited in the ocean: from all these we cannot doubt, that strata are now forming in those regions, to which nature seems to have confined the powers of mineral reproduction; from which, after being consolidated, they are again destined to emerge, and to exhibit a series of changes similar to the past.

How often these vicissitudes of decay and renovation have been repeated, is not for us to determine: they constitute a series, of which, as the author of this theory has remarked, we neither see the beginning nor the end; a circumstance that accords well with what is known concerning other parts of the economy of the world. In the continuation of the different species of animals and vegetables that inhabit the earth, we discern neither a beginning nor an end; and, in the planetary motions, where geometry has carried the eye so far both into the future and the past, we discover no mark, either of the commencement or the termination of the present order. It is unreasonable, indeed, to suppose, that such marks should any where exist. The Author of nature has not given laws to the universe, which, like the institutions of men, carry in themselves the elements of their own destruction. He has not permitted, in his works, any symptom of infancy or of old age, or any sign by which we may estimate either their future or their past duration. He may put an end, as he no doubt gave a beginning, to the present system, at some determinate period; but we may safely conclude, that this great *catastrophe* will not be brought about by any of the laws now existing, and that it is not indicated by any thing which we perceive.

To assert, therefore, that, in the economy of the world, we see no mark, either of a beginning or an end, is very different from affirming, that the world had no beginning, and will have no end. The first is a conclusion justified by common sense, as well as sound philosophy; while the second is a presumptuous and unwarrantable assertion, for which no reason from experience or analogy can ever be assigned. Dr. Hutton might, therefore, justly complain of the uncandid criticism, which, by substituting the one of these assertions for the other, endeavoured to load his theory with the reproach of atheism and impiety. Mr. Kirwan,[3] in bringing forward this harsh and ill founded censure, was neither animated by the spirit, nor guided by the maxims of true philosophy. By the spirit of philosophy, he must have been induced to reflect, that such poisoned weapons as he was preparing to use, are hardly ever allowable in scientific contest, as having a less direct tendency to overthrow the system, than to hurt the person of an adversary, and to wound, perhaps incurably, his mind, his reputation, or his peace. By the maxims of philosophy, he must have been reminded, that, in no part of the history of nature, has any mark been discovered, either of the beginning or the end of the present *order;* and that the geologist sadly mistakes, both the object of his science and the limits of his understanding, who thinks it his business to explain the means employed by infinite wisdom for establishing the laws, which now govern the world.

By attending to these obvious considerations, Mr. Kirwan would have avoided a very illiberal and ungenerous proceeding; and, however he might have differed from Dr. Hutton as to the *truth* of his opinions, he would not have censured their *tendency* with such rash and unjustifiable severity.

But, if this author may be blamed for wanting the temper, or neglecting the rules, of philosophic investigation, he is hardly

3 Richard Kirwan (1733–1812), an Irish-born chemist and mineralogist, wrote a strident attack upon the Huttonian theory. Among other objections, based upon physical and chemical theories, Kirwan included a denunciation of Hutton's ideas as being contradictory to the Biblical account of the earth's origin. By proposing almost unlimited time for development, Kirwan claimed the Biblical chronology was denied, as was the universal deluge, the theory favored by Kirwan as an explanation of the present structure of the earth.

less culpable, for having so slightly considered the scope and spirit of a work which he condemned so freely. In that work, instead of finding the world represented as the result of necessity or chance, which might be looked for, if the accusations of atheism or impiety were well founded, we see every where the utmost attention to discover, and the utmost disposition to admire, the instances of wise and beneficent design manifested in the structure, or economy of the world. The enlarged views of these, which his geological system afforded, appeared to Dr. Hutton himself as its most valuable result. They were the parts of it which he contemplated with greatest delight; and he would have been less flattered, by being told of the ingenuity and originality of his theory, than of the addition which it had made to our knowledge of *final causes.* It was natural, therefore, that he should be hurt by an attempt to accuse him of opinions, so different from those which he had always taught; and if he answered Mr. Kirwan's attack with warmth or asperity, we must ascribe it to the indignation excited by unmerited reproach.

But to return to the natural history of the earth: Though there be in it no *data,* from which the commencement of the present order can be ascertained, there are many by which the existence of that order may be traced back to an antiquity extremely remote. The beds of primitive schistus, for instance, contain sand, gravel, and other materials, collected, as already shewn, from the dissolution of mineral bodies; which bodies, therefore, must have existed long before the oldest part of the present land was formed. Again, in this gravel we sometimes find pieces of sandstone, and of other compound rocks, by which we are of course carried back a step farther, so as to reach a system of things, from which the present is the third in succession; and this may be considered as the most ancient epocha, of which any memorial exists in the records of the fossil kingdom.

Next in the order of time to the consolidation of the primary strata, we must place their elevation, when, from being horizontal, and at the bottom of the sea, they were broken, set on edge, and raised to the surface. It is even probable, as formerly observed, that to this succeeded a depression of the same strata, and a second elevation, so that they have twice visited the superior, and twice the inferior regions. During the second immersion, were formed, first, the great bodies of pudding-stone, that in so many instances lie immediately above them; and next were deposited the strata that are strictly denominated secondary.

The third great event, was the raising up of this compound body of old and new strata from the bottom of the sea, and forming it into the dry land, or the continents, as they now exist. Contemporary with this, we must suppose the injection of melted matter among the strata, and the consequent formation of the crystallized and unstratified rocks, namely, the granite, metallic veins, and veins of porphyry and whinstone. This, however, is to be considered as embracing a period of great duration; and it must always be recollected, that veins are found of very different formation; so that when we speak generally, it is perhaps impossible to state any thing more precise concerning their antiquity, than that they are posterior to the strata, and that the veins of whinstone seem to be the most recent of all, as they traverse every other.

In the fourth place, with respect to time, we must class the facts that regard the detritus and waste of the land, and must carefully distinguish them from the more ancient phenomena of the mineral kingdom. Here we are to reckon the shaping of all the present inequalities of the surface; the formation of hills of gravel, and of what have been called tertiary strata, consisting of loose and unconsolidated materials; also collections of shells not mineralized, like those in Turaine; such petrifactions as those contained in the rock of Gibraltar, on the coast of Dalmatia, and in the caves of Bayreuth. The bones of land animals found in the soil, such as those of Siberia, or North America, are probably more recent than any of the former.

These phenomena, then, are all so many marks of the lapse of time, among which the principles of geology enable us to distinguish a certain order, so that we know some of them to be more, and others to be less distant, but without being able to ascertain, with any exactness, the proportion of the immense intervals which separate them. These intervals admit of no comparison with the astronomical measures of time; they cannot be expressed by the revolutions of the sun or of the moon; nor is there any synchronism between the most recent epochas of the mineral kingdom, and the most ancient of our ordinary chronology.

On what is now said is grounded another objection to Dr. Hutton's theory, namely, that the high antiquity ascribed by it to the earth, is inconsistent with that system of chronology which rests on the authority of the Sacred Writings. This objection would no doubt be of weight, if the high antiquity in question were not restricted merely to the globe of the earth, but were also extended to the human race. That the origin of mankind does not go back beyond six or seven thousand years, is a position so involved in the narrative of the Mosaic books, that any thing inconsistent with it, would no doubt stand in opposition to the testimony of those ancient records. On this subject, however, geology is silent; and the history of arts and sciences, when traced as high as any authentic monuments extend, refers the beginnings of civilization to a date not very different from that which has just been mentioned, and infinitely within the limits of the most recent of the epochas, marked by the physical revolutions of the globe.

On the other hand, the authority of the Sacred Books seems to be but little interested in what regards the mere antiquity of the earth itself; nor does it appear that their language is to be understood literally concerning the *age* of that body, any more than concerning its *figure* or its *motion*. The theory of Dr. Hutton stands here precisely on the same footing with the system of Copernicus; for there is no reason to suppose, that it was the purpose of revelation to furnish a standard of geological, any more than of astronomical science. It is admitted, on all hands, that the Scriptures are not intended to resolve physical questions, or to explain matters in no way related to the morality of human actions; and if, in consequence of this principle, a considerable latitude of interpretation were not allowed, we should continue at this moment to believe, that the earth is flat; that the sun moves round the earth; and that the circumference of a circle is no more than three times its diameter.

It is but reasonable, therefore, that we should extend to the geologist the same liberty of speculation, which the astronomer and mathematician are already in possession of; and this may be done, by supposing that the chronology of Moses relates only to the human race. This liberty is not more necessary to Dr. Hutton than to other theorists. No ingenuity has been able to reconcile the natural history of the globe with the opinion of its recent origin; and accordingly the cosmologies of Kirwan and De Luc, though contrived with more mineralogical skill, are not less forced and unsatisfactory than those of Burnet Whiston.[4]

It is impossible to look back on the system which we have thus endeavoured to illustrate, without being struck with the novelty and beauty of the views which it sets before us. The very plan and scope of it distinguish it from all other theories of the earth, and point it out as a work of great and original invention. The sole object of such theories has hitherto been, to explain the manner in which the present laws of the mineral kingdom were first established, or began to exist, without treating of the manner in which they now proceed, and by which their continuance is provided for. The authors of these theories have accordingly gone back to a state of things altogether unlike the present, and have confined their reasonings, or their fictions, to a crisis which never has existed but once, and which never can return. Dr. Hutton, on the other hand, has guided his investigation by the philosophical maxim, *Causam naturalem et assiduam quærimus, non raram et fortuitam.* His theory, ac-

4 Jean André de Luc (1763–1847), like Kirwan a critic of Hutton, proposed a cosmogony which he hoped would be in close harmony with the Biblical account. The earth, he believed, attained its current configuration no more than 4000 years ago and this through the collapse of the water-covered crust, thus leaving the present mountains and continents. Thomas Burnet (1635–1715) and William Whiston (1666–1753), both writing in the late seventeenth century, had proposed cosmogonical theories which relied upon a catastrophic occurrence to account for the present structure of the earth. Their theories were two among many which suggested a recent date for the origin of the earth as then known.

cordingly, presents us with a system of wise and provident economy, where the same instruments are continually employed, and where the decay and renovation of fossils being carried on at the same time in the different regions alloted to them, preserve in the earth the conditions essential for the support of animal and vegetable life. We have been long accustomed to admire that beautiful contrivance in nature, by which the water of the ocean, drawn up in vapour by the atmosphere, imparts, in its descent, fertility to the earth, and becomes the great cause of vegetation and of life; but now we find, that this vapour not only fertilizes, but creates the soil; prepares it from the solid rock, and, after employing it in the great operations of the surface, carries it back into the regions where all its mineral characters are renewed. Thus, the circulation of moisture through the air, is a prime mover, not only in the annual succession of the seasons, but in the great geological cycle, by which the waste and reproduction of entire continents is circumscribed. Perhaps a more striking view than this, of the wisdom that presides over nature, was never presented by any philosophical system, nor a greater addition ever made to our knowledge of final causes. It is an addition which gives consistency to the rest, by proving, that equal foresight is exerted in providing for the whole and for the parts, and that no less care is taken to maintain the constitution of the earth, than to preserve the tribes of animals and vegetables which dwell on its surface. In a word, it is the peculiar excellence of this theory, that it ascribes to the phenomena of geology an order similar to that which exists in the provinces of nature with which we are best acquainted; that it produces seas and continents, not by accident, but by the operations of regular and uniform causes; that it makes the decay of one part subservient to the restoration of another, and gives stability to the whole, not by perpetuating individuals, but by reproducing them in succession.

CHARLES LYELL

Methods of Theorizing in Geology*

Charles Lyell (1797–1875), the son of a Scottish landowner, studied at Oxford and received training for the law. After a short period at the bar he abandoned the law and returned to the study of geology, a subject to which he had been attracted by the lectures of William Buckland at Oxford. Despite severe difficulty with his vision, Lyell carried on a full life as a scientist, undertaking numerous lengthy field trips to the Continent as well as to North America. Although he gave a course of lectures in geology at King's College, London, in 1831, he did not assume a professorship and remained a private scholar throughout the whole of his scientific career. As the principal spokesman for the uniformitarian theory in geology, Lyell believed that all the processes of change which occurred on the earth's surface in the past must be referable to causes still in operation. In concluding that the same forces, in approximately the same degree, have always been operative, the uniformitarians provided a substitute for the "castastrophic" schools in geology and laid a sound basis for evolutionary theories. The *Principles of Geology* (1830–1833) was a remarkably successful work. During Lyell's lifetime eleven editions were published and a twelfth appeared shortly after his death.

Having considered, in the preceding volumes, the actual operation of the causes of change which affect the earth's surface and its inhabitants, we are now about to enter upon a new division of our inquiry, and shall therefore offer a few preliminary observations, to fix in the reader's mind the connexion

* From *Principles of Geology, being an Attempt to Explain the Former Changes of the Earth's Surface, by Reference to Causes now in Operation* (1833).

between two distinct parts of our work, and to explain in what manner the plan pursued by us differs from that more usually followed by preceding writers on Geology.

All naturalists, who have carefully examined the arrangement of the mineral masses composing the earth's crust, and who have studied their internal structure and fossil contents, have recognized therein the signs of a great succession of former changes; and the causes of these changes have been the object of anxious inquiry. As the first theorists possessed but a scanty acquaintance with the present economy of the animate and inanimate world, and the vicissitudes to which these are subject, we find them in the situation of novices, who attempt to read a history written in a foreign language, doubting about the meaning of the most ordinary terms; disputing, for example, whether a shell was really a shell, — whether sand and pebbles were the result of aqueous trituration, — whether stratification was the effect of successive deposition from water; and a thousand other elementary questions which now appear to us so easy and simple, that we can hardly conceive them to have once afforded matter for warm and tedious controversy.

In the first volume we enumerated many prepossessions which biassed the minds of the earlier inquirers, and checked an impartial desire of arriving at truth. But of all the causes to which we alluded, no one contributed so powerfully to give rise to a false method of philosophizing as the entire unconsciousness of the first geologists of the extent of their own ignorance respecting the operations of the existing agents of change.

They imagined themselves sufficiently acquainted with the mutations now in progress in the animate and inanimate world, to entitle them at once to affirm, whether the solution of certain problems in geology could ever be derived from the observation of the actual economy of nature, and having decided that they could not, they felt themselves at liberty to indulge their imaginations, in guessing at what *might be,* rather than in inquiring *what is;* in other words, they employed themselves in conjecturing what might have been the course of nature at a remote period, rather than in the investigation of what was the course of nature in their own times.

It appeared to them more philosophical to speculate on the possibilities of the past, than patiently to explore the realities of the present, and having invented theories under the influence of such maxims, they were consistently unwilling to test their validity by the criterion of their accordance with the ordinary operations of nature. On the contrary, the claims of each new hypothesis to credibility appeared enhanced by the great contrast of the causes or forces introduced to those now developed in our terrestrial system during a period, as it has been termed, of *repose.*

Never was there a dogma more calculated to foster indolence, and to blunt the keen edge of curiosity, than this assumption of the discordance between the former and the existing causes of change. It produced a state of mind unfavourable in the highest conceivable degree to the candid reception of the evidence of those minute, but incessant mutations, which every part of the earth's surface is undergoing, and by which the condition of its living inhabitants is continually made to vary. The student, instead of being encouraged with the hope of interpreting the enigmas presented to him in the earth's structure, — instead of being prompted to undertake laborious

[219]

inquiries into the natural history of the organic world, and the complicated effects of the igneous and aqueous causes now in operation, was taught to despond from the first. Geology, it was affirmed, could never rise to the rank of an exact science, — the greater number of phenomena must for ever remain inexplicable, or only be partially elucidated by ingenious conjectures. Even the mystery which invested the subject was said to constitute one of its principal charms, affording, as it did, full scope to the fancy to indulge in a boundless field of speculation.

The course directly opposed to these theoretical views consists in an earnest and patient endeavour to reconcile the former indications of change with the evidence of gradual mutations now in progress; restricting us, in the first instance, to known causes, and then speculating on those which may be in activity in regions inaccessible to us. It seeks an interpretation of geological monuments by comparing the changes of which they give evidence with the vicissitudes now in progress, or *which may be* in progress.

We shall give a few examples in illustration of the practical results already derived from the two distinct methods of theorizing, for we have now the advantage of being enabled to judge by experience of their respective merits, and by the relative value of the fruits which they have produced.

In our historical sketch of the progress of geology, the reader has seen that a controversy was maintained for more than a century, respecting the origin of fossil shells and bones — were they organic or inorganic substances? That the latter opinion should for a long time have prevailed, and that these bodies should have been supposed to be fashioned into their present form by a plastic virtue,[1] or some other mysterious agency, may appear absurd; but it was, perhaps, as reasonable a conjecture as could be expected from those who did not appeal, in the first instance, to the analogy of the living creation, as affording the only source of authentic information. It was only by an accurate examination of living testacea,[2] and by a comparison of the osteology of the existing vertebrated animals with the remains found entombed in ancient strata, that this favourite dogma was exploded, and all were, at length, persuaded that these substances were exclusively of organic origin.

In like manner, when a discussion had arisen as to the nature of basalt and other mineral masses, evidently constituting a particular class of rocks, the popular opinion inclined to a belief that they were of aqueous, not of igneous origin.[3] These rocks, it was said, might have been precipitated from an aqueous solution, from a chaotic fluid, or an ocean which rose over the continents, charged with the requisite mineral ingredients. All are now agreed that it would have been impossible for human ingenuity to invent a theory more distant from the truth; yet we must cease to wonder, on that account, that it gained so many proselytes, when we remember that its claims to probability arose partly from its confirming the assumed want of all analogy between geological causes and those now in action.

By what train of investigation were all theorists brought round

1 Plastic virtue; i.e., a shaping power inherent in the material itself.

2 Testacea is a generic term for shelled animals.

3 The aqueous or igneous origin of the rock in question refers to a major controversy in the history of geology between those who believed that the present configuration of the earth's surface is ultimately due to the agency of water (Neptunists), and those who believed that the agency of fire, heat and volcanic eruptions (Vulcanists or Plutonists) as well as water served to provide structure for the crust of the earth.

at length to an opposite opinion, and induced to assent to the igneous origin of these formations? By an examination of the structure of active volcanos, the mineral composition of their lavas and ejections, and by comparing the undoubted products of fire with the ancient rocks in question.

We shall conclude with one more example. When the organic origin of fossil shells had been conceded, their occurrence in strata forming some of the loftiest mountains in the world, was admitted as a proof of a great alteration of the relative level of sea and land, and doubts were then entertained whether this change might be accounted for by the partial drying up of the ocean, or by the elevation of the solid land. The former hypothesis, although afterwards abandoned by general consent, was at first embraced by a vast majority. A multitude of ingenious speculations were hazarded to show how the level of the ocean might have been depressed, and when these theories had all failed, the inquiry, as to what vicissitudes of this nature might now be taking place, was, as usual, resorted to in the last instance. The question was agitated, whether any changes in the level of sea and land had occurred during the historical period, and, by patient research, it was soon discovered that considerable tracts of land had been permanently elevated and depressed, while the level of the ocean remained unaltered. It was therefore necessary to reverse the doctrine which had acquired so much popularity, and the unexpected solution of a problem at first regarded as so enigmatical, gave perhaps the strongest stimulus ever yet afforded to investigate the ordinary operations of nature. For it must have appeared almost as improbable to the earlier geologists, that the laws of earthquakes should one day throw light on the origin of mountains, as it must to the first astronomers, that the fall of an apple should assist in explaining the motions of the moon.

Of late years the points of discussion in geology have been transferred to new questions, and those, for the most part, of a higher and more general nature; but, notwithstanding the repeated warnings of experience, the ancient method of philosophising has not been materially modified.

We are now, for the most part, agreed as to what rocks are of igneous, and what of aqueous origin, — in what manner fossil shells, whether of the sea or of lakes, have been imbedded in strata, — how sand may have been converted into sandstone, — and are unanimous as to other propositions which are not of a complicated nature; but when we ascend to those of a higher order, we find as little disposition, as formerly, to make a strenuous effort, in the first instance, to search out an explanation in the ordinary economy of Nature. If, for example, we seek for the causes why mineral masses are associated together in certain groups; why they are arranged in a certain order which is never inverted; why there are many breaks in the continuity of the series; why different organic remains are found in distinct sets of strata; why there is often an abrupt passage from an assemblage of species contained in one formation to that in another immediately superimposed, — when these and other topics of an equally extensive kind are discussed, we find the habit of indulging conjectures, respecting irregular and extraordinary causes, to be still in full force.

We hear of sudden and violent revolutions of the globe, of the instantaneous elevation of mountain chains, of paroxysms of volcanic energy, declining according to some, and according to others increasing in violence, from the earliest to the latest ages.[4] We are also told of general catastrophes and a succession of deluges, of the alternations of periods of repose and disorder, of the refrigeration of the globe, of the sudden annihilation of whole races of animals and plants, and other hypotheses, in which we see the ancient spirit of speculation revived, and a desire manifested to cut, rather than patiently to untie, the Gordian knot.

In out attempt to unravel these difficult questions, we shall adopt a different course, restricting ourselves to the known or possible operations of existing causes; feeling assured that we have not yet exhausted the resources which the study of the present course of nature may provide, and therefore that we are not authorized, in the infancy of our science, to recur to extraordinary agents. We shall adhere to this plan, not only on the grounds explained in the first volume, but because, as we have above stated, history informs us that this method has always put geologists on the road that leads to truth, — suggesting views which, although imperfect at first, have been found capable of improvement, until at last adopted by universal consent. On the other hand, the opposite method, that of speculating on a former distinct state of things, has led invariably to a multitude of contradictory systems, which have been overthrown one after the other, — which have been found quite incapable of modification, — and which are often required to be precisely reversed.

In regard to the subjects treated of in our first two volumes,

[4] The belief that there had occurred in the earth's history sudden and major violent changes on the surface of the earth, whether eruptions, deluges or freezings, was at basis of the theories which relied upon such natural "catastrophes" to explain the succession of geological and palaeontological strata.

if systematic treatises had been written on these topics, we should willingly have entered at once upon the description of geological monuments properly so called, referring to other authors for the elucidation of elementary and collateral questions, just as we shall appeal to the best authorities in conchology and comparative anatomy, in proof of many positions which, but for the labours of naturalists devoted to these departments, would have demanded long digressions. When we find it asserted, for example, that the bones of a fossil animal at Œningen[5] were those of man, and the fact adduced as a proof of the deluge, we are now able at once to dismiss the argument as nugatory, and to affirm the skeleton to be that of a reptile, on the authority of an able anatomist; and when we find among ancient writers the opinion of the gigantic stature of the human race in times of old, grounded on the magnitude of certain fossil teeth and bones, we are able to affirm these remains to belong to the elephant and rhinoceros, on the same authority.

But since in our attempt to solve geological problems, we shall be called upon to refer to the operation of aqueous and igneous causes, the geographical distribution of animals and plants, the real existence of species, their successive extinction, and so forth, we were under the necessity of collecting together a variety of facts, and of entering into long trains of reasoning, which could only be accomplished in preliminary treatises.

These topics we regard as constituting the alphabet and grammar of geology; not that we expect from such studies to

5 Clearly the town of Öhingen near Tübingen in Germany. The area is well-known for its limestone outcropping and has been called the "Schwabischen Alps." Bernhard Hauff established a museum in the area which has supplied fossil reptiles and fishes for many other museums.

obtain a key to the interpretation of all geological phenomena, but because they form the groundwork from which we must rise to the contemplation of more general questions relating to the complicated results to which, in an indefinite lapse of ages, the existing causes of change may give rise.

Concluding Remarks. — In our history of the progress of geology, in the first volume, we stated that the opinion originally promulgated by Hutton, "that the strata called *primitive* were mere altered sedimentary rocks," was vehemently opposed for a time, the main objection to the theory being its supposed tendency to promote a belief in the past eternity of our planet. Previously the absence of animal and vegetable remains in the so-called primitive strata, had been appealed to, as proving that there had been a period when the planet was uninhabited by living beings, and when, as was also inferred, it was uninhabitable, and, therefore, probably in a nascent state.

The opposite doctrine, that the oldest visible strata might be the monuments of an antecedent period, when the animate world was already in existence, was declared to be equivalent to the assumption, that there never was a beginning to the present order of things. The unfairness of this charge was clearly pointed out by Playfair, who observed, "that it was one thing to declare that we had not yet discovered the traces of a beginning, and another to deny that the earth ever had a beginning."

We regret, however, to find that the bearing of our arguments in the first volume has been misunderstood in a similar manner, for we have been charged with endeavouring to establish the proposition, that "the existing causes of change have operated with absolute uniformity from all eternity."[6]

It is the more necessary to notice this misrepresentation of our views, as it has proceeded from a friendly critic whose theoretical opinions coincide in general with our own, but who has, in this instance, strangely misconceived the scope of our argument. With equal justice might an astronomer be accused of asserting, that the works of creation extend throughout *infinite* space, because he refuses to take for granted that the remotest stars now seen in the heavens are on the utmost verge of the material universe. Every improvement of the telescope has brought thousands of new worlds into view, and it would, therefore, be rash and unphilosophical to imagine that we already survey the whole extent of the vast scheme, or that it will ever be brought within the sphere of human observation.

But no argument can be drawn from such premises in favour of the infinity of the space that has been filled with worlds; and if the material universe has any limits, it then follows that it must occupy a minute and infinitesimal point in infinite space. So, if in tracing back the earth's history, we arrive at the monuments of events which may have happened millions of ages before our times, and if we still find no decided evidence of a commencement, yet the arguments from analogy in support of the probability of a beginning remain unshaken; and if the past duration of the earth be finite, then the aggregate of geological epochs, however numerous, must constitute a mere moment of the past, a mere infinitesimal portion of eternity.

It has been argued, that as the different states of the earth's surface, and the different species by which it has been inhabited,

[6] *Quarterly Review*, no. 86 (October, 1830), p. 464.

have had each their origin, and many of them their termination, so the entire series may have commenced at a certain period. It has also been urged, that as we admit the creation of man to have occurred at a comparatively modern epoch — as we concede the astonishing fact of the first introduction of a moral and intellectual being, so also we may conceive the first creation of the planet itself.

We are far from denying the weight of this reasoning from analogy; but although it may strengthen our conviction, that the present system of change has not gone on from eternity, it cannot warrant us in presuming that we shall be permitted to behold the signs of the earth's origin, or the evidences of the first introduction into it of organic beings.

In vain do we aspire to assign limits to the works of creation in *space*, whether we examine the starry heavens, or that world of minute animalcules which is revealed to us by the microscope. We are prepared, therefore, to find that in *time* also, the confines of the universe lie beyond the reach of mortal ken. But in whatever direction we pursue our researches, whether in time or space, we discover everywhere the clear proofs of a Creative Intelligence, and of His foresight, wisdom, and power.

As geologists, we learn that it is not only the present condition of the globe that has been suited to the accommodation of myriads of living creatures, but that many former states also have been equally adapted to the organization and habits of prior races of beings. The disposition of the seas, continents, and islands, and the climates have varied; so it appears that the species have been changed, and yet they have all been so modelled, on types analogous to those of existing plants and animals, as to indicate throughout a perfect harmony of design and unity of purpose. To assume that the evidence of the beginning or end of so vast a scheme lies within the reach of our philosophical inquiries, or even of our speculations, appears to us inconsistent with a just estimate of the relations which subsist between the finite powers of man and the attributes of an Infinite and Eternal Being.

V

Biology

ROBERT BROWN

Remarks on Active Molecules*

A Scot, educated in medicine at Edinburgh University, Robert Brown (1773–1858) did his early work in systematic and geographical botany. As it was custom at the time for a naturalist to participate in a voyage of exploration, Brown went as botanist on an expedition to Australia. He later served as librarian to the Linnean Society of London and as botanical curator at the British Museum. His discovery of the universality of the plant cell nucleus came as a by-product of the study of the mode of fecundation in orchids and other plants. The description of the movement of small particles was probably stimulated by observation of plant pollen, and the random motion described in the paper below bears the name of its discoverer, "Brownian motion."

ABOUT twelve months ago I printed an account of Microscopical Observations made in the summer of 1827, on the Particles contained in the Pollen of Plants; and on the general Existence of active Molecules in Organic and Inorganic Bodies.

In the present Supplement to that account, my objects are, to explain and modify a few of its statements, to advert to some of the remarks that have been made, either on the correctness or originality of the observations, and to the causes that have been considered sufficient for the explanation of the phænomena.

In the first place, I have to notice an erroneous assertion of

---

* From "Additional Remarks on Active Molecules" (1829).

more than one writer, namely, that I have stated the active Molecules to be animated. This mistake has probably arisen from my having communicated the facts in the same order in which they occurred, accompanied by the views which presented themselves in the different stages of the investigation; and in one case, from my having adopted the language, in referring to the opinion, of another inquirer into the first branch of the subject.

Although I endeavoured strictly to confine myself to the statement of the facts observed, yet in speaking of the active Molecules I have not been able, in all cases, to avoid the introduction of hypothesis; for such is the supposition, that the equally active particles of greater size, and frequently of very different form, are primary compounds of these Molecules, — a supposition which, though professedly conjectural, I regret having so much insisted on, especially as it may seem connected with the opinion of the absolute identity of the Molecules, from whatever source derived.

On this latter subject, the only two points that I endeavoured to ascertain, were their size and figure: and although I was, upon the whole, inclined to think that in these respects the Molecules were similar from whatever substances obtained, yet the evidence then adduced in support of the supposition was far from satisfactory; and I may add, that I am still less satisfied now that such is the fact. But even had the uniformity of the Molecules in those two points been absolutely established, it did not necessarily follow, nor have I any where stated, as has been imputed to me, that they also agreed in all their other properties and functions.

I have remarked, that certain substances, namely, sulphur,

resin, and wax, did not yield active particles, which, however, proceeded merely from defective manipulation; for I have since readily obtained them from all these bodies: at the same time I ought to notice that their existence in sulphur was previously mentioned to me by my friend Mr. Lister.[1]

In prosecuting the inquiry subsequent to the publication of my Observations, I have chiefly employed the simple microscope mentioned in the Pamphlet, as having been made for me by Mr. Dolland,[2] and of which the three lenses that I have generally used, are of a 40th, 60th, and 70th of an inch focus.

Many of the observations have been repeated and confirmed with other simple microscopes having lenses of similar powers, and also with the best achromatic compound microscopes, either in my own possession or belonging to my friends.

The result of the inquiry at present essentially agrees with that which may be collected from my printed account, and may be here briefly stated in the following terms: namely,

That extremely minute particles of solid matter, whether obtained from organic or inorganic substances, when suspended in pure water, or in some other aqueous fluids, exhibit motions for which I am unable to account, and which from their irregularity and seeming independence resemble in a remarkable degree the less rapid motions of some of the simplest animalcules of infusions. That the smallest moving particles observed, and which I have termed Active Molecules, appear to be spherical, or nearly so, and to be between 1-20,000dth and

1 Joseph J. Lister (1786–1869), an important contributor to the development of the achromatic microscope.
2 George Dolland (1774–1852) was partner with his uncle Peter Dolland (1730–1820) in an optical firm. Both men made contributions in the field of microscope and telescope manufacture.

1-30,000dth of an inch in diameter; and that other particles of considerably greater and various size, and either of similar or of very different figure, also present analogous motions in like circumstances.

I have formerly stated my belief that these motions of the particles neither arose from currents in the fluid containing them, nor depended on that intestine motion which may be supposed to accompany its evaporation.

These causes of motion, however, either singly or combined with others, — as, the attractions and repulsions among the particles themselves, their unstable equilibrium in the fluid in which they are suspended, their hygrometrical or capillary action, and in some cases the disengagement of volatile matter, or of minute air bubbles, — have been considered by several writers as sufficiently accounting for the appearances. Some of the alleged causes here stated, with others which I have considered it unnecessary to mention, are not likely to be overlooked or to deceive observers of any experience in microscopical researches: and the insufficiency of the most important of those enumerated, may, I think, be satisfactorily shown by means of a very simple experiment.

This experiment consists in reducing the drop of water containing the particles to microscopic minuteness, and prolonging its existence by immersing it in a transparent fluid of inferior specific gravity, with which it is not miscible, and in which evaporation is extremely slow. If to almond-oil, which is a fluid having these properties, a considerably smaller proportion of water, duly impregnated with particles, be added, and the two fluids shaken or triturated together, drops of water of various sizes, from 1-50th to 1-2000dth of an inch in diameter, will be immediately produced. Of these, the most minute necessarily contain but few particles, and some may be occasionally observed with one particle only. In this manner minute drops, which if exposed to the air would be dissipated in less than a minute, may be retained for more than an hour. But in all the drops thus formed and protected, the motion of the particles takes place with undiminished activity, while the principal causes assigned for that motion, namely, evaporation, and their mutual attraction and repulsion, are either materially reduced or absolutely null.

It may here be remarked, that those currents from centre to circumference, at first hardly perceptible, then more obvious, and at last very rapid, which constantly exist in drops exposed to the air, and disturb or entirely overcome the proper motion of the particles, are wholly prevented in drops of small size immersed in oil, — a fact which, however, is only apparent in those drops that are flattened, in consequence of being nearly or absolutely in contact with the stage of the microscope.

That the motion of the particles is not produced by any cause acting on the surface of the drop, may be proved by an inversion of the experiment; for by mixing a very small proportion of oil with water containing the particles, microscopic drops of oil of extreme minuteness, some of them not exceeding in size the particles themselves, will be found on the surface of the drop of water, and nearly or altogether at rest; while the particles in the centre or towards the bottom of the drop continue to move with their usual degree of activity.

By means of the contrivance now described for reducing the size and prolonging the existence of the drops containing the particles, which, simple as it is, did not till very lately occur to me, a greater command of the subject is obtained, sufficient perhaps to enable us to ascertain the real cause of the motions in question.

Of the few experiments which I have made since this manner of observing was adopted, some appear to me so curious, that I do not venture to state them until they are verified by frequent and careful repetition.

I shall conclude these supplementary remarks to my former Observations, by noticing the degree in which I consider those observations to have been anticipated.

That molecular was sometimes confounded with animalcular motion by several of the earlier microscopical observers, appears extremely probable from various passages in the writings of Leeuwenhoek, as well as from a very remarkable Paper by Stephen Gray, published in the 19th volume of the Philosophical Transactions.[3]

Needham also, and Buffon, with whom the hypothesis of organic particles originated, seem to have not unfrequently fallen into the same mistake.[4] And I am inclined to believe that Spallanzani, notwithstanding one of his statements respecting them, has under the head of *Animaletti d'ultimo ordine* included the active Molecules as well as true Animalcules.[5]

I may next mention that Gleichen, the discoverer of the mo-

[3] Anton van Leeuwenhoek (1632–1723), the famous Dutch microscopist. Stephen Gray (d. 1736), as well as conducting microscopical observations, carried out an early series of studies in electricity.

[4] John Tuberville Needham (1713–1781) and George Louis Leclerc de Buffon (1707–1788) collaborated in a series of studies on spontaneous generation, one basis for which was Buffon's theory of organic molecules.

[5] Lazzaro Spallanzani (1729–1799) challenged the idea of spontaneous generation in a series of studies on microorganisms.

tions of the Particles of the Pollen, also observed similar motions in the particles of the ovulum of Zea Mays.[6]

Wrisberg and Muller, who adopted in part Buffon's hypothesis, state the globules, of which they supose all organic bodies formed, to be capable of motion; and Muller distinguishes these moving organic globules from real Animalcules, with which, he adds, they have been confounded by some very respectable observers.[7]

In 1814 Dr. James Drummond, of Belfast, published in the 7th volume of the Transactions of the Royal Society of Edinburgh, a valuable Paper, entitled "On certain Appearances observed in the Dissection of the Eyes of Fishes."[8]

In this Essay, which I regret I was entirely unacquainted with when I printed the account of my Observations, the author gives an account of the very remarkable motions of the spicula which form the silvery part of the choroid coat of the eyes of fishes.

These spicula were examined with a simple microscope, and as opake objects, a strong light being thrown upon the drop of water in which they were suspended. The appearances are minutely described, and very ingenious reasoning employed to show that, to account for the motions, the least improbable conjecture is to suppose the spicula animated.

As these bodies were seen by reflected and not by transmitted light, a very correct idea of their actual motions could hardly

6 Friedrich Wilhelm von Gleichen (1717–1783). *Zea mays* is the botanical name for Indian corn or maize.

7 Heinrich August Wrisberg (1739–1808), German anatomist. Otto Frederik Müller (1730–1784), Danish microscopist.

8 James Lawson Drummond (1783–1853), a Belfast physician, submitted a paper on the comparative anatomy of the eye for his M.D. dissertation.

be obtained; and with the low magnifying powers necessarily employed with the instrument and in the manner described, the more minute nearly spherical particles or active Molecules which, when higher powers were used, I have always found in abundance along with the spicula, entirely escaped observation.

Dr. Drummond's researches were strictly limited to the spicula of the eyes and scales of fishes; and as he does not appear to have suspected that particles having analogous motions might exist in other organized bodies, and far less in inorganic matter, I consider myself anticipated by this acute observer only to the same extent as by Gleichen, and in a much less degree than by Muller, whose statements have been already alluded to.

All the observers now mentioned have confined themselves to the examination of the particles of organic bodies. In 1819, however, Mr. Bywater, of Liverpool, published an account of Microscopical Observations, in which it is stated that not only organic tissues, but also inorganic substances, consist of what he terms animated or irritable particles.[9]

A second edition of this Essay appeared in 1828, probably altered in some points, but it may be supposed agreeing essentially in its statements with the edition of 1819, which I have never seen, and of the existence of which I was ignorant when I published my pamphlet.

From the edition of 1828, which I have but lately met with, it appears that Mr. Bywater employed a compound microscope of the construction called Culpeper's, that the object was examined in a bright sunshine, and the light from the mirror

[9] John Bywater, *Physiological Fragments; or, Sketches of various subjects intimately connected with the study of Physiology* (London: Baldwin, Cradock & Joy, 1819).

thrown so obliquely on the stage as to give a blue colour to the infusion.[10]

The first experiment I here subjoin in his own words.

"A small portion of flour must be placed on a slip of glass, and mixed with a drop of water, then instantly applied to the microscope; and if stirred and viewed by a bright sun, as already described, it will appear evidently filled with innumerable small linear bodies, writhing and twisting about with extreme activity."

Similar bodies, and equally in motion, were obtained from animal and vegetable tissues, from vegetable mould, from sandstone after being made red hot, from coal, ashes, and other inorganic bodies.

I believe that in thus stating the manner in which Mr. Bywater's experiments were conducted, I have enabled microscopical observers to judge of the extent and kind of optical illusion to which he was liable, and of which he does not seem to have been aware. I have only to add, that it is not here a question of priority; for if his observations are to be depended on, mine must be entirely set aside.

[10] Edward Culpeper, a prominent microscope maker who flourished in the first half of the eighteenth century, constructed a type of compound microscope which became associated with his name.

ROBERT CHAMBERS

Hypothesis of the Development of the Vegetable and Animal Kingdoms[*]

Robert Chambers (1802–1871) was a Scot whose name is most widely known for biographical dictionaries, collections of Scottish ballads, and other works printed by the publishing house which he ran jointly with his brother. His *Vestiges,* published anonymously in 1844, received wide attention and drew bitter attack because it was viewed as being contradictory of the Biblical account of the Creation. In the preface to the tenth edition (1853) the still anonymous author claimed: "It seemed to him logically necessary that we should regard the organic part of nature as having been instituted in the manner of law also, though not less under the providential care of the Supreme than the physical phenomena. . . ." His speculations were not done ". . . in an irreverent spirit, or with a hostile design to any form or code of morals." However, the author laments that the book became the subject of obloquy and controversy. "It has never had a single declared adherent — and nine editions have been sold." *Vestiges* is essentially a compilation of all the data and theories which would support the idea of the mutability of species and the gradual evolution of lower forms into higher ones. Missing from this work is the important theory of natural selection provided by Darwin and Wallace as a causal mechanism for evolution.

I T HAS been . . . intimated, as a general fact, that there is an obvious gradation amongst the families of both the vegetable and animal kingdoms, from the simple lichen and ani-

[*] From *Vestiges of the Natural History of Creation* (1844).

[243]

malcule respectively up to the highest order of dicotyledonous[1] trees and the mammalia. Confining our attention, in the meantime, to the animal kingdom — it does not appear that this gradation passes along one line, on which every form of animal life can be, as it were, strung. There seems to be a plurality of lines; how many there are it is not necessary at present to decide. There may be two or more lines; or the lines may be branching; or the whole may be in a circle composed of minor circles, as has been recently suggested. But still it is incontestable that there are general appearances of a scale beginning with the simple and advancing to the complicated. The animal kingdom was divided by Cuvier[2] into four sub-kingdoms, or divisions, and these exhibit an unequivocal gradation in the order in which they are here enumerated: —

RADIATA, (polypes, &c.)
MOLLUSCA, (pulpy animals.)   ARTICULATA, (jointed animals.)
VERTEBRATA, (animals with internal skeleton.)

the mollusca and articulata being, as it were, two distinct parallel lines by which we pass from the radiata to the vertebrata. The gradation can, in like manner, be clearly traced in the *classes* into which the sub-kingdoms are subdivided, as, for instance, when we take those of the vertebrata in this order — fishes, reptiles, birds, mammals.

While the external forms of all these various animals are so different, it is very remarkable that the whole are, after all, variations of a fundamental plan, which can be traced as a basis

[1] Refers to the two cotyledons, or seed leaves, common to most shrubs and trees.
[2] Georges Cuvier (1769–1832), an important student of comparative anatomy, published *La règne animal* (4 vols., Paris, 1817), a major systematic work.

throughout the whole, the variations being merely modifications of that plan to suit the particular conditions in which each particular animal has been designed to live. Starting from the primeval germ, which, as we have seen, is the representative of a particular order of full-grown animals, we find all others to be merely advances from that type, with the extension of endowments and modification of forms which are required in each particular case; each form, also, retaining a strong affinity to that which precedes it, and tending to impress its own features on that which succeeds. This unity of structure, as it is called, becomes the more remarkable, when we observe that the organs, while preserving a resemblance, are often put to different uses. For example: the ribs become, in the serpent, organs of locomotion, and the snout is extended, in the elephant, into a prehensile instrument.

It is equally remarkable that analogous purposes are served in different animals by organs essentially different. Thus, the mammalia breathe by lungs; the fishes, by gills. These are not modifications of one organ, but distinct organs. In mammifers, the gills exist and act at an early stage of the fœtal state, but afterwards go back and appear no more; while the lungs are developed. In fishes, again, the gills only are fully developed; while the lung structure either makes no advance at all, or only appears in the rudimentary form of an air-bladder. So, also, the baleen of the whale and the teeth of the land mammalia are different organs. The whale, in embryo, shews the rudiments of teeth; but these, not being wanted, are not developed, and the baleen is brought forward instead. The land animals, we may also be sure, have the rudiments of baleen in their organization. In many instances, a particular structure is found advanced to a certain point in a particular set of animals, (for instance, feet in the serpent tribe,) although it is not there required in any degree; but the peculiarity, being carried a little farther forward, is perhaps useful in the next set of animals in the scale. Such are called rudimentary organs. With this class of phenomena are to be ranked the useless mammæ of the male human being, and the unrequired process of bone in the male opossum, which is needed in the female for supporting her pouch. Such curious features are most conspicuous in animals which form links between various classes.

These facts clearly shew how all the various organic forms of our world are bound up in one — how a fundamental unity pervades and embraces them all, collecting them, from the humblest lichen up to the highest mammifer, in one system, the whole creation of which must have depended upon one law or decree of the Almighty, though it did not all come forth at one time. After what we have seen, the idea of a separate exertion for each must appear totally inadmissible. The single fact of abortive or rudimentary organs condemns it; for these, on such a supposition, could be regarded in no other light than as blemishes or blunders — the thing of all others most irreconcilable with that idea of Almighty Perfection which a general view of nature so irresistibly conveys. On the other hand, when the organic creation is admitted to have been effected by a general law, we see nothing in these abortive parts but harmless peculiarities of development, and interesting evidences of the manner in which the Divine Author has been pleased to work.

We have yet to advert to the most interesting class of facts connected with organic development. It is only in recent times that physiologists have observed that each animal passes, in the course of its germinal history, through a series of changes resembling the *permanent forms,* first of the various orders inferior to it in the entire scale, and then of its own order. This is a department of natural history in which only a few facts have been collected; but these are of such a nature, that we cannot doubt of their being the indications of some great general law. Thus for instance, the comatula, a free-swimming starfish, is, at one stage of its early progress, a crinoid — that is, a star-fish fixed upon a stalk to the botton of the sea. It advances from the form of one of the lower to that of one of the higher echinodermata. The animals of its first form were, as we have seen, among the most abundant in the earliest fossiliferous rocks: they began to decline in the new red sandstone era, and they were succeeded in the oolitic age by animals *of the form of the mature comatula.* Thus, too, the insect, standing at the head of the articulated animals, is, in the larva state, an annelid or worm, the annelida being the lowest in the same class. The higher crustacea, as the crab or lobster, at their escape from the ovum, resemble the perfect animal of the inferior order entomostraca, and pass through all the forms of transition which characterize the intermediate tribes of crustacea. The salmon, a highly organized fish, exhibits, in its early stages, as has been remarked, the gelatinous dorsal cord, the heterocercal tail, and inferior position of the mouth, which mark the mature example of the lower tribes of fishes, the placoids and ganoids. The frog, again, for some time after its birth, is a fish with external gills, and other organs fitting it for an aquatic life, all of which are changed as it advances to maturity, and becomes a land animal. The mammifer only passes through still more stages, according to its higher place in the scale. Nor is man himself exempt from this law. His first form is that which is permanent in the animalcule. His organization gradually passes through conditions generally resembling a fish, a reptile, a bird, and the lower mammalia, before it attains its specific maturity. At one of the last stages of his fœtal career, he exhibits an intermaxillary bone, which is characteristic of the perfect ape; this is suppressed, and he may then be said to take leave of the simial type, and become a true human creature. Even, as we shall see, the varieties of his race are represented in the progressive development of an individual of the highest, before we see the adult Caucasian, the highest point yet attained in the animal scale.

It is certainly very remarkable that, corresponding generally to these progressive forms in the development of individuals, has been the succession of animal forms in the course of time. Our earth, as we have seen, bore crinoidea before it bore the higher echinodermata. It presented crustacea before it bore fishes, and when fishes came, the first forms were those ganoidal and placoidal types which correspond with the early fœtal condition of higher orders. Afterwards there were reptiles, then mammifers, and finally, as we know, came man. The tendency of all these illustrations is to make us look to *development* as the principle which has been immediately concerned in the peopling of this globe, a process extending over a vast space of time, but which is nevertheless connected in character with the briefer process by which an individual being is evoked from a simple germ. What mystery is there here — and how shall I proceed to enunciate the conception which I have ventured to form of what may prove to be its proper solution! It is an idea by no means calculated to impress by its greatness, or to puzzle by its profoundness. It is an idea more marked by simplicity than perhaps any other of those which have explained the great secrets of nature. But in this lies, perhaps, one of its strongest claims to our faith.

The whole train of animated beings, from the simplest and oldest, up to the highest and most recent, are, then, to be regarded as a series of *advances of the principle of development,* which have depended upon external physical circumstances, to which the resulting animals are appropriate. I contemplate the whole phenomena as having been in the first place arranged in the counsels of Divine Wisdom, to take place, not only upon this sphere, but upon all the others in space, under necessary modifications, and as being carried on, from first to last, here and elsewhere, under immediate favour of the creative will or energy. The nucleated vesicle, the fundamental form of all organization, we must regard as the meeting-point between the inorganic and the organic — the end of the mineral and beginning of the vegetable and animal kingdoms, which thence start in different directions, but in perfect parallelism and analogy. We have already seen that this nucleated vesicle is itself a type of mature and independent being in the infusory animalcules, as well as the starting point of the fœtal progress of every higher individual in creation, both animal and vegetable. We have seen that it is a form of being which there is some reason to believe electric agency will produce — though not perhaps usher into full life — in albumen, one of those compound elements of animal bodies, of which another (urea) has been made by artificial means. Remembering these things, we are drawn on to the supposition, that the fist step in the creation of life upon this planet was *a chemico-electric operation, by which simple germinal vesicles were produced.* This is so much, but what were the next steps? Let a common vegetable infusion help us to an answer. There, as we have seen, simple forms are produced at first, but afterwards they become more complicated, until at length the life-producing powers of the infusion are exhausted. Are we to presume that, in this case, the simple engender the complicated? Undoubtedly, this would not be more wonderful as a natural process than one which we never think of wondering at, because familiar to us — namely, that in the gestation of the mammals, the animalcule-like ovum of a few days is the parent, in a sense, of the chick-like form of a few weeks, and that in all the subsequent stages — fish, reptile, &c. — the one may, with scarcely a metaphor, be said to be the progenitor of the other. I suggest, then, as an hypothesis already countenanced by much that is ascertained, and likely to be further sanctioned by much that remains to be known, that the first step was *an advance under favour of peculiar conditions, from the simplest forms of being, to the next more complicated, and this through the medium of the ordinary process of generation.*

It has been seen that, in the reproduction of the higher animals, the new being passes through stages in which it is successively fish-like and reptile-like. But the resemblance is not to the adult fish or the adult reptile, but to the fish and reptile at a certain point in their fœtal progress; this holds true with regard to the vascular, nervous, and other systems alike. It seems as if gestation consisted of two distinct and independent stages — one devoted to the development of the new being through the conditions of the inferior types, or, rather, through the corresponding *first stages of their development;* another perfecting and bringing the new being to a healthy maturity, on the basis of the point of development reached. This may be illustrated by a simple diagram. The fœtus of all the four classes may be supposed to advance in an identical condition to the point A. The fish there diverges and passes along a line apart, and peculiar to itself, to its mature state at F. The reptile, bird, and mammal, go on together to C, where the reptile diverges in like manner, and advances by itself to R. The bird diverges at D, and goes on to B. The mammal then goes forward in a straight line to the highest point of organization at M. This diagram shews only the main ramifications; but the reader must suppose minor ones, representing the subordinate differences of orders, tribes, families, genera, &c., if he wishes to extend his views to the whole varieties of being in the animal kingdom. Limiting ourselves at present to the outline afforded by this diagram, it is apparent that the only thing required for an advance from one type to another in the generative process is that, for example, the fish embryo should not diverge at A, but go on to C before it diverges, in which case the progeny will be, not a fish, but a reptile. To protract the *straightforward part of the gestation over a small space* — and from species to species the space would be small indeed — is all that is necessary.

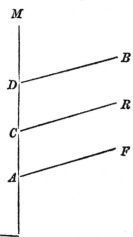

This might be done by the force of certain external conditions operating upon the parturient system. The nature of these conditions we can only conjecture, for their operation, which in the geological eras was so powerful, has in its main strength been long interrupted, and is now perhaps only allowed to work in some of the lowest departments of the organic world, or under extraordinary casualties in some of the higher, and to these points the attention of science has as yet been little directed. But though this knowledge were never to be clearly attained, it need not much affect the present argument, provided it be satisfactorily shewn that there must be some such influence within the range of natural things.

We shall now see an instance of development operating within the production of what approaches to the character of variety of species. It is fully established that a human family, tribe, or nation is liable, in the course of generations, to be either advanced from a mean form to a higher one, or degraded from a higher to a lower, by the influence of the physical conditions in which it lives. The coarse features, and other structural peculiarities of the negro race only continue while these people live amidst the circumstances usually associated with barbarism. In a more temperate clime, and higher social state, the face and figure become greatly refined. The few African nations which possess any civilization also exhibit forms approaching the European; and when the same people in the United States of America have enjoyed a within-door life for several generations, they assimilate to the whites amongst whom they live. On the other hand, there are authentic instances of a people originally well-formed and good-looking, being brought, by imperfect diet and a variety of physical hardships, to a meaner form. It is remarkable that prominence of the jaws, a recession and diminution of the cranium, and an elongation and attenuation of the limbs, are peculiarities always produced by these miserable conditions, for they indicate an unequivocal retrogression towards the type of the lower animals. Thus we see nature alike willing to go back and to go forward. Both effects are simply the result of the operation of the law of development in the generative system. Give good conditions, it advances; bad ones, it recedes. Now, perhaps, it is only because there is no longer a possibility, in the higher types of being, of giving sufficiently favourable conditions to carry on species to species, that we see the operation of the law so far limited.

Let us trace this law also in the production of certain classes of monstrosities. A human fœtus is often left with one of the most important parts of its frame imperfectly developed: the heart, for instance, goes no farther than the three-chambered form, so that it is the heart of a reptile. There are even instances of this organ being left in the two-chambered or fish-form. Such defects are the result of nothing more than a failure of the power of development in the system of the mother, occasioned by weak health or misery, and bearing with force upon that sub-stage of the gestation at which the perfecting of the heart to its right form ought properly to have taken place. Here we have apparently a realization of the converse of those conditions which carry on species to species, so far, at least, as one organ is concerned. Seeing a complete specific retrogression in this one point, how easy it is to suppose an access of favourable conditions sufficient to reverse the phenomenon, and make a fish mother develop a reptile heart, or a reptile mother develop a mammal one. It is no great boldness that a super-adequacy in the measure of this under-adequacy (and the one thing seems as natural an occurrence as the other) would suffice in a goose to give its progeny the body of a rat, and produce the ornithorhynchus,[3] or might give the progeny of an ornithorhynchus the mouth and feet of a true rodent, and thus complete at two stages the passage from the aves to the mammalia.

Perhaps even the transition from species to species does still take place in some of the obscurer fields of creation, or under extraordinary casualties, though science professes to have no such facts on record. It is here to be remarked, that such facts might often happen, and yet no record be taken of them, for so strong is the prepossession for the doctrine of invariable like-production, that such circumstances, on occurring, would be almost sure to be explained away on some other supposition, or, if presented, would be disbelieved and neglected. Science, therefore, has no such facts, for the very same reason that some small sects are said to have no discreditable members — namely, that they do not receive such persons, and extrude all who begin to verge upon the character. There are, nevertheless, some facts which have chanced to be reported without any reference to this hypothesis, and which it seems extremely difficult to explain satisfactorily upon any other. One of these has already been mentioned — a progression in the forms of the animalcules in a vegetable infusion from the simpler to the more complicated, a sort of microcosm, representing the whole history of the progress of animal creation as displayed by geology. Another is given in the history of the Acarus Crossii,[4] which may be only the ultimate stage of a series of similar transformations

---

[3] A family of the order Monotrema, more commonly known as the duck-billed platypus.

[4] *Acarus crossii,* the mite.

effected by electric agency in the solution subjected to it. There is, however, one direct case of a translation of species, which has been presented with a respectable amount of authority.[5] It appears that, whenever oats sown at the usual time are kept cropped down during summer and autumn, and allowed to remain over the winter, a thin crop of rye is the harvest presented at the close of the ensuing summer. This experiment has been tried repeatedly, with but one result; invariably the *secale cereale* is the crop reaped where the *avena sativa,* a recognised different genera, was sown. Now it will not satisfy a strict inquirer to be told that the seeds of the rye were latent in the ground, and only superseded the dead product of the oats; for if any such fact were in the case, why should the usurping grain be always rye? Perhaps those curious facts which have been stated with regard to forests of one kind of trees, when burnt down, being succeeded (without planting) by other kinds, may yet be found most explicable, as this is, upon the hypothesis of a progression of species which takes place under certain favouring conditions, now apparently of comparatively rare occurrence. The case of the oats is the more valuable, as bearing upon the suggestion as to a protraction of the gestation at a particular part of its course. Here, the generative process is, by the simple mode of cropping down, kept up for a whole year beyond its usual term. The type is thus allowed to advance, and what was oats becomes rye.

The idea, then, which I form of the progress of organic life upon the globe — and the hypothesis is applicable to all similar theatres of vital being — is, *that the simplest and most primitive*

[5] W. Weissenborn, "On the Alleged Transformation of Avena sativa into Secale cereale," *Magazine of Natural History,* I (1837), 574–577.

type, under a law to which that of like-production is subordinate, gave birth to the type next above it, that this again produced the next higher, and so on to the very highest, the stages of advance being in all cases very small — namely, from one species only to another; so that the phenomenon has always been of a simple and modest character. Whether the whole of any species was at once translated forward, or only a few parents were employed to give birth to the new type, must remain undetermined; but, supposing that the former was the case, we must presume that the moves along the line or lines were simultaneous, so that the place vacated by one species was immediately taken by the next in succession, and so on back to the first, for the supply of which the formation of a new germinal vesicle out of inorganic matter was alone necessary. Thus, the production of new forms, as shewn in the pages of the geological record, has never been anything more than a new stage of progress in gestation, an event as simply natural, and attended as little by any circumstances of a wonderful or startling kind, as the silent advance of an ordinary mother from one week to another of her pregnancy. Yet, be it remembered, the whole phenomena are, in another point of view, wonders of the highest kind, for in each of them we have to trace the effect of an Almighty Will which had arranged the whole in such harmony with external physical circumstances, that both were developed in parallel steps — and probably this development upon our planet is but a sample of what has taken place, through the same cause, in all the other countless theatres of being which are suspended in space.

Early in this century, M. Lamarck, a naturalist of the highest character, suggested an hypothesis of organic progress which deservedly incurred much ridicule, although it contained a glimmer of the truth.[6] He surmised, and endeavoured, with a great deal of ingenuity, to prove, that one being advanced in the course of generations to another, in consequence merely of its experience of wants calling for the exercise of its faculties in a particular direction, by which exercise new developments of organs took place, ending in variations sufficient to constitute a new species. Thus he thought that a bird would be driven by necessity to seek its food in the water, and that, in its efforts to swim, the outstretching of its claws would lead to the expansion of the intermediate membranes, and it would thus become web-footed. Now it is possible that wants and the exercise of faculties have entered in some manner into the production of the phenomena which we have been considering; but certainly not in the way suggested by Lamarck, whose whole notion is obviously so inadequate to account for the rise of the organic kingdoms, that we only can place it with pity among the follies of the wise. Had the laws of organic development been known in his time, his theory might have been of a more imposing kind. It is upon these that the present hypothesis is mainly founded. I take existing natural means, and shew them to have been capable of producing all the existing organisms, with the simple and easily conceivable aid of a higher generative law, which we perhaps still see operating upon a limited scale. I also go beyond the French philosopher to a very important point, the original Divine conception of all the forms of being which these natural laws were only instruments in working out and realizing. The actuality of such a conception receives a remark-

---

[6] Jean Baptiste Pierre Antoine de Monet, Chevalier de Lamarck (1744–1829) first proposed a theory of organic evolution in 1801.

able support from the glimpses which we obtain, through the medium of the discoveries of Mr. Macleay,[7] with regard to the affinities and analogies of animal (and by implication vegetable) organisms. Such a regularity in the *structure*, as we may call it, of the *classification of animals*, as is there beginning to be revealed to us, is totally irreconcilable with the idea of form going on to form merely as needs and wishes in the animals themselves dictated. Had such been the case, all would have been irregular, as things arbitrary necessarily are. But, lo, the whole plan of being appears to be as symmetrical as the plan of a house, or the laying out of an old-fashioned garden! This must needs have been devised and arranged for beforehand. And what a preconception or forethought have we here! For let us only for a moment consider how various are the external physical conditions in which animals live — climate, soil, temperature, land, water, air; the peculiarities of food, and the various ways in which it is to be sought; the peculiar circumstances in which the business of reproduction and the care-taking of the young are to be attended to: all these requiring to be taken into account, and thousands of animals to be formed suitable in organization and mental character for the concerns they were to have with these various conditions and circumstances — here a tooth fitted for crushing nuts: there a claw fitted to serve as a hook for suspension; here to repress teeth and develop a bony net-work instead; there to arrange for a bronchial apparatus, to last only for a certain brief time; and all these animals were to

[7] William Sharp Macleay (1792–1865), a zoologist whose primary studies were on insects. Author of a number of studies attempting to illustrate affinities and analogies among living forms; see, e.g., "A Reply to Some Observations of Mr. Virey in *Bulletin des Sciences Naturelles*, 1825, on Analogy and Affinity," *Zoological Journal*, IV (1828–1829), 47–52.

be schemed out, each as a part of a great range, which was on the whole to be rigidly regular: let us, I say, only consider these things, and we shall see that the decreeing of laws to bring the whole about was an act involving such a degree of wisdom and device as we only can attribute, adoringly, to the one Eternal and Unchangeable. It may be asked, how does this reflection comport with that timid philosophy which would have us to draw back from the investigation of God's works, lest the knowledge of them should make us undervalue his greatness and forget his paternal character? Does it not rather appear that our ideas of the Deity can only be worthy of him in the ratio in which we advance in a knowledge of his works and ways; and that the acquisition of this knowledge is consequently an available means of our growing in a genuine reverence for him!

But the idea that any of the lower animals have been concerned in any way with the origin of man — is not this degrading? Degrading is a term, expressive of a notion of the human mind, and the human mind is liable to prejudices which prevent its notions from being invariably correct. Were we acquainted for the first time with the circumstances attending the production of an individual of our race, we might equally think them degrading, and be eager to deny them, and exclude them from the admitted truths of nature. Knowing this fact familiarly and beyond contradiction, a healthy and natural mind finds no difficulty in regarding it complacently. Creative Providence has been pleased to order that it should be so, and it must therefore be submitted to. Now the idea as to the progress of organic creation, if we become satisfied of its truth, ought to be received precisely in this spirit. If it has pleased Providence to arrange that one species should give birth to another, until the second

[259]

highest gave birth to man, who is the very highest; be it so; it is our part to admire and to submit. The very faintest notion of there being anything ridiculous or degrading in the theory — how absurd does it appear when we remember that every individual amongst us actually passes through the characters of the insect, the fish, and reptile, (to speak nothing of others,) before he is permitted to breathe the breath of life! But such notions are mere emanations of false pride and ignorant prejudice. He who conceives them little reflects that they, in reality, involve a contempt for the works and ways of God. For it may be asked, if He, as appears, has chosen to employ inferior organisms as a generative medium for the production of higher ones, even including ourselves, what right have we, his humble creatures, to find fault? There is, also, in this prejudice, an element of unkindliness towards the lower animals, which is utterly out of place. These creatures are all of them part products of the Almighty Conception, as well as ourselves. All of them display wondrous evidences of his wisdom and benevolence. All of them have had assigned to them by their Great Father a part in the drama of the organic world, as well as ourselves. Why should they be held in such contempt? Let us regard them in a proper spirit, as parts of the grand plan, instead of contemplating them in the light of frivolous prejudices, and we shall be altogether at a loss to see how there should be any degradation in the idea of our race having been genealogically connected with them.

CHARLES BELL

The Anatomy and Philosophy of Expression as Connected with the Fine Arts*

The material excerpted from *The Anatomy and Philosophy of Expression as Connected with the Fine Arts* by Sir Charles Bell is from the fifth (London) edition of 1865. The work was first published in 1806; Bell died in 1842; and a preface to the third edition, which is identical with the fifth, opens with the charming statement: "These Essays formed the earliest and latest occupation of the lamented author's leisure hours."

T HE violent passions are exhibited so distinctly in the countenance of both man and animals, that we are led to consider the movements by which they are made obvious, as characteristic signs provided by nature for the express purpose of intimating the inward emotions: that they may be interpreted by a peculiar and intuitive faculty in the observer.

This view, however, so natural at first, is not altogether satisfactory; and an opposite theory has been proposed, in which such special provision is denied, and the appearances are accounted for, as the effect of certain actions which are performed in obedience to the common laws of the animal economy. It is also said, that we are taught by experience

* From *The Anatomy and Philosophy of Expression as Connected with the Fine Arts* (1806–1865).

[261]

alone to distinguish the signs of the passion in man: that in infancy we learn that smiles are expressive of kindness, because accompanied by endearments, and that frowns are the reverse, because they are followed by blows. The expression of anger in a brute is alleged to be merely the cast of features which precedes his biting; and the character of fondness, that which is seen in his fawning and licking of the hand. In short, it has been maintained that what are called the external signs of passion, are only the concomitants of those voluntary movements which the structure renders necessary. That, for example, the glare of the lion's eye proceeds from his effort to see his prey more clearly; and his grin or snarl from the natural act of unsheathing his fangs before using them.

But, if we attend to the evidence of anatomical investigation, we shall perceive a remarkable difference between the provision for giving motion to the features in animals, and that for bestowing expression in man. In the lower creatures, there is no expression, but what may be referred, more or less plainly, to their acts of volition, or necessary instincts; while in man there seems to be a special apparatus, for the purpose of enabling him to communicate with his fellow-creatures, by that natural language, which is read in the changes of his countenance. There exist in his face, not only all those parts, which by their action produce expression in the several classes of quadrupeds, but there is added a peculiar set of muscles to which no other office can be assigned than to serve for expression.

In brutes the most marked expression is that of rage; the object of which is opposition, resistance, and defence. But on examination it will be found that the force of the expression is in proportion to the strength of the principal action in the creature when thus excited.

The graminivorous animals, which seek their subsistence, not by preying upon others, or by the ferocity, contest, and victory, which supply the carnivorous with food, have in their features no strong expression of rage; it is chiefly confined to the effect produced on the general system. Thus the inflamed eye and the breathing nostrils of the bull are induced by the excitement of the whole frame; his only proper expression of rage is in the position of the head, with the horns turned obliquely to the ground, ready to strike; and indeed it may be observed, that animals which strike with the horns shew little indication either of fear or rage, except in the position of the head; for the breath ejected from the expanded nostril is the effect of mere exertion, and may belong to different conditions of the frame. In all graminivorous animals, the skin of the head is closely attached to the skull, and capable of very limited motion: the eye is almost uniformly mild, and the lips are unmoved by passion.

It is in the carnivorous animals, with whose habits and manner of life ferocity is instinctively connected, as suited to their mode of subsistence, that rage is distinguished by remarkable strength of expression. The eyeball is terrible, and the retraction of the flesh of the lips indicates the most savage fury. The action of the respiratory organs, the heaving and agony of breathing, the deep and harsh motion of the air drawn through the throat in the growl, declare the universal excitement of the animal. It is wrong to imagine that all this is a mere preparatory exposure of the canine teeth. Brutes may have expression, properly so called, as well as man, though in

[263]

a more limited degree; but in them, expression is so moulded to their natures and their necessities, that it seems accessory to their needful and voluntary actions.

The horse is universally held to be a noble animal, as he possesses the expression of courage, without the ferociousness of the beast of prey; and as there is a consent between the motions of the ear and the eye, which resembles the exertion of mind, and the movements of the human countenance. But even this expression is the result of an incidental consent of animal motions; and no more proves intelligence, than the diminutive eye and the unexpressive face of the elephant denote the contrary. We admire it, because there is as much animation as in the tiger, without the ferocity. The consent of motions between the eye and the ear of the horse is a physical consequence of the necessities of the animal. His defence lies in the hind feet, and there is an arrangement both in the muscles, and in the form of the skull, for that retroverted direction of the eye, which seems so expressive in the horse, but which merely serves to guide the blow. The inflation of the nostrils, and the fleshiness of the lips, belong to the peculiar provision for his respiration and mode of feeding.

Artists bestow an expression on the eye of the lion which they suppose gives dignity — a kind of knitting of the eyebrows, whilst the eyelids are straining wide. This is quite incompatible with the powers of expression in brutes. When the lion closes his eyes in repose, the fleshiness about the eyelids and the hair of the skin produce the effect of a morose human expression, but when he is excited, and the eye is fixed, there is no such character.

I observed above, that some painters have thought it allowable to give human expression to the heads of lions, and others have presented it in their heads of horses. I think this is done on a mistaken view, and that it will never enhance the peculiar beauty of any animal to engraft upon it some part of human expression. Rubens, in his picture of Daniel in the lions' den, has given this character to the heads of the lions.[1]

It is more than doubtful whether it be in the true spirit of that principle of association which should govern the adaptation of expression and character in producing an ideal form, thus to mingle human expression with the features of the savage animals. It seems, however, that a distinction is to be made when the lion is represented in its natural state and when sculptured emblematically. Represented in his den, or in the forest, the picture should possess all the natural character; when couched amidst the insignia of empire, there may be a difference.

Referring to the remarkable difference between the range of expression in man and in animals, and considering that in brutes it proceeds from necessity or voluntary action, while in man there is a special provision for bestowing it, — a peculiar set of muscles to which no other office can be assigned, it is proper to reduce the muscles of several quadrupeds into classes, that we may distinguish the characteristics of mere animal expression from those in man.

They may be distinguished as, Ist. Those which raise the lips from the teeth; 2d. Those which surround the eyelids; and 3d. Those which move the nostrils.

1 Bell presumably saw this picture in England. It was, when he wrote, in the collection of Lord Hamilton.

1. The first of these classes, viz. *the muscles which raise the lips from the teeth,* admit of a subdivision. In the carnivorous animals the muscles of the lips are so directed as to raise the lip from the canine teeth. In the graminivorous they are directed so as to raise the lips from the incisor teeth. The former I would distinguish by the name *ringentes,* snarling muscles: the latter by the name *depascentes,* muscles simply for feeding.

The snarling muscles arise from the margin of the orbit, and from the upper jaw; they are inserted into that part of the upper lip from which the moustaches grow, and which is opposite to the canine teeth. Their sole office is to raise the upper lip from the canine teeth; and although they are assisted in this by others (the masticating muscles), I have ventured to distinguish them particularly as the muscles of snarling. This action of snarling is quite peculiar to the ferocious and carnivorous animals. The graminivorous are incapable of it, and consequently these muscles are to be found largely developed only in the former class, not in the latter. In the carnivorous animals it can scarcely be said that there is a perfect or regular orbicular muscle, as in man, for contracting the lips; the lips hang loose and relaxed, unless when drawn aside by the snarling muscles, and they fall back into this state of relaxation, with the remission of the action of these muscles.

The chief muscles of the lips, which in carnivorous animals are directed to the side of the mouth, are, in graminivorous animals, directed to the middle of the lip over the front teeth. I call them *depascentes,* from their use, which is to enable the creature to open its lips so as to gather food, and to bite the grass. They are long muscles; one set come down upon each side of the face, and joining in a broad tendon, pass over the nose to be inserted into the upper lip. Another set run along the lower jaw, to be inserted by a peculiar feathered tendon into the under lip. These muscles are very strong in the horse. They give a peculiar and characteristic expression to the stallion, when he snuffs the breeze, with his head high in air; when he bites, the expression is entirely different from that of the carnivorous animal; instead of exposing the teeth corresponding with the canine, he lifts the lips from the fore teeth, and protrudes them. The carnivorous animals have not these muscles of the fore part of the lip; in them, the lips covering the incisor teeth are not fleshy like those of the graminivorous animals, but are tied down to the gums, and the fore teeth are exposed only in consequence of the straining occasioned by retraction of the side of the mouth.

Although the graminivorous animals do not possess those muscles which so powerfully retract the lips in the carnivorous class, they have a more perfect orbicular muscle surrounding the mouth, and regulating the motion of their fleshy lips.

2. *Muscles which surround the eyelid.* — In man, the upper eyelid is raised by a muscle coming from the back of the orbit. But animals of prey, in whose eyes there is the peculiar and ferocious splendour, which distinguishes the tiger or the lion, have, in addition to this muscle, three others attached to the eyelids, which, stretching the coats and drawing the eyelids backward upon the prominent eyeball, produce a fixed straining of the eye, and a greater brightness. These muscles I have termed *scintillantes*, because by retracting the eyelids, they expose the brilliant white of the eye, which reflects a sparkling light. In the sheep, besides the proper muscle coming

from the bottom of the orbit, there is only a web of fibres to assist in raising the eyelid. In the horse, there is a muscle to pull down the lower eyelid; and another, which, passing from the ear to the outer angle of the eyelid, retracts it, and enables the animal to direct the pupil backward, where his defence lies. In the feline tribe light is reflected from the bottom of the eye, when the pupil is dilated; and as the pupil dilates in obscure light, there is a brilliant reflection from the cat's eye, which we mistake for indication of passion. All these may be partially displayed in the human eye, as in the bloodshot redness combined with the circle of reflected light from the margin of the corner, like a flame or angry spark, as Charon is described by Dante, —

"Ch' intorno agli occhi avea di fiamme ruote,"[2]

Or as lighted charcoal, from the bottom of the eye, —

"Caron demonio con occhi di bragia."[3]

It is in this way that a touch of true expression will illustrate a whole passage; so Milton,

"With head uplift above the wave, and eyes
That sparkling blazed."[4]

3. *Muscles of the Nostrils.* — These are not less distinct and peculiar, in different classes of animals, than the muscles of the eye and lips. In the carnivorous animals, the nose is comparatively insignificant, provision being made in the open

[2] *Inferno* III:99. Around whose eyes two fiery circles shone (Plumptre).
[3] *Inferno* III:109. Charon, fiend with eyes that flamed all o'er (Plumptre).
[4] *Paradise Lost* I:193–194. Also Spenser, *Faerie Queene*, Book vi, cant. 7, stanza 42.

mouth for any occasional increase of respiration above the uniform play of the lungs; while in the inoffensive animals, which are the prey of the more ferocious, the inflation of the nostril is provided for by the action of another set of muscles.

For example, in the horse "the glory of whose nostrils is terrible,"[5] the muscles which inflate the nostril are very peculiar. They arise like the *ringentes;* but instead of being fixed into the lips, as in carnivorous animals, whose lips are to be raised from the canine teeth, they pass to the nostrils, and in combination with some lesser muscles, powerfully inflate them when the animal is pushed to his speed, excited by fear, or inflamed to rage.

In the gallery of Florence, there is the head of a horse in bronze, and antique; it is very fine, and in all respects as natural as those of the Elgin Marbles;[6] the mouth is open, but there is a bit in it.

Over the fountain, in the Piazza of the Grand Duke, is placed a group of Neptune, drawn by four horses;[7] the mouths of all the horses are open, and as they are free agents, without bit or harness, they seem to be of one mind, and to be expressing the same thing, whatever that may be. They would have been much finer, had the artist given them animation through the eye and nostril, without opening the mouth.

The horse's mouth is never seen open when the animal is free. Nothing can be finer than the action of a charger in

5 Job XXXIX: 20.

6 The Elgin Marbles are in the British Museum. They are, of course, the frieze of the Parthenon.

7 The author's note: "Milan. The four horses in the triumphal arch have their mouths gaping wide; not so the coursers last night in the Circus." Probably extracted from the journal of his Continental visit of 1840.

the field: but though he should snort and neigh and throw up his head and mane, with all his excitement he does not open his mouth. In the antiquities of Count Caylus, the horse's head is represented naturally.[8]

We may notice here, that most of the carnivorous animals hunt their prey. For this object, they not only require a peculiar and extended organ of smelling, but the air must be drawn forcibly over the surface on which the olfactory nerve is spread. It appears to me, that this accounts for their small confined nostril, and their breathing freely through the mouth. In smelling, an action of the nostrils takes place which directs the stream of air upwards into the cells of the nose, where the olfactory nerve is distributed. This is especially the case in the conformation of the dog's nostrils.

Returning now to the muscles in the human countenance, we perceive that, although the motions of the lips and nostrils in man may not be so extensive as in other classes of animals, there is in his face a capacity for all the varieties of expression which distinguish these creatures. He stands, as we have said, between the carnivorous and graminivorous animals; or, rather, he partakes the nature of both. He has the snarling muscles which so peculiarly distinguish the carnivorous class, while he is able to protrude the lips, and uncover the teeth, like the graminivorous. We have seen that in the carnivorous animals, the muscles descending from the cheek-bones and upper jaw to raise the lip are strong, and that the orbicular or circular fibres of the mouth are feeble, the lip being attached

[8] The *Recueil d'antiquités égyptiennes, étrusques, grècques et romaines*, by the Count de Caylus, was published in Paris from 1752 to 1767 in seven volumes. It is difficult to identify the engraving Bell has in mind.

to the forepart of the gums. In the graminivorous animals, on the contrary, the obicular muscle has great power; while the elevating and depressing muscles of the side of the mouth are weak. But in man, both classes of muscles are combined; the elevating and depressing muscles are fully developed, while the orbicular muscle completely antagonises them, modulating and qualifying their actions, and bestowing the utmost perfection on the motions of the lips.

Whether we look to the form of the features or to their power of expression, the consideration of these two classes of muscles alone will account for certain varieties in the human face. In one man, the excitement of passion may be indicated chiefly by the prevalence of one class, while in a second, another class will predominate in the expression.

If it be allowable to give examples, I would say that in the countenance of Mrs. Siddons or Mr. John Kemble,[9] there was presented the highest character of beauty which belongs to the true English face. In that family the upper lip and nostrils were very expressive: the class of muscles which operate on the nostrils was especially powerful, and both these great tragedians had a remarkable capacity for the expression of the nobler passions. In their cast of features there was never seen that blood-thirsty look which Cooke[10] could throw into his face. In him, the *ringentes* prevailed: and what determined hate could he express, when, combined with the oblique cast of his eyes, he drew up the outer part of the upper lip, and disclosed a sharp angular tooth! And is it not this lateral

[9] Sarah Kemble Siddons (1755–1831). Reynolds painted her as "The Tragic Muse." John Philip Kemble (1757–1823), famous for his Shakespearian roles.
[10] Presumably George Frederick Cooke (1756–1812), famous tragic actor.

drawing of the lips, and stretching them upon the closed teeth, which make the blood start from them, in remorseless hate and rancour?

But besides the muscles analogous to those of brutes, others are introduced into the human face, which indicate emotions and sympathies of which the lower animals are not susceptible; and as they are peculiar to man, they may be considered as the index of mental energy, in opposition to mere animal expression.

The most moveable and expressive features are the inner extremity of the eyebrow and the angle of the mouth; and these are precisely the parts which have least expression in brutes; for they have no eyebrows, and no power of elevating or depressing the angle of the mouth. It is therefore in these features that we should expect to find the muscles of expression peculiar to man.

The most remarkable muscle of the human face is the corrugator supercilii, arising from the frontal bone, near its union with the nasal bones, and inserted into the skin of the eyebrow; it knits the eyebrows with an energetic effect, which unaccountably, but irresistibly, conveys the idea of mind.

The frontal portion of the occipito-frontalis muscle is the antagonist of the orbicular muscle of the eyelids. It is wanting in the animals which we have examined; and in its stead, fibres, more or less strong, are found to be inserted directly into the eyelids.

The motion of the features which, next to that produced by the corrugator supercilii, is most expressive of human passion and sentiment, is to be seen in the angle of the mouth. At one time I conceived that this distinctive expression was chiefly owing to the superbus, which elevates and protrudes the under lip, but I was deceived. The character of human expression in the mouth is given by the *triangularis oris,* or *depressor anguli oris,* a muscle which I have not found in any of the lower animals; I believe it to be peculiar to man, and I can assign no other use for it than that which belongs to expression. It arises from the base of the lower jaw, and passes up to be inserted, with the converging fibres of almost all the muscles of the side of the face, into the corner of the mouth: it produces that arching of the lip so expressive of contempt, hatred, jealousy; and in combination with the elevator of the under lip, or superbus, and the orbicularis, it has a larger share than any other muscle in producing the infinite variety of motions in the mouth, expressive of sentiment.

We have already observed, that the faces of animals seem chiefly capable of expressing rage and fear; even pain is indicated more in the voice, and in writhing and struggling.

The rage of the graminivorous animal is chiefly visible in the eye, in the inflation of the nostril, and in the disturbed state of the body. It is expressed most strongly by the carnivorous animals: in them it is wild, ferocious, and terrifying. Their expression of rage, so far as it appears in the face, is shown by the strong action of the *ringentes,* or snarling muscles, the exposure of the canine teeth, the gnashing of the tusks, and the brilliant excitement of the eye. The expression of human rage partakes of both; the corresponding muscles of the lips and nostrils producing a similar action to that in animals; an exposure and clenching of the teeth; a degree of sparkling of the eye, and an inflation of the nostrils. Of a face under the influence of such actions, a spectator would infallibly say, that the aspect was brutal, savage, and cruel. But when the corrugator supercilii, a muscle peculiar to human expression, is brought into action, the sign is altered. The eyebrows are knit, the energy of mind is apparent, and there is the mingling of thought and emotion with the savage and brutal rage of the mere animal.

In man, the actions of the frontal muscle of the corrugator supercilii, and of the orbicular muscle of the mouth, give much expression. If instead of the retraction of the lips and the exposure of the teeth, as in the rage or pain of animals, the mouth is half closed, the lips inflected by the circular fibres, and drawn down by the action of the peculiarly human muscle, the depressor anguli oris, then there is expressed more agony of mind than of mere bodily suffering, by a combination of muscular actions of which animals are incapable.

The action of the orbicular muscle of the lips is, indeed, the most characteristic of agony of mind, and of all those passions which partake of sentiment; in grief, in vexation of spirit, in weeping, it modifies the effect of the muscles of animal expression, and produces human character.

Fear is characterised in animals by a mingling of anger, and of preparation for defence, with a shrinking of alarm in the more ferocious, and a straining of the eye and inflation of the nostril, with trembling, in the milder. In human fear and suspicion, the nostril is inflated, and the eye has that backward, jealous, and timid character which we see in the horse, and in the gentler classes of animals.

The orbicular muscle of the lips, with the system of elevating and depressing muscles in man, lead to expressions peculiarly human. And here I may observe, that expression is not always the effect of a contraction of the muscles of the face, either general or partial. It proceeds rather from a combined action of the muscles when under passion: for it is often the relaxation of a certain class, more than their excitement, which gives expression; and of this, smiling and laughter furnish the most apposite examples.

The capacity of receiving ludicrous ideas is as completely denied to animals as they are utterly incapable of the accompanying action of laughter. Dogs, in their expression of fondness, have a slight eversion of the lips, and grin and snuff amidst their frolic and gambols, in a way that resembles laughter; but in all this there is nothing which truly approaches to human expression. That is produced by the relaxation of the orbicular muscle of the lips, and the consequent preponderating action of the elevating muscles; and, of course, it can exist only in a face which possesses both the orbicular and the straight muscles of the lips in perfection.

In the emotions of contempt, pride, suspicion, and jealousy, the orbicular muscle and the triangularis oris, produce by their combination the arching of the lips, and the depression of the angle of the mouth. The horizontal drawing of the lips, which just discloses the teeth, and betrays the severe or bitter and malignant passions, is owing to a more general action of the muscles overcoming the opposition of the orbicularis.

In grief, the muscles of the eyebrow and those of the lips are combined in expression; hence the union of that upward direction of the extremity of the eyebrow characterising peevishness, discontent, and sinking of the spirits, with the depression of the angle of the mouth, which so distinctly indicates the harassed and subdued state of mind.

By the combination of those muscles of expression, much of that various play of the features expressive of human passions, as joy, hope, admiration, anxiety, fear, horror, despair, is produced; and thus, while the human countenance is capable of expressing both the rage of the more ferocious animals, and the timidity of the milder, it possesses, by the consentaneous action of a few superadded muscles, powers of expression varying almost to infinity.

It is curious to observe how the muscles thus afford a new occasion of distinguishing the classes of animals; and how, as signs of superior intelligence, they give proofs of the endowments of man, and the excellence of his nature. The full clear eye; the arched and moveable eyebrow; the smooth and polished forehead; as indicating susceptibility of emotion, and power of expression, are grand features of human character and beauty; and it is the perfection of beauty when the spectator is made sensible of this inherent, this latent power, even while no prevailing passion affects the features. But a great portion of the beauty of the human face is in the nose and the mouth; in a nostril which has a capacity for expression, without being too membranous and inflatable, for that produces a mean and imbecile kind of fierceness; and in lips, at once full and capable of those various modulations of form which are necessary to speech and the indication of human feeling.

The form of the face and the features are but the ground work of expression. The influence of passion on the body is a subject which has been discussed from the first dawnings of philosophy. The Greeks did not confine their study to the outward form of man; they also speculated on the habit of the body as affecting the mind: and we insensibly use their language, although the course of their ideas may be rejected or forgotten. There are varieties in the forms, strength, temper, and capacities of man. It has been well said that you cannot tread on a man's toes without learning something of his temper. One man will have his joke, although it may hurt his dearest friend, and another has so little imagination, that even in the delirium of fever he is dull. Some are generous to profligacy, or frugal to meanness, or gallant and true, or cowardly and insincere: these varieties are a part of human nature, and necessary to the constitution of society. But the ingenious reasoners of Ancient Greece ascribed the diversity of disposition to the texture of the frame; not to the features, nor to the proportions or shape of the skull, but rather to the mixture of the elements of the body; and more to the fluids than to the solids. Those distinctions, familiar to all, have in every succeeding age been attributed to the humours. When we speak of the constitution, the temper, the humour of a man, we are in truth adopting the language of Hippocrates,[11] who treated of the four radical humours, — the sanguineous, phlegmatic, choleric, and melancholic.

Other philosophers have imagined that the dispositions of man might have their source in his greater or less resemblance to the brutes. It was then allowable to fancy that a lion-like frame, strong hair, deep voice, and powerful limbs, were com-

[11] Hippocrates (460–377 B.C.), the "Father of Medicine," the author of one or more of the famous series of medical texts known as the Hippocratic corpus and clearly exhibiting the hands of numerous authors.

bined with courage. But our heroes are not of that mould. To be collected amidst fire and smoke, and the deafening sounds of battle — to marshal thousands — or to direct the vessel's course, whilst exposed not only to wounds but to death, is true courage; and, in these days, it is witnessed in the pale and fragile, more than in the strong and sanguineous, or the bulky and hairy savage. We can better estimate true courage since combatants have been divested of the helmet and mail.

Let us attend more especially to the human passions. I do not mean to treat of all those conditions of mind which are considered under the head of the passions, sentiments, or emotions; but to limit my inquiry to that kind or degree of mental excitement, which draws the frame into action, and which is interpreted by its agitation; when the spirits, by their vehemence, produce uncontrollable movements of the body, not determined by the will, but spontaneously arising with the state of feeling, which they strengthen and direct.

We shall begin, by marking the most extreme expression of the passions, — *laughter* and *weeping*. They suit our purpose as being peculiarly human, arising from sentiments not participated by the brutes.

We have seen that the muscles which operate upon the mouth are distinguishable into two classes, — those which surround and control the lips, and those which oppose them, and draw the mouth widely open. The effect of a ludicrous idea is to relax the former, and to contract the latter; hence, by a lateral stretching of the mouth, and a raising of the cheek to the lower eyelid, a smile is produced. The lips are, of all the

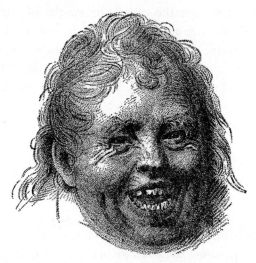

features, the most susceptible of action, and the most direct index of the feelings.

If the idea be exceedingly ridiculous, it is in vain that we endeavour to restrain this relaxation, and to compress the lips. The muscles concentring to the mouth prevail; they become more and more influenced; they retract the lips, and display the teeth. The cheeks are more powerfully drawn up, the eyelids wrinkled, and the eye almost concealed. The lacrymal gland within the orbit is compressed by the pressure on the eyeball, and the eye suffused with tears.

Simple and passive pleasures, the delight of meeting or the contemplation of innocence, relax the lips and dimple the cheek, whilst the eyes are bright and intelligent. The dimple is formed by the muscles which are inserted in the angle of the mouth acting on the plump integument of infancy and youth.

Observe the condition of a man convulsed with laughter,

and consider what are the organs or system of parts affected. He draws a full breath, and throws it out in interrupted, short, and audible cachinnations; the muscles of his throat, neck, and chest, are agitated; the diaphragm is especially convulsed. He holds his sides, and, from the violent agitation, he is incapable of a voluntary act.

It is impossible to avoid the conclusion, that it is the respiratory organs and their muscles which are affected during the paroxysm of laughter. Physiologists, in all former times, attributed the line of sympathetic relations which draw these remote parts into action, to a nerve called the sympathetic. But I have proved, that there is a machinery altogether distinct; and that the expression, not only of this, but of all the other passions, arises from that system of nerves, which, from their great office, I have called *respiratory*.

The respiratory nerves spring from a common centre in the medulla oblongata, and pass off divergingly to all the parts just enumerated, and to every organ employed in respiration. They combine these distant parts in the ordinary action of breathing; and they are the agents in all the effects of passion, when these organs give the outward signs of the condition of the mind.

In man, the expression of mere bodily fear is like that of animals, without dignity; it is the mean anticipation of pain. The eyeball is largely uncovered, the eyes are staring, and the eyebrows elevated to the utmost stretch. There is a spasmodic affection of the diaphragm and muscles of the chest, disturbing the breathing, producing a gasping in the throat, with an inflation of the nostril, convulsive opening of the mouth, and dropping of the jaw; the lips nearly conceal the teeth, yet allow the tongue to be seen, the space between the nostril and the lip being full. There is a hollowness and convulsive motion of the cheeks, and a trembling of the lips, and muscles on the

side of the neck. The lungs are kept distended, while the breathing is short and rapid. From the connexion of the nerves of the lungs and diaphragm with those of the side of the neck, and with the branches which supply the cutaneous muscle of the cheek and neck, we may comprehend the cause of the convulsive motion of this muscle. The aspect is pale and cadaverous from the receding of the blood. The hair is lifted up by the creeping of the skin, and action of the occipito-frontalis.

But if we should suppose the fear there represented, to have

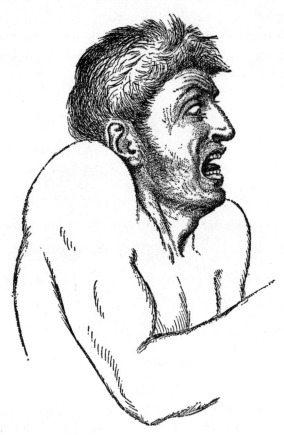

arisen from apprehended danger still remote, and that the object of fear approaches, and is now about to cleave to the person,
he trembles, looks pale, has a cold sweat on his face, and in
proportion as the imagination has less room to range in, as
the danger is more distinctly visible, the expression partakes
more of actual bodily pain. The scream of fear is heard, the
eyes start forward, the lips are drawn wide, the hands are

clenched, and the expression becomes more strictly animal, and indicative of such fear as is common to brutes.

I should apply the name of terror to that kind of fear, in which there is a strong working of the imagination, and which is therefore peculiar to man. The eye is bewildered; the inner extremity of the eyebrows is elevated, and strongly knit by the action of the corrugator; thus producing an expression of distracting thought, anxiety, and alarm, and one which does not belong to animals. The cheek is a little raised, and all the muscles which are concentred about the mouth are active; there being a kind of modulating action in the circular muscle of the lips, which keeps the mouth partially open. The cutaneous muscle of the neck, the platysma myoides, is strongly contracted, and its fibres may be seen starting into action like cords, under the skin, and dragging powerfully on the angles of the mouth. The imagination wanders; there is an indecision in the action, the steps are furtive and unequal, there is a spasm which hinders speech, and the colour of the cheeks vanishes.

> Canst thou quake and change thy colour,
> Murther thy breath in middle of a word,
> And then again begin, and stop again,
> As if thou wast distraught and mad with terror?[12]

When mingled with astonishment, terror is fixed and mute. The fugitive and unnerved steps of mere terror are then changed for the rooted and motionless figure of a creature appalled and stupified. Spenser characterises well this kind of terror: —

> He answer'd nought at all: but adding new
> Fear to his first amazement, staring wide

[12] *Richard III*, Act III, Sc. 5.

With stony eyes, and heartless hollow hue,
Astonish'd stood, as one that had espy'd
Infernal furies with their chains unty'd.

*   *   *   *

But trembling every joint did inly quake,
And falt'ring tongue at last these words seem'd
forth to shake.[13]

Horror differs from both fear and terror, although more
nearly allied to the last than to the first. It is superior to both in
this, that it is less imbued with personal alarm. It is more full
of sympathy with the sufferings of others, than engaged with our
own. We are struck with horror even at the spectacle of artificial
distress, but it is peculiarly excited by the real danger or pain of
another. We see a child in the hazard of being crushed by an
enormous weight, with sensations of extreme horror. Horror is
full of energy; the body is in the utmost tension, not unnerved,
by fear. The flesh creeps, and a sensation of cold seems to chill
the blood; the term is applicable of "damp horror."

Despair is a mingled emotion. While terror is in some measure the balancing and distraction of a mind occupied with an
uncertainty of danger, despair is the total wreck of hope, the
terrible assurance of ruin having closed around, beyond all
power of escape. The expression of despair must vary with the
nature of the distress of which it forms the acmé. In certain circumstances it will assume a bewildered, distracted air, as if mad-
ness were likely to be the only close to the mental agony. Sometimes there is at once a wildness in the looks and total relaxation,
as if falling into insensibility; or there is upon the countenance
of the desperate man a horrid gloom; the eye is fixed, yet he

[13] *Faerie Queene*, Book i, cant. 9, stanza 24.

neither sees nor hears aught, nor is sensible of what surrounds him. The features are shrunk and livid, and convulsion and tremors affect the muscles of the face. Hogarth has chosen well the scene of his picture of despair.[14] In a gaming-house, the wreck of all hope affects, in a thousand various ways, the victims of this vice; but in every representation of despair, an inconsolable and total abandonment of those exertions to which hope inspirits and excites a man, forms an essential feature. We have two fine descriptions of despair given in detail by English poets. One is by Spenser:

> The darksome cave they enter, where they find
> That cursed man, low sitting on the ground,
> Musing full sadly in his sullen mind;
> His greazy locks, long growing and unbound,
> Disorder'd hung about his shoulders round,
> And hid his face; through which his hollow eyne
> Look, deadly dull, and stared as astound;
> His raw-bone cheeks, through penury and pine,
> Were shrunk into his jaws, as he did never dine.[15]

The other is in the tragedy of the "Gamester," where Beverley,[16] after heart-rending reiteration of hope and disappointment, having staked the last resource of his wife and family on one fatal throw, finds himself suddenly plunged into ruin.

"When all was lost, he fixed his eyes upon the ground, and stood some time with folded arms stupid and motionless: then snatching his sword that hung against the wainscot, he sat him down, and with a look of fixed attention drew figures on the

---

14 The fifth episode in Hogarth's set of plates *The Rake's Progress* (1735).

15 *Faerie Queene*, Book i, cant. 9, stanza 35.

16 The titular hero of *The Gamester* (1753) of Edward Moore, famous as an acting part.

floor. At last he started up; looked wild and trembled; and, like a woman seized with her sex's fits, laughed out aloud, while the tears trickled down his face. So he left the room."

A painter may have to represent terror, despair, astonishment, and supernatural awe, mingled in one powerful expression of emotion. In a mind racked with deep despair, conscious of strength and courage, but withered and subdued by supernatural agency, the expression is quite removed from all meanness; it must be preserved grand and terrific; the hero may still appear, though palpitating and drained of vigour.

Milton has admirably sketched the nerveless stupefaction of mingled astonishment and horror: —

> On th' other side, Adam, soon as he heard
> The fatal trespass done by Eve, amaz'd,
> Astonied stood and blank, while horror chill
> Ran through his veins, and all his joints relax'd;
> From his slack hand the garland wreath'd for Eve
> Down dropp'd, and all the faded roses shed:
> Speechless he stood and pale, till thus at length
> First to himself he inward silence broke.[17]

In admiration, the faculty of sight is enjoyed to the utmost, and all else is forgotten. The brow is expanded and unruffled, the eyebrow gently raised, the eyelid lifted so as to expose the coloured circle of the eye, while the lower part of the face is relaxed in a gentle smile. The mouth is open, the jaw a little fallen, and by the relaxation of the lower lip we just perceive the edge of the lower teeth and the tongue. The posture of the body is most expressive when it seems arrested in some familiar action.

[17] *Paradise Lost*, Book ix., ver. 888–896.

VI

Science: Its Organization and Support

WILLIAM VERNON HARCOURT

Objects and Plans of the British Association for the Advancement of Science*

Fourth son of the Archbishop of York, William Vernon Harcourt (1789–1871) became a cleric in the Church of England. He acquired a lifelong taste for science through a friendship with Dr. John Kidd, a teacher of chemistry at Christ Church, Oxford, from which Harcourt was graduated in 1811. In Yorkshire, where he settled, he was instrumental in founding the Yorkshire Philosophical Society, one of the many provincial scientific societies which came into being in the first decades of the nineteenth century. It was largely through the efforts of these groups that the British Association for the Advancement of Science came into being at a meeting held at York in September, 1831. Harcourt, portions of whose address to that meeting are presented below, became the first general secretary of the B.A.A.S. and has been referred to as its "virtual founder." He succeeded to the presidency of the Association in 1839. In obvious criticism of the membership qualifications of the Royal Society, Harcourt proposed a single principle for guidance of the new group: "It is not our desire in the general composition of the Society to separate writers from readers, the professor of natural knowledge from the student. A public testimonial of reputable character and zeal for science is the only passport into our camp which we would require." The subscription charge was low, and the governing power of the Association was placed in the hands of those who had contributed scientific papers which had been published under the auspices of any "Philosophical Society." Harcourt left no important body of scientific work, but as the architect of the B.A.A.S. he made an impressive contribution to the pursuit of science in England.

I PROPOSE, Gentlemen, in the first place, that we should found a BRITISH ASSOCIATION FOR THE ADVANCEMENT OF SCIENCE, having for its objects, to give a stronger impulse and more

* From *Report of the First and Second Meetings of the British Association for the Advancement of Science; at York in 1831, and at Oxford in 1832.*

systematic direction to scientific inquiry, to obtain a greater degree of national attention to the objects of science, and a removal of those disadvantages which impede its progress, and to promote the intercourse of the cultivators of science with one another, and with foreign philosophers.

On the first and most important of these objects, some difference of opinion may exist; a difference of opinion, I mean, as to the want in which we stand of a new Association, to give a stronger impulse and more systematic direction to scientific inquiry.

I do not rest my opinion, Gentlemen, of this want upon any complaint of the decline of science in England. It would be a strange anomaly if the science of the nation were declining, whilst the general intelligence and prosperity increase. There is good reason, indeed, to regret that it does not make more rapid progress in so favourable a soil, and that its cultivation is not proportionate to the advantages which this country affords, and the immunity from vulgar cares which a mature state of social refinement implies. But, in no other than this relative sense, can I admit science to have declined in England. What three names, if we except the name of NEWTON, can be shown in any one age of our scientific history which rank higher than those of men whose friendship we have enjoyed, by whose genius we have been warmed, and whose loss it has been our misfortune prematurely to deplore, the names of DAVY, WOLLASTON, and YOUNG! And there are men still remaining among us, individuals whom I must not mention, present in this Meeting, and absent from this Meeting, whose names are no less consecrated to immortality than theirs.

But it is not by counting the great luminaries who may

chance to shine in this year, or that, — in a decade of years, or a generation of men, — that we are to inform ourselves of the state of national science. Let us look rather to the numbers engaged, effectually, though less conspicuously, in adding by degrees to our knowledge of nature; let us look to the increase of scientific transactions and journals; let us look, Gentlemen, at the list produced this day of Philosophical Societies which have grown up in all parts of the kingdom.[1] The multiplication of these new and numerous institutions indicates a wide extension of scientific pursuits. The funds so liberally contributed to their support bear evidence of an enlarged disposition in the public to promote such pursuits.

It is on this very ground I rest the necessity and the practicability of establishing in science a new impulsive and directive force, that there are new and more abundant materials to be directed and impelled. The mining-field of discovery seems to me to show, on the one part, the ore breaking out on every side; veins of the precious metal scarcely opened or imperfectly wrought; and on the other a multitude of hands ready to work it; but no one engaging them to labour, or showing them in what manner they may employ their industry to the best advantage. And therefore it is that I propose to you to found an Association including all the scientific strength of Great Britain, which shall employ a short period of every year in pointing out the lines of direction in which the researches of science should move, in indicating the particulars which most immediately demand investigation, in stating problems to be solved and data to be fixed, in assigning to every class of mind a definite task, and suggesting to its members, that there is here a shore of which

[1] Presented at a different session of the meetings.

the soundings should be more accurately taken, and there a line of coast along which a voyage of discovery should be made.

I am not aware, Gentlemen, that in executing such a plan we should intrude upon the province of any other Institution. There is no Society at present existing among us, which undertakes to lend any guidance to the individual efforts of its members, and there is none perhaps which can undertake it. Consider the difference, Gentlemen, between the limited circle of any of our scientific councils, or even the Annual Meetings of our Societies, and a Meeting at which all the science of these kingdoms should be convened, which should be attended, as this first Meeting you see already promises, by deputations from every other Society, and in which foreign talent and character should be tempted to mingle with our own. With what a momentum would such an Association urge on its purpose! what activity would it be capable of exciting! how powerfully would it attract and stimulate those minds, which either thirst for reputation or rejoice in the light and sunshine of truth!

The eldest of our scientific Institutions contemplated, in its origin, the objects which we now propose to pursue. The foundation, Gentlemen, of the Royal Society was an attempt to reduce to practice the splendid fiction of the New Atlantis.[2] The

2 In the *New Atlantis* (1626) Francis Bacon used fiction, as his chaplain tells us, "to the end that he might exhibit therein a model or description of a college instituted for the interpreting of nature and the producing of great and marvellous works for the benefit of men, under the name of Salomon's House, or the College of the Six Days' Works." So strong was the image that more than one of its founders saw in Salomon's House "a Prophetick Scheam of the Royal Society." At the time that its Royal charter was granted, in 1662, the Society adopted the Baconian plan which called for groups of men to set to work in common for the collecting of natural knowledge. Robert Hooke's proposed statutes for the Society also reflect the utilitarian image of Bacon's *New Atlantis:* "The business and design of the Royal Society is to improve the

same comprehensive mind which first developed the true method of interpreting nature, sketched also the first draught of a national Association for undertaking, by a system of distributed and combined exertion, the labour of that work.

This philosophical romance was not composed by its great author to amuse the fancy, but to dispose the minds of the legislature towards the foundation of a public establishment for the advancement of science. The basis of the great Institution, which Bacon meditated, was a public provision for the maintenance and promotion of science. It was one of the defects noted by him in his masterly survey of the state of learning, that science had never possessed a *whole man;* and he exerted all the influence of his high station and commanding talents, to promote the supply of that defect. In a letter to the king respecting the foundation of the hospital at Dulwich by Alleyn[3] the actor, he remarked, that though he was glad to see him play the last act of life so well, yet he thought Sir H. Savile's endowments of geometrical and astronomical Professorships[4] of much greater

knowledge of natural things, and all useful Arts, Manufactures, Mechanick practices, Engynes, and Inventions by Experiments — (not meddling with Divinity, Metaphysics, Moralls, Politicks, Grammar, Rhetorick, or Logick)."

But the Baconian influence rapidly declined as its members became more involved in the newly developing sciences of the seventeenth century. There was no Royal patronage given, and Fellows received no pensions or privileges. Well into the nineteenth century, the Society was financially poor so that, included among the qualifications for Fellowship, were wealth as well as scientific merit. It was this difficulty, among others, which brought about severe criticism of the Royal Society in the early decades of the nineteenth century and in some measure was responsible for the founding of the B.A.A.S.

3 Edward Alleyn (1566–1626), an actor of some prominence, instituted actions in 1613 which ultimately brought into being the college at Dulwich.

4 Sir Henry Savile (1549–1622), educated at Brasenose College, Oxford, and a Fellow of Merton College, Oxford, showed an early interest in mathematics and classical Greek. This combination of interests later led him to establish two Savilian professorships at Oxford in 1619, one of geometry and the other of astronomy. He also endowed a mathematical library.

necessity and more deserving of royal encouragement; and his own last bequest was one which, had it been executed, would have endowed two similar offices with salaries of two hundred pounds a year. In his opinion it was "necessary to the progression of sciences, that those who are to generate and propagate them should be placed in such a condition as may content the ablest man to appropriate his whole labour, and continue his whole age, in that function and attendance;" and he added, "there will hardly be any main proficiency in the disclosing of nature, except there be some allowances for expenses about experiments, whether they be experiments appertaining to Vulcan or Dædalus, furnace or engine, or any other kind; and therefore, as secretaries and spials of princes and states bring in bills for intelligence, so you must allow the spials and intelligencers of nature to bring in their bills, or else you shall be ill advertised."

These desiderata no means have yet been found of supplying in an adequate degree; and science, even to the present day, can scarcely be said to possess more than *fractions of men.* The Royal Society did not attempt to execute this part of Bacon's plan; but in other respects it copied as closely as possible, the model of the *six days College.*[5] It was not then an association of individuals throwing their contributions casually into a common stock, but a body politic of philosophers acting in a corporate capacity and with systematic views, allotting to its members their respective tasks, and conjunctively debating and consulting for the advancement of knowledge. It had, in the figurative lan-

5 The College of the Six Days' Works was an alternate title for Salomon's House, referring of course to the Biblical account of God having created the world and all therein in six days. Since the members of the order or society were to find out the nature of natural things (or things created in the six days) the alternate name is descriptive of their enterprise.

guage of Bacon, its *merchants of light*,[6] who were dispatched in various directions at home and abroad, to gather information and bring back specimens of the productions of nature; it had its *depredators* who were deputed to examine histories of countries, and to question the travellers who had visited them, in order that queries might be framed which were then addressed to the Society's correspondents in foreign lands, among whom Consuls and Ambassadors were proud to be numbered. It employed some of its members as auxiliaries to the arts; to some it proposed the solution of the most important problems in mathematics, whilst it referred to others the charge of experimental researches, the mode of conducting which was discussed before-hand, and the results re-examined by a public Meeting. I may mention as examples of the effect of this system, that we are indebted to it, practically, for *Evelyn's History of Forest Trees*,[7] by which the planting of the country was so materially promoted, and, theoretically, for the determination of *the law of the collision of bodies*, simultaneously obtained from Huygens, Wallis, and Wren.[8]

[6] The "merchants of light" were the fellows of Salomon's House who ventured forth every twelfth year to collect from abroad " . . . knowledge of the affairs and state of those countries to which they were designed, and especially of the sciences, arts, manufactures, and inventions of all the world; to bring . . . books, instruments, and patterns in every kind." They maintained ". . . a trade, not for gold, silver, or jewels; nor for silks; nor for spices; nor for any other commodity of matter; but only for God's first creature, which was *Light*: to have *light* . . . of the growth of all parts of the world."

[7] John Evelyn (1620–1706), *Silva, or a Discourse of Forest-trees, and the Propagation of Timber in this Majesty's Dominions* . . . , (London, 1664 and later editions). He was one of the founders of the Royal Society.

[8] The search for the law of impact, or the law foretelling the course of events whenever two bodies collide, was one of the major topics in physics between the time of Galileo and Descartes and the time of Newton. Leading to the concept of momentum, this quest bore fruit in three major papers published in the *Philosophical Transactions*, (the journal of the Royal Society of London)

This was indeed to execute a noble plan in the spirit in which it was designed. The noise of works and inventions resounded on every side; new facts and original discoveries of the laws of the universe were daily brought to light; the conveniences and safeguards of life, the measurements of time, the construction of ships, the tilling and planting of the earth began to be rapidly improved. But the vigour of these exertions soon declined, and within thirty years we find Leibnitz[9] suggesting to one of the original founders of the Royal Society that it wanted new warmth to be infused into its constitution, and recommending that it should be remodelled after the example of the French Academy.

Leibnitz indeed had no right to consider a Society effete, which within a few years had elicited a work[10] from Newton, that eclipsed the fame even of the great German philosopher. Nor to this hour has it ever lost its title to public respect. It still embodies in its list every name which stands high in British science; it still communicates to the world the most important of our discoveries; it still crowns with the most coveted honours the ambition of successful talent; and when the public service

in 1669, by Christian Huygens (1629–1695), Dutch physicist and astronomer and creator of the wave theory of light; John Wallis (1616–1703), mathematician and divine, one of the founders of the Royal Society; and Christopher Wren (1632–1723), geometer, experimenter, and architect, also one of the founders of the Royal Society.

9 Gottfried Wilhelm Leibniz (1646–1716), German polymath who made important contributions as scientist, inventor, philologist, logician and philosopher. He carried on a scientific correspondence with Huygens, von Guericke, Mariotte, Perrault, Papin and Boyle and was engaged in a lengthy controversy with Newton over the discovery of the infinitesimal calculus, and with the Newtonian Samuel Clarke about the adequacy of a mechanical world view.

10 Isaac Newton agreed to write and to publish his *magnum opus, The Mathematical Principles of Natural Philosophy,* only after a direct solicitation of the Royal Society.

requires the aid of philosophy, it still renders to the nation the ablest assistance, and the soundest counsel. Nevertheless it must be admitted, Gentlemen, that the Royal Society no longer performs the part of promoting natural knowledge by any such exertions as those which we now propose to revive. As a body, it scarcely labours itself, and does not attempt to guide the labours of others.

Hence it happens, that when any science becomes popular, and those who interest themselves in its advancement perceive the necessity of working for it by united exertions, that science is detached from the central body; first one fragment falls off, and then another; colony after colony dissevers itself from the declining empire, and by degrees the commonwealth of science is dissolved. The new Societies distinguish themselves by their diligence and activity; the parts of knowledge which thus receive more distinct attention, and are propelled by more undivided labour, make rapid advances; and each separate undertaking justifies itself by the most promising appearances and undeniable fruits.

This is a new stage, Gentlemen, in the progress of science; a new state of things, which, whilst it is attended certainly with great advantages, has some consequences of doubtful aspect to the highest aims of philosophy. As the facts and speculations in any department of knowledge are multiplied, the study of it has a tendency to engross and confine the views of those by whom it is cultivated; and if the system of separate Societies shall encourage this insulation, science will be in the end retarded by them more than it is at first advanced. The chief Interpreters of nature have always been those who grasped the widest field of inquiry, who have listened with the most universal curiosity to all information, and felt an interest in every question which the one great system of nature presents. Nothing, I think, could be a more disastrous event for the sciences, than that one of them should be in any manner dissociated from another; and nothing can conduce more to prevent that dissociation, than the bringing into mutual contact men who have exercised great and equal powers of mind upon different pursuits; nothing more fitted to shame men out of that unphilosophical contempt which they are too apt to feel for each other's objects; nothing more likely to open to them new veins of thought, which may be of the utmost importance to the very inquiries on which they are more peculiarly intent.

I remember, at the Meeting of a foreign Society, to have heard a memoir read, in which a specific and original difference was inferred between two animals (commonly considered of one species), not from any difference in the higher and more essential parts of their organization, but from a dissimilarity of colour in the skin or fur, and from minute anatomical distinctions; and I heard the error of the Zoologist corrected by a Botanist, one of the most eminent in Europe, who illuminated the whole subject of generic, specific and individual difference, by the light of a powerful mind which had been directed to the study of the question, considered in a different aspect, and with a more extensive survey. In like manner, it is easy to conceive, on the one hand, how much advantage might be derived to geological debates from the presence of a sober and rigorous mathematician; and how, on the other hand, the abstract analyst and geometer might have his calculations restricted or promoted by listening to the detail of facts, which those could give him who cultivate the sciences more directly dependent on observation and experiment.

But there is a defect in these separate Societies, in respect to their own immediate objects, which I am sure no member of them would wish to dissemble, and which arises from the narrow basis on which they are of necessity built. It is not only that the constant converse of men, who, to borrow the expression of Goldsmith, have often travelled over each other's minds, is not half so effectual in striking out great and unexpected lights, as the occasional intercourse of those who have studied nature at a distance from each other, under various circumstances and in different views; but it is also, Gentlemen, that none of our existing Societies is able to concentrate the scattered forces even of its own science: they do not know, much less can they connect or employ that extensive and growing body of humble labourers who are ready, whenever they shall be called upon, to render their assistance. I have the pleasure of seeing here the President of the Geological Society of London; and I beg leave to ask him, whether in a science, the most complex of all sciences in its object, because it aims at deciphering the history of nature not only as it is but as it has been, in a science of which very few even among the lowest generalizations are as yet so settled as to be able to bear the weight of any theoretical superstructure whatever, — I ask him whether in the science of Geology there is not a multitude of facts to be ascertained in every district, on which he would be glad to see a much greater number of observers employed? And if it be so, let me remind him that we have heard today of nine Philosophical Societies in this county alone, which could doubtless find members ready to prosecute any local inquiry that this Meeting might, at his suggestion, request them to undertake. It is the same with all parts of Natural History, with Meteorology, and indeed with every science which is founded upon observation, or even upon experiment; for the lower order of experiments, in subjects of the utmost ultimate abstractness, — such as the relations, for instance, of heat and of light, — are not only abundantly wanted, but by a moderate degree of industry and talent are by no means difficult to be supplied.

What numberless suggestions, what a crowd of valuable but abortive hints are continually floating in the thoughts of philosophers, for the pursuit of which time is wanting to themselves! Now I say, Gentlemen, that we have among us, scattered through the country, men willing to adopt these unexecuted hints, as they arise out of the profound and varied meditations of more experienced minds, men not incapable of surveying with accuracy a limited district, though they may not pretend to draw the general outline of the map, or fill up the whole of its details. Many such there are who only wait for instructions, and who require no other stimulus than that of being invited, to render the most essential service to researches and calculations of the highest order; and it is upon this ground especially that we venture to pronounce an Institution wanting, which shall not hesitate to make such invitations and to offer such instructions; it is upon this ground that if we now propose to revive in the nineteenth century a plan devised two centuries ago, — we see a difference, Gentlemen, in the probability of success. Scientific knowledge has of late years been more largely infused into the education of every class of society, and the time seems to be arrived for taking advantage of the intellectual improvement of the nation. Let Philosophy at length come forth and

show herself in public; let her hold her court in different parts
of her dominions; and you will see her surrounded by loyal
retainers, who will derive new light and zeal from her presence
and contribute to extend her power on every side.

One great benefit, at least, in addition to her maritime ex-
peditions, England, as a nation, has conferred on the science of
the world. She has had reason to be proud of her astronomical
observations; though perhaps it is not equally gratifying to reflect that these observations have been turned to account, of late
year, less by her own geometers than by the national school of
mathematicians in France. But there are many other sciences,
Gentlemen, on which the resources of states are no less dependent; and in them also there are physical data, which require to
be ascertained by masters in science, with the most rigorous precision, and not without the most persevering labour. And I may
be permitted to think with Mr. Herschel, that "it may very
reasonably be asked, why the direct assistance afforded by gov-
ernments to the execution of continued series of observations,
adapted to this especial end, should continue to be, as it has
hitherto almost exclusively been, confined to Astronomy."

The Chairman of the Meeting adverting to this subject, has
said that "there are enterprises in science which none but a
nation can undertake;" let me add also, that there are establishments for science which none but a nation can support. I
remember, Gentlemen, to have heard the greatest philosopher of
this age for variety and extent of attainments, M. de Humboldt,[11] speak of Great Britain, as he was showing me the splen-

---

[11] Alexander von Humboldt (1769–1859) German natural scientist, made his
most important scientific contributions in the study of the geographical distribution of plants.

did collections of natural history in the Louvre. What country in the world, said he, has such opportunities as England for collecting in her capital specimens of all the productions of the earth! I reflected, Gentlemen, on those unrivalled advantages, — but felt, I confess, no elation of national pride when I recollected the state of the British Museum.[12] Since that time, however, one material step has been taken towards improvement; and when an adequate building shall have been prepared, let us hope that we may at length see a public school of natural history in London, so furnished, and so appointed, as not to be unworthy of the British nation. I am persuaded that even our statesmen would have no cause for regret, if, whilst the stores of this national repository were replenished by scientific missions judiciously employed, a more accurate knowledge were at the same time obtained of our distant possessions, and of their natural riches, than has been sometimes discovered in our diplomatic transactions.

All the remarks, Gentlemen, which I have this day made, have been made with an anxious desire to say neither more nor less than the truth. I have spoken both of scientific societies and of the national policy with all freedom, because I take free speech upon points in which the interests of science are deeply concerned, to be one of the principal purposes for which we are now assembled; but I hope I have spoken also without any disposition to exaggerate the deficiencies which I have

[12] The British Museum was founded in 1753 by the government through its purchase of the library and collections of Sir Hans Sloane (1660–1753), onetime President of the Royal Society. The impressive building in Bloomsbury was begun in 1828 and completed in 1852. The natural history collections were separated from the main museum and moved to their own quarters at the Natural History Museum, South Kensington, in 1881.

thought it right to notice, or to elevate a new institution by detracting from the merits of elder establishments. It only remains for me to lay before you the particulars of the plan by which we propose to accomplish the objects which I have stated; the subordinate details would be most advantageously revised by a Committee, but the material principles on which it is framed are points to which I would request the attention of this Meeting.

The material principles of the plan are included in the *composition of the Association, in the constitution of its government, and in the selection of the work on which it is to be employed.*

An enterprise like this has no danger to fear, but from a deficiency of zeal and union in carrying it into effect. It must undoubtedly fail, if it meets only with imperfect cooperation and cold support. But if it shall recommend itself to the full approbation of men of science, if it appears to you, Gentlemen, desirable to undertake it, the Association will have competent sponsors in the present assembly, who will stand pledged not only for its early encouragement, but for those future exertions which will be required to ensure its success. The Council of the Yorkshire Philosophical Society have not the presumption to dictate to this Meeting the course which it may be for the interests of Philosophy to pursue. They collected, in the first instance, the best opinions which they could obtain, before they proceeded to mature their plan; and they now wait for the opinion of the eminent persons who are here assembled, before they can assure themselves that it is as feasible in practice as it appears in theory. My own judgement waits with theirs, Gentlemen, on that of the High Priests of the temple, in the porch of which I am only an humble worshiper, — "parcus Deorum cultor et infrequens",[13] — and I shall be the first to withdraw the resolutions which I am now ready to propose, unless I find them, by the deliberate and cordial concurrence of this Meeting, stamped with authority and endued with permanence.

A string of Resolutions in which were embodied the Objects and Rules of the Association as stated in Mr. Harcourt's speech, were then moved by him *seriatim,* and seconded by Dr. Brewster, by Mr. Murchison, President of the Geological Society of London, by Dr. Pearson, Vice-President of the Astronomical Society of London, by Mr. Robison, Secretary to the Royal Society of Edinburgh, &c. It was resolved unanimously — "that an Association be formed, to be called The British Association for the Advancement of Science, the objects of which shall be to give a stronger impulse and more systematic direction to scientific inquiry, to promote the intercourse of those who cultivate science in different parts of the British Empire, with one another, and with foreign philosophers, and to obtain a greater degree of national attention to the objects of science and a removal of any disadvantages of a public nature which impede its progress."

[13] Horace, *Odes,* I, 34, 1. The meaning is: an infrequent worshipper of heaven.

WILLIAM WHEWELL

Of the Transformation of Hypotheses in the History of Science*

William Whewell (1794–1866), master of Trinity College, Cambridge, chose mathematics for his field of specialization while a Cambridge student. Appointed mathematical lecturer at Trinity, he was the author of books on mathematics and mechanics and became a fellow of the Royal Society. After a period of study in Germany, he changed his field to mineralogy and was appointed professor of the subject at Cambridge in 1828, a chair he held until his resignation in 1832. He then became active in the work of the newly formed British Association for the Advancement of Science, and within a few years became Knightsbridge Professor of Moral Philosophy. In the meanwhile, he had gone deep into the study of German philosophy, had translated Goethe's *Hermann und Dorothea,* and had written the first (1833) of the *Bridgewater Treatises.* His best known book is the *History of the Inductive Sciences,* which was published in three volumes in 1837, followed by a sequel called *Philosophy of the Inductive Sciences,* in two volumes, published in 1840. After he was made master of Trinity in 1841, he became active in the field of educational reform and university administration. Known to scientists primarily for his study of the theory of the tides, Whewell was "rather a critic than an original investigator in science," and he is remembered today for his historical and philosophical writings, of which the following selection, read in 1854 to the Cambridge Philosophical Society, is a representative sample.

$\mathbf{T}$HE history of science suggests the reflection that it is very difficult for the same person at the same time to do justice to two conflicting theories. Take for example the Cartesian hypoth-

* From *Transactions of the Cambridge Philosophical Society* (1856).

esis of vortices and the Newtonian doctrine of universal gravitation.[1] The adherents of the earlier opinion resisted the evidence of the Newtonian theory with a degree of obstinacy and captiousness which now appears to us quite marvellous: while on the other hand, since the complete triumph of the Newtonians, *they* have been unwilling to allow any merit at all to the doctrine of vortices. It cannot but seem strange, to a calm observer of such changes, that in a matter which depends upon mathematical proofs, the whole body of the mathematical world should pass over, as in this and similar cases they seem to have done, from an opinion confidently held, to its opposite. No doubt this must be, in part, ascribed to the lasting effects of education and early prejudice. The old opinion passes away with the old generation: the new theory grows to its full vigour when its congenital disciples grow to be masters. John Bernoulli[2] continues a Cartesian to the last; Daniel, his son, is a

[1] When the Newtonian doctrine of universal gravitation was announced in Isaac Newton's *Mathematical Principles of Natural Philosophy*, printed in London in 1687, the chief rival theory was the Cartesian, disseminated in many books on philosophy and physical science, and discussed by René Descartes in his *Principles of Philosophy*. According to the Cartesian doctrine, the planets swim about in vortices or whirlpools of an ethereal matter, which causes them to move in the observed fashion. Newton displayed a proof that any ethereal matter that would have this effect would also slow down the motion of comets as they passed through the solar system. He substituted for the Cartesian vortices a doctrine of attraction, according to which the planets are attracted by the sun, each planet attracts its moons, and in general any piece of matter attracts any other piece of matter in the universe in proportion to the masses of the two bodies attracting and being attracted and inversely proportional to the square of the distance between them.

[2] The Bernoullis were a famous family of mathematicians in the seventeenth and eighteenth centuries. Johann or John (1667–1748) and Jakob or Jacques (1654–1705) were professors of mathematics at Basel, the former being a pioneer in studies of the calculus, the latter the author of many works of physics and a classic treatise on the theory of probability. Daniel (1700–1782), the second son of Johann, was professor of mathematics at St. Petersburg and eventually

Newtonian from the first. Newton's doctrines are adopted at once in England, for they are the solution of a problem at which his contemporaries have been labouring for years. They find no adherents in France, where Descartes is supposed to have already explained the constitution of the world; and Fontenelle,[3] the secretary of the Academy of Sciences at Paris, dies a Cartesian seventy years after the publication of Newton's *Principia*. This is, no doubt, a part of the explanation of the pertinacity with which opinions are held, both before and after a scientific revolution: but this is not the whole, nor perhaps the most instructive aspect of the subject. There is another feature in the change, which explains, in some degree, how it is possible that, in subjects, mainly at least mathematical, and therefore claiming demonstrative evidence, mathematicians should hold different and even opposite opinions. And the object of the present paper is to point out this feature in the successions of theories, and to illustrate it by some prominent examples drawn from the history of science.

The feature to which I refer is this; that when a prevalent theory is found to be untenable, and consequently, is succeeded by a different, or even by an opposite one, the change is not made suddenly, or completed at once, at least in the minds of the most tenacious adherents of the earlier doctrine; but is effected by a transformation, or series of transformations, of the

professor of physics and then of philosophy at Basel; he wrote works on various aspects of physics and astronomy.

3 Bernard Le Bovier de Fontenelle (1657–1757) was a famous popularizer of the sciences, and for many decades the Permanent Secretary of the French Academy of Sciences. Part of his duty was to write the *Éloge* of each academician; thus on Newton's death in 1727 he wrote the first biography of the founder of modern science.

earlier hypothesis, by means of which it is gradually brought nearer and nearer to the second; and thus, the defenders of the ancient doctrine are able to go on as if still asserting their first opinions, and to continue to press their points of advantage, if they have any, against the new theory. They borrow, or imitate, and in some way accommodate to their original hypothesis, the new explanations which the new theory gives, of the observed facts; and thus they maintain a sort of verbal consistency; till the original hypothesis becomes inextricably confused, or breaks down under the weight of the auxiliary hypotheses thus fastened upon it, in order to make it consistent with the facts.

This often-occurring course of events might be illustrated from the history of the astronomical theory of epicycles and eccentrics,[4] as is well known. But my present purpose is to give one or two brief illustrations of a somewhat similar tendency from other parts of scientific history; and in the first place, from that part which has already been referred to, the battle of the Cartesian and Newtonian systems.

The part of the Cartesian system of vortices which is most familiarly known to general readers is the explanation of the motions of the planets by supposing them carried round the sun by a kind of whirlpool of fluid matter in which they are immersed: and the explanation of the motions of the satellites round their primaries by similar subordinate whirlpools, turning round the primary, and carried, along with it, by the pri-

4 The system of epicycles and eccentrics was invented in Greek antiquity to "save the appearances" in the domain of astronomy. An epicycle is a curve formed by a point moving around a circle whose center moves around another circle. An eccentric is a circle, such as the apparent orbit of the sun around the earth, whose center would not coincide with the earth itself; by this manner in the ancient Greek astronomy the apparent departures from simple regularity of motion could be explained for sun and planets.

mary vortex. But it should be borne in mind that a part of the Cartesian hypothesis which was considered quite as important as the cosmical explanation, was the explanation which it was held to afford of terrestrial gravity. Terrestrial gravity was asserted to arise from the motion of the vortex of subtle matter which revolved round the earth's axis and filled the surrounding space. It was maintained that by the rotation of such a vortex, the particles of the subtle matter would exert a centrifugal force, and by virtue of that force, tend to recede from the center: and it was held that all bodies which were near the earth, and therefore immersed in the vortex, would be pressed towards the center by the effort of the subtle matter[5] to recede from the center.

These two assumed effects of the Cartesian vortices — to carry bodies in their stream, as straws are carried round by a whirlpool, and to press bodies to the center by the centrifugal effort of the whirling matter — must be considered separately, because they were modified separately, as the progress of discussion drove the Cartesians from point to point. The former effect indeed, the *dragging* force of the vortex, as we may call it, would not bear working out on mechanical principles at all; for as soon as the law of motion was acknowledged (which Descartes himself was one of the loudest in proclaiming), that a body in motion keeps all the motion which it has, and receives in addition all that is impressed upon it; as soon, in short, as philoso-

[5] The "subtle matter" was the stuff of which Cartesian vortices was supposedly made, by the action of which the observed planetary motions were caused. The physics of the seventeenth and eighteenth centuries knew many "subtle" forms of matter, such as electrical and magnetic effluvia, the matter of heat, and (according to some scientists) the matter of light. These forms of matter were "subtle" to the extent that they could penetrate ordinary matter owing to their property of being rare, tenuous, or refined.

phers rejected the notion of an inertness in matter which constantly retards its movements, — it was plain that a planet perpetually dragged onwards in its orbit by a fluid moving quicker than itself, must be perpetually accelerated; and therefore could not follow those constantly-recurring cycles of quicker and slower motion which the planets exhibit to us.

The Cartesian mathematicians, then, left untouched the calculation of the progressive motion of the planets; and, clinging to the assumption that a vortex would produce a tendency of bodies to the center, made various successive efforts to construct their vortices in such a manner that the centripetal forces produced by them should coincide with those which the phenomena required, and therefore of course, in the end, with those which the Newtonian theory asserted.

In truth, the Cartesian vortex was a bad piece of machinery for producing a central force: from the first, objections were made to the sufficiency of its mechanism, and most of these objections were very unsatisfactorily answered, even granting the additional machinery which its defenders demanded. One formidable objection was soon started, and continued to the last to be the torment of the Cartesians. If terrestrial gravity, it was urged, arise from the centrifugal force of a vortex which revolves about the earth's axis, terrestrial gravity ought to act in planes perpendicular to the earth's axis, instead of tending to the earth's center. This objection was taken by James Bernoulli,[6] and by Huyghens not long after the publication of Descartes's

6 James Bernoulli was the brother of John (see note 2, above). Christian Huygens, or Huyghens, (1629–1695), a Dutch mathematician and physicist, invented the escapement for the pendulum clock, improved the telescope so as to be the first man to resolve the rings of Saturn, and is generally considered to be the founder of the wave theory of light, which he announced in a famous treatise written in 1678, though not published until 1690.

Principia. Huyghens (who adopted the theory of vortices with modifications of his own) supposes that there are particles of the fluid matter which move about the earth in every possible direction, within the spherical space which includes terrestrial objects; and that the greater part of these motions being in spherical surfaces concentric with the earth, produces a tendency towards the earth's center.

This was a procedure tolerably arbitrary, but it was the best which could be done. Saurin, a little later,[7] gave nearly the same solution of this difficulty. The solution, identifying a vortex of some kind with a central force, made the hypothesis of vortices applicable wherever central forces existed; but then, in return, it deprived the image of a vortex of all that clearness and simplicity which had been its first great recommendation.

But still there remained difficulties not less formidable. According to this explanation of gravity, since the tendency of bodies to the earth's center arose from the superior centrifugal forces of the whirling matter which pushed them inward as water pushes a light body upward, bodies ought to tend more strongly to the center in proportion as they are less dense. The rarest bodies should be the heaviest; contrary to what we find.

Descartes's original solution of this difficulty has a certain degree of ingenuity. According to him a terrestrial body consists of particles of the *third element,* and the more it has of such particles, the more it excludes the parts of the *celestial matter,* from the revolution of which matter gravity arises; and therefore the denser is the terrestrial body, and the heavier it will be.

But though this might satisfy him, it could not satisfy the

[7] Joseph Saurin (1659–1737) published in 1709 a "Study of a considerable difficulty proposed by Mr. Huyghens against the Cartesian system with regard to the cause of gravity."

mathematicians who followed him, and tried to reduce his system to calculation on mechanical principles. For how could they do this, if the celestial matter, by the operation of which the phenomena of force and motion were produced, was so entirely different from ordinary matter, which alone had supplied men with experimental illustrations of mechanical principles? In order that the celestial matter, by its whirling, might produce the gravity of heavy bodies, it was mechanically necessary that it must be very dense; and *dense* in the ordinary sense of the term; for it was by regarding density in the ordinary sense of the term that the mechanical necessity had been established.

The Cartesians tried to escape this result by saying that there were two meanings of *density* and *rarity;* that some fluids might be rare by having their particles far asunder, others, by having their particles very small though in contact. But it is difficult to think that they could, as persons well acquainted with mechanical principles, satisfy themselves with this distinction; for they could hardly fail to see that the mechanical effect of any portion of fluid depends upon the total mass moved, not on the size of its particles.

Attempts made to exemplify the vortices experimentally only showed more clearly the force of this difficulty. Huyghens had found that certain bodies immersed in a whirling fluid tended to the center of the vortex. But when Saulmon[8] a little later made similar experiments, he had the mortification of finding that the heaviest bodies had the greatest tendency to recede from the axis

8 Saulmon, associated with the Academy of Sciences in Paris, died in 1725; his first name is unknown, as is also the date of his birth. His chief contribution was a paper published in 1712 in the *Mémoires* of the Academy of Sciences in Paris on "The movement of a cylinder plunged into a cylindric whirlpool," followed by various other papers on the effects of whirlpools.

of the vortex. "The result is," as the Secretary of the Academy (Fontenelle) says, "exactly the opposite of what we could have wished, for the [Cartesian] system of gravity: but we are not to despair; sometimes in such researches disappointment leads to ultimate success."[9]

But, passing by this difficulty, and assuming that in some way or other a centripetal force arises from the centrifugal force of the vortex, the Cartesian mathematicians were naturally led to calculate the circumstances of the vortex on mechanical principles; especially Huyghens, who had successfully studied the subject of centrifugal force. Accordingly, in his little treatise on the *Cause of Gravitation*[10] he calculates the velocity of the fluid matter of the vortex, and finds that, at a point in the equator, it is 17 times the velocity of the earth's rotation.

It may naturally be asked, how it comes to pass that a stream of fluid, dense enough to produce the gravity of bodies by its centrifugal force, moving with a velocity 17 times that of the earth (and therefore moving round the earth in 85 minutes), does not sweep all terrestrial objects before it. But to this Huyghens had already replied, that there are particles of the fluid moving *in all directions,* and therefore that they neutralize each other's action, so far as lateral motion is concerned.

9 This quotation from Fontenelle is taken from the historical survey, which it was his duty as Secretary of the Academy to write, in the volume containing Saulmon's discussion of whirlpools.

10 Huyghens's treatise on the cause of gravity (*pésanteur*) was published in 1690. Although Huyghens approved of Newton's mathematics, he did not like the idea of bodies attracting one another over such vast spaces as that from the sun to Saturn. Incidentally, it was to Huyghens that the philosopher John Locke turned to find whether the mathematics of Newton's *Principia* was sound. Whewell's translation "gravitation" is a little unfortunate, because Huyghens did not subscribe to the Newtonian doctrine of universal gravitation, and was writing on gravity in the sense of weight, as when an object has a downward inclination (from whatever cause) towards the earth's center.

And thus, as early as this treatise of Huyghens, that is, in three years from the publication of Newton's *Principia,* a vortex is made to mean nothing more than some machinery or other for producing a central force. And this is so much the case, that Huyghens commends as confirming his own calculation of the velocity of his vortex, Newton's proof that at the Moon's orbit the centripetal force is equal to the centrifugal; and that thus, this force is less than the centripetal force at the earth's surface in the inverse proportion of the squares of the distances.

John Bernoulli, in the same manner, but with far less clearness and less candour, has treated the hypothesis of vortices as being principally a hypothetical cause of central force. He had repeated occasions given him of propounding his inventions for propping up the Cartesian doctrine, by the subjects proposed for prizes by the Paris Academy of Sciences;[11] in which competition Cartesian speculations were favourably received. Thus the subject of the Prize Essays for 1730 was, the explanation of the Elliptical Form of the planetary orbits and of the Motion of their Aphelia, and the prize was assigned to John Bernoulli, who gave the explanation on Cartesian principles. He explains the elliptical figure, not as Descartes himself had done, by supposing the vortex which carries the planet round the sun to be itself squeezed into an elliptical form by the pressure of contiguous vortices; but he supposes the planet, while it is carried round by the vortex, to have a limited oscillatory motion to and from the center, produced by its being originally, not at the distance at which it would float in equilibrium in the

11 It was the custom of the French Academy of Sciences to hold prize competitions on various scientific subjects. In this way, it was hoped, the leading men of science would be stimulated to make significant contributions in special fields.

vortex, but above or below that point. On this supposition, the planet would oscillate to and from the center, Bernoulli says, like the mercury when deranged in a barometer: and it is evident that such an oscillation, combined with a motion round the center, might produce an oval curve, either with a fixed or with a moveable aphelion. All this however merely amounts to a possibility that the oval *may* be an ellipse, not to a proof that it will be so; nor does Bernoulli advance further.

It was necessary that the vortices should be adjusted in such a manner as to account for Kepler's laws;[12] and this was to be done by making the velocity of each stratum of the vortex depend in a suitable manner on its radius. The Abbé de Molières[13] attempted this on the supposition of elliptical vortices, but could not reconcile Kepler's first two laws, of equal elliptical areas in equal times, with his third law, that the squares of the periodic times are as the cubes of the mean distance. Bernoulli, with his circular vortices, could accommodate the velocities at different distances so that they should explain Kepler's laws. He pretended to prove that Newton's investigations respecting vortices (in the ninth Section of the Second Book of the *Principia*) were mechanically erroneous; and in truth, it must be allowed that, besides several arbitrary assumptions, there are some errors of reasoning in them. But for the most part, the more

12 Kepler's first two laws state: planets move in elliptical paths, with the sun located at one of the foci; furthermore, a line from the sun to the planet describes equal areas in any equal times. It is this second law which accounts for the fact that planets move more rapidly when near the sun than when they are far from the sun. These two laws were announced by Johann Kepler in 1609. A third law, published in 1619, relates the average distance of the planets from the sun to their periodic times of revolution about the sun.

13 The Abbé Joseph Privat de Molières (1677–1742), an Oratorien, attempted to answer Newton's objections to the Cartesian vortices.

enlightened Cartesians were content to accept Newton's account of the motions and forces of the solar system as part of their scheme; and to say only that the hypothesis of vortices explained the origin of the Newtonian forces; and that thus theirs was a philosophy of a higher kind. Thus it is asserted that M. de Molières retains the beautiful theory of Newton entire, only he renders it in a sort less Newtonian, by disentangling it from attraction, and transferring it from a vacuum[14] into a plenum. This plenum, though not its native region, frees it from the need of attraction, which is all the better for it. These points were the main charms of the Cartesian doctrine in the eyes of its followers; — the getting rid of attractions, which were represented as a revival of the Aristotelian "occult qualities," "substantial forms,"[15] or whatever else was the most disparaging way of describing the bad philosophy of the dark ages — and the providing some material intermedium, by means of which a body may affect another at a distance; and thus avoid the reproach urged against the Newtonians, that they made a body

[14] One of the aspects of the Cartesian philosophy was to deny the existence of a vacuum. Newton, like many other British scientists of his day, accepted the concept of vacuum and supposed that there could be a nothingness between the particles of matter. The Cartesian point of view, based on a "plenum" rather than a "vacuum" was traditional, having ancestry in medieval and ancient days.

[15] The doctrine of "substantial forms" descended from the "four qualities" of Aristotle — moist, dry, cold, and warm — which were related to the Aristotelian "four elements": air, water, fire, earth. It came to be thought that an object had these and still other "qualities" because its matter had the proper "form" — thus the matter of heavy bodies had the proper "form" for the quality of "heaviness." Allied with the doctrine of "substantial forms" was that of "occult qualities," hidden from ordinary perception, and which in the eyes of seventeenth-century men of science was held to be so poor a concept that it was used only in a pejorative sense. In the discussions at the end of the seventeenth and early part of the eighteenth centuries of the cause of gravitation, the worst epithet that could be used in describing another theory was to say it was based on "occult qualities."

act where it was not. And we are the less called upon to deny that this last feature in the Newtonian theory was a difficulty, inasmuch as Newton himself was never unwilling to allow that gravity might be merely an effect produced by some ulterior cause.

With such admissions on the two sides, it is plain that the Newtonian and Cartesian systems would coincide, if the hypothesis of vortices could be modified in such a way as to produce the force of gravitation. All attempts to do this, however, failed: and even John Bernoulli, the most obstinate of the mathematical champions of the vortices, was obliged to give them up. In his Prize Essay for 1734, (on the Inclinations of the Planetary Orbits,) he says, "The gravitation of the Planets towards the center of the Sun and the weight of bodies towards the center of the earth has not, for its cause, either the attraction of M. Newton, or the centrifugal force of the matter of the vortex according to M. Descartes;" and he then goes on to assert that these forces are produced by a perpetual torrent of matter tending to the center on all sides, and carrying all bodies with it. Such a hypothesis is very difficult to refute. It has been taken up in more modern times by Le Sage;[16] with some modifications; and may be made to account for the principal facts of the universal gravitation of matter. The great difficulty in the way of such a hypothesis is, the overwhelming thought of the whole universe filled with torrents of an invisible but material and tangible substance, rushing in every direction in infinitely

16 George Louis Le Sage (1724–1803) was the author of many works in physical science, chiefly on gravity. His father, who had the same name (1676–1759), was the author of works on mathematics, light, and astronomy. The younger Le Sage was the author of a particularly attractive attempt to reconcile the ancients and the moderns, called "Lucrèce newtonien" and published in the Mémoires of the Academy of Berlin in 1782.

prolonged straight lines and with immense velocity. Whence can such matter come, and whither can it go? Where can be its perpetual and infinitely distant fountain, and where the ocean into which it pours itself when its infinite course is ended? A revolving whirlpool is easily conceived and easily supplied; but the central torrent of Bernoulli, the infinite streams of particles of Le Sage, are an explanation far more inconceivable than the thing explained.

But however the hypothesis of vortices, or some hypothesis substituted for it, was adjusted to explain the facts of attraction to a center, this was really nearly all that was meant by a vortex or a "tourbillion,"[17] when the system was applied. Thus in the case of the last act of homage to the Cartesian theory which the French Academy rendered in the distribution of its prizes, the designation of a Cartesian Essay in 1741 (along with three Newtonian ones) as worthy of a prize for an explanation of the Tides; the difference of high and low water was not explained, as Descartes has explained it, by the pressure, on the ocean, of the terrestrial vortex, forced into a strait where it passes the Moon; but the waters were supposed to rise towards the Moon, the terrestrial vortex being disturbed and broken by the Moon, and therefore less effective in forcing them down. And in giving an account of a Tourmaline from Ceylon, when it has been ascertained that it attracts and repels substances, the writer adds, as a matter of course, "It would seem that it has a vortex." As another example, the elasticity of a body was ascribed to vortices between its particles: and in general, as I have said, a vortex implied what we now imply by speaking of a central force.

In the same manner vortices were ascribed to the Magnet,

[17] The "tourbillion" or whirlpool was another name given to the vortex.

in order to account for its attractions and repulsions. But we may note a circumstance which gave a special turn to the hypothesis of vortices as applied to this subject, and which may serve as a further illustration of the manner in which a transition may be made from one to the other of two rival hypotheses.

If iron filings be brought near a magnet, in such a manner as to be at liberty to assume the position which its polar action assigns to them; (for instance, by strewing them upon a sheet of paper while the two poles of the magnet are close below the paper;) they will arrange themselves in certain curves, each proceeding from the N. to the S. pole of the magnet, like the meridians in a map of the globe. It is easily shown, on the supposition of magnetic attraction and repulsion, that these *magnetic curves*, as they are termed, are each a curve whose tangent at every point is the direction of a small line or particle, as determined by the attraction and repulsion of the two poles. But if we suppose a *magnetic vortex* constantly to flow out of one pole and into the other, in streams which follow such curves, it is evident that such a vortex, being supposed to exercise material pressure and impulse, would arrange the iron filings in corresponding streams, and would thus produce the phenomenon which I have described. And the hypothesis of *central torrents* of Bernoulli or Le Sage which I have referred to, would, in its application to magnets, really become this hypothesis of a magnetic vortex, if we further suppose that the matter of the torrents which proceed to one pole and from the other, mingles its streams, so as at each point to produce a stream in the resulting direction. Of course we shall have to suppose two sets of magnetic torrents; — a boreal torrent, proceeding to the north pole, and from the south pole of a magnet; and an austral torrent proceeding to the south and from the north pole: — and with these suppositions, we make a transition from the hypothesis of attraction and repulsion, to the Cartesian hypothesis of vortices, or at least, torrents, which determine bodies to their magnetic positions by impulse.

Of course it is to be expected that, in this as in the other case, when we follow the hypothesis of impulse into detail, it will need to be loaded with so many subsidiary hypotheses, in order to accommodate it to the phenomena, that it will no longer seem tenable. But the plausibility of the hypothesis in its first application cannot be denied: — for, it may be observed, the two *opposite* streams would counteract each other so as to produce no local *motion,* only *direction.* And this case may put us on our guard against other suggestions of forces acting in curve lines, which may at first appear to be discerned in magnetic and electric phenomena. Probably such curve lines will all be found to be only resulting lines, arising from the direct action and combination of elementary attraction and repulsion.

There is another case in which it would not be difficult to devise a mode of transition from one to the other of two rival theories; namely, in the case of the emission theory and the undulation theory of Light. Indeed several steps of such a transition have already appeared in the history of optical speculation; and the conclusive objection to the emission theory of light, as to the Cartesian theory of vortices, is, that no amount of additional hypotheses will reconcile it to the phenomena. Its defenders had to go on adding one piece of machinery after another, as new classes of facts came into view, till it became more complex and unmechanical than the theory of epicycles and eccentrics at its worst period. Otherwise, as I have said, there was nothing to prevent the emmission theory from migrating into the undulatory theory, and as the theory of vortices did into the theory of attraction. For the emissionists allow that rays may *interfere;* and that these interferences may be modified by alternate *fits* in the rays; now these fits are already a kind of *undulation.* Then again the phenomena of polarized light show that the fits or undulations must have a *transverse* character: and there is no reason why emitted rays should not be subject to *fits* of *transverse* modification as well as to any other fits.[18] In short, we may add to the emitted rays of the one theory, all the properties which belong to the undulations of the other, and thus account for all the phenomena on the emission theory; with this limitation only, that the emission will have no share in the explanation, and the undulations will have the whole. If, instead of conceiving the universe full of a *stationary* ether, we suppose it to be full of etherial particles moving in every direction; and if we suppose, in the one case and in the other, this ether to be susceptible of undulations proceeding from every luminous point; the results of the two hypotheses will be the same; and all we shall have to say is, that the supposition of the emissive motion of the particles is superfluous and useless.

This view of the manner in which rival theories pass into one another appears to be so unfamiliar to those who have only slightly attended to the history of science, that I have thought it might be worth while to illustrate it by a few examples.

It might be said, for instance, by such persons,[19] "Either the

18 In the early nineteenth century, when the wave theory of light of Huyghens was revived by Thomas Young and J.-A. Fresnel, it was held that light consists of vibrations in the luminiferous ether which fills all of space. Young had believed that the light waves were merely longitudinal pulses in the ether, but Fresnel was forced to the conclusion that the waves or undulations must be transverse (at right angles) to the direction in which the disturbance moves, such as water waves. The difficulty with the transverse theory was that a medium which can support transverse vibrations must be extremely rigid.

planets are not moved by vortices, or they do not move by the law by which heavy bodies fall. It is impossible that both opinions can be true." But it appears, by what has been said above, that the Cartesians did hold both opinions to be true; and one with just as much reason as the other, on their assumptions. It might be said in the same manner, "Either it is false that the planets are made to describe their orbits by the above quasi-Cartesian theory of Bernoulli, or it is false that they obey the Newtonian theory of gravitation." But this would be said quite erroneously; for if the hypothesis of Bernoulli be true, it is so because it agrees in its result with the theory of Newton. It is not only possible that both opinions may be true, but it is certain that if the first be so, the second is. It might be said again, "Either the planets describe their orbits by an inherent virtue, or according to the Newton theory." But this again would be erroneous, for the Newtonian doctrine decided nothing as to whether the force of gravitation was inherent or not. Cotes held that it was, though Newton strongly protested against being supposed to hold such an opinion. The word *inherent* is no part of the physical theory, and will be asserted or denied according to our metaphysical views of the essential attributes of matter and force.

Of course, the possibility of two rival hypotheses being true, one of which takes the explanation a step higher than the other, is not affected by the impossibility of two contradictory assertions of the *same order* of generality being both true. If there be a new-discovered comet, and if one astronomer asserts that

19 This quotation is taken from John Stuart Mill's *Logic*. Mill (1806–1873) and Whewell were engaged in a celebrated controversy, which lasted many years, on the subject of the logic of science.

it will return once in *every* twenty years, and another, that it will return once in every thirty years, both cannot be right. But if an astronomer says that though its interval was in the last instance 30 years, it will only be 20 years to the next return, in consequence of perturbation and resistance, he may be perfectly right.

And thus, when different and rival explanations of the same phenomena are held, till one of them, though long defended by ingenious men, is at last driven out of the field by the pressure of facts, the defeated hypothesis is transformed before it is extinguished. Before it has disappeared, it has been modified so as to have all palpable falsities squeezed out of it, and subsidiary provisions added, in order to reconcile it with the phenomena. It has, in short, been penetrated, infiltrated, and metamorphosed by the surrounding medium of truth, before the merely arbitrary and erroneous residuum has been finally ejected out of the body of permanent and certain knowledge.

VII

The New Age

JAMES CLERK MAXWELL

On Faraday's Lines of Force[*]

James Clerk Maxwell (1831–1879), a Scottish physicist, first professor of
experimental physics at Cambridge University, is known today chiefly for
his studies of electromagnetism, epitomized in "Maxwell's equations."
Basing his work on the concepts and experiments of Faraday, Maxwell conceived a mathematical theory encompassing the related phenomena of
electricity and magnetism, in which he predicted the possible existence of
electromagnetic waves, the basis of transmission of radio, radar, and
television. Above all, this theory had a unifying influence on physical
thought by showing that light itself could be considered as an electromagnetic effect. In 1859 and 1860 Maxwell read a two-part paper entitled
"Illustrations of the Dynamical Theory of Gases" to the British Association. In many ways as revolutionary for science as the theory of evolution, Maxwell's marked the first full-scale presentation of a physical
theory in which the basic laws were shown to have a statistical rather than
a causal basis. The following selection, taken from Maxwell's first
electrical paper, was read to the Cambridge Philosophical Society on
December 10, 1855 and on February 11, 1856, just a year after the author,
aged twenty-three, had received his Bachelor of Arts degree. The present
selection includes the whole of the introductory part of the paper, the
remainder being unintelligible to those unskilled in the language of
mathematical abstraction.

T HE present state of electrical science seems peculiarly unfavourable to speculation. The laws of the distribution of
electricity on the surface of conductors have been analytically
deduced from experiment; some parts of the mathematical

* From *Transactions of the Cambridge Philosophical Society* (1856).

theory of magnetism[1] are established, while in other parts the experimental data are wanting; the theory of the conduction of galvanism and that of the mutual attraction of conductors have been reduced to mathematical formulæ, but have not fallen into relation with the other parts of the science. No electrical theory can now be put forth, unless it shews the connexion not only between electricity at rest and current electricity, but between the attractions and inductive effects of electricity in both states.[2] Such a theory must accurately satisfy those laws, the mathematical form of which is known, and must afford the means of calculating the effects in the limiting cases where the known formulæ are inapplicable. In order therefore to appreciate the requirements of the science, the student must make himself familiar with a considerable body of most intricate mathematics, the mere retention of which in the memory materially interferes with further progress. The first process therefore in the effectual study of the science, must be one of simplification and reduction of the results of previous investigation to a form in which the mind can grasp them. The results of this simplification may take the form of a purely mathematical formula or of a physical hypothesis. In the first case we entirely lose sight of the phenomena to be explained; and though we may trace out the consequences of given laws, we can never obtain more extended views of the connexions of

[1] In Maxwell's day the word *galvanism* was used to denote electricity evolved by chemical action, as in the case of a battery.

[2] In the case of "electricity at rest," two insulated charged bodies with opposite charges will attract each other, just as in "current electricity" parallel wires bearing electric currents in the same direction will attract each other. By "inductive effect," Maxwell referred to the fact that a body with an electric charge will, by being in the neighborhood of a conducting body, produce the effects of charge in it.

the subject. If, on the other hand, we adopt a physical hypothesis, we see the phenomena only through a medium, and are liable to that blindness to facts and rashness in assumption which a partial explanation encourages. We must therefore discover some method of investigation which allows the mind at every step to lay hold of a clear physical conception, without being committed to any theory founded on the physical science from which that conception is borrowed, so that it is neither drawn aside from the subject in pursuit of analytical subtleties, nor carried beyond the truth by a favourite hypothesis.

In order to obtain physical ideas without adopting a physical theory we must make ourselves familiar with the existence of physical analogies. By a physical analogy I mean that partial similarity between the laws of one science and those of another which makes each of them illustrate the other. Thus all the mathematical sciences are founded on relations between physical laws and laws of numbers, so that the aim of exact science is to reduce the problems of nature to the determination of quantities by operations with numbers. Passing from the most universal of all analogies to a very partial one, we find the same resemblance in mathematical form between two different phenomena giving rise to a physical theory of light.

The changes of direction which light undergoes in passing from one medium to another, are identical with the deviations of the path of a particle in moving through a narrow space in which intense forces act. This analogy, which extends only to the direction, and not to the velocity of motion, was long believed to be the true explanation of the refraction of light;[3]

---

[3] According to Newton's theory of light, in which optical phenomena were thought to be due to the motion of a series of particles, it was held that when

and we still find it useful in the solution of certain problems, in which we employ it without danger, as an artificial method. The other analogy, between light and the vibrations of an elastic medium, extends much farther, but, though its importance and fruitfulness cannot be over-estimated, we must recollect that it is founded only on a resemblance *in form* between the laws of light and those of vibrations. By stripping it of its physical dress and reducing it to a theory of "transverse alternations,"[4] we might obtain a system of truth strictly founded on observation, but probably deficient both in the vividness of its conceptions and the fertility of its method. I have said thus much on the disputed questions of Optics, as a preparation for the discussion of the almost universally admitted theory of attraction at a distance.

We have all acquired the mathematical conception of these attractions. We can reason about them and determine their appropriate forms or formulæ. These formulæ have a distinct mathematical significance, and their results are found to be in accordance with natural phenomena. There is no formula in applied mathematics more consistent with nature than the formula of attractions, and no theory better established in the minds of men than that of the action of bodies on one another

light goes from air into glass or water it must suffer an increase in speed, as a material particle would. In fact, however, unlike the stream of particles in the circumstances described by Maxwell, light suffers a diminution of speed when it is refracted and enters water or glass from air — a fact only recently discovered in Maxwell's day.

4 In Maxwell's day, the theory that light consists of a series of vibrations of some kind of an elastic or ethereal medium had been generally accepted. By "transverse," it was meant that the vibrations were at right angles to the direction of motion, much as water waves cause when a stone is dropped on the surface and the waves spread out in a direction at right angles to the motion of the stone.

at a distance. The laws of the conduction of heat in uniform media appear at first sight among the most different in their physical relations from those relating to attractions. The quantities which enter into them are *temperature, flow of heat, conductivity.* The word *force* is foreign to the subject. Yet we find that the mathematical laws of the uniform motion of heat in homogeneous media are identical in form with those of attractions varying inversely as the square of the distance. We have only to substitute *source of heat* for *centre of attraction, flow of heat* for *accelerating effect of attraction* at any point, and *temperature* for *potential,* and the solution of a problem in attractions is transformed into that of a problem in heat.[5]

Now the conduction of heat is supposed to proceed by an action between contiguous parts of a medium, while the force of attraction is a relation between distant bodies, and yet, if we knew nothing more than is expressed in the mathematical formulæ, there would be nothing to distinguish between the one set of phenomena and the other.

It is true, that if we introduce other considerations and observe additional facts, the two subjects will assume very different aspects, but the mathematical resemblance of some of their laws will remain, and may still be made useful in exciting appropriate mathematical ideas.

It is by the use of analogies of this kind that I have attempted to bring before the mind, in a convenient and manageable form, those mathematical ideas which are necessary to the study of the phenomena of electricity. The methods are generally those suggested by the processes of reasoning which are found in the

---

[5] Maxwell at this point noted that the analogy between heat and attraction had first been pointed out by Professor William Thomson, later Lord Kelvin.

researches of Faraday, and which, though they have been interpreted mathematically by Prof. Thomson and others, are very generally supposed to be of an indefinite and unmathematical character, when compared with those employed by the professed mathematicians. By the method which I adopt, I hope to render it evident that I am not attempting to establish any physical theory of a science in which I have hardly made a single experiment, and that the limit of my design is to shew how, by a strict application of the ideas and methods of Faraday, the connexion of the very different orders of phenomena which he has discovered may be clearly placed before the mathematical mind. I shall therefore avoid as much as I can the introduction of anything which does not serve as a direct illustration of Faraday's methods, or of the mathematical deductions which may be made from them. In treating the simpler parts of the subject I shall use Faraday's mathematical methods as well as his ideas. When the complexity of the subject requires it, I shall use analytical notation, still confining myself to the development of ideas originated by the same philosopher.

I have in the first place to explain and illustrate the idea of "lines of force."

When a body is electrified in any manner, a small body charged with positive electricity, and placed in any given position, will experience a force urging it in a certain direction. If the small body be now negatively electrified, it will be urged by an equal force in a direction exactly opposite.

The same relations hold between a magnetic body and the north or south poles of a small magnet. If the north pole is urged in one direction, the south pole is urged in the opposite direction.

In this way we might find a line passing through any point of space, such that it represents the direction of the force acting on a positively electrified particle, or on an elementary north pole, and the reverse direction of the force on a negatively electrified particle or an elementary south pole. Since at every point of space such a direction may be found, if we commence at any point and draw a line so that, as we go along it, its direction at any point shall always coincide with that of the resultant force at that point, this curve will indicate the direction of that force for every point through which it passes, and might be called on that account a *line of force*. We might in the same way draw other lines of force, till we had filled all space with curves indicating by their direction that of the force at any assigned point.

We should thus obtain a geometrical model of the physical phenomena, which would tell us the *direction* of the force, but we should still require some method of indicating the *intensity* of the force at any point. If we consider these curves not as mere lines, but as fine tubes of variable section carrying an incompressible fluid, then, since the velocity of the fluid is inversely as the section of the tube, we may make the velocity vary according to any given law, by regulating the section of the tube, and in this way we might represent the intensity of the force as well as its direction by the motion of the fluid in these tubes. This method of representing the intensity of a force by the velocity of an imaginary fluid in a tube is applicable to any conceivable system of forces, but it is capable of great simplification in the case in which the forces are such as can be explained by the hypothesis of attractions varying inversely as the square of the distance, such as those observed in electrical and magnetic phenomena. In the case of a perfectly arbitrary system of forces, there will generally be interstices between the tubes; but in the case of electric and magnetic forces it is possible to arrange the tubes so as to leave no interstices. The tubes will then be mere surfaces, directing the motion of a fluid filling up the whole space. It has been usual to commence the investigation of the laws of these forces by at once assuming that the phenomena are due to attractive or repulsive forces acting between certain points. We may however obtain a different view of the subject, and one more suited to our more difficult inquiries, by adopting for the definition of the forces of which we treat, that they may be represented in magnitude and direction by the uniform motion of an incompressible fluid.

I propose, then, first to describe a method by which the motion of such a fluid can be clearly conceived; secondly to trace the consequences of assuming certain conditions of motion, and to point out the application of the method to some of the less complicated phenomena of electricity, magnetism, and galvanism; and lastly to shew how by an extension of these methods, and the introduction of another idea due to Faraday, the laws of the attractions and inductive actions of magnets and currents may be clearly conceived, without making any assumptions as to the physical nature of electricity, or adding anything to that which has been already proved by experiment.

By referring everything to the purely geometrical idea of the motion of an imaginary fluid, I hope to attain generality and precision, and to avoid the dangers arising from a premature theory professing to explain the cause of the phenomena. If the results of mere speculation which I have collected are found to be of any use to experimental philosophers, in arranging and interpreting their results, they will have served their purpose, and a mature theory, in which physical facts will be physically explained, will be formed by those who by interrogating Nature herself can obtain the only true solution of the questions which the mathematical theory suggests.

CHARLES ROBERT DARWIN
and ALFRED RUSSEL WALLACE

On the Tendency of Species to Form Varieties; and on the Perpetuation of Varieties and Species by Natural Means of Selection[*]

The academic preparation of Charles Robert Darwin (1809–1882) gave no indication of the major contributions he was later to make in science; he had an undistinguished school career at Shrewsbury; he abandoned his attempt to prepare in medicine at Edinburgh University; of his time at Cambridge University, where he was reading for orders in the Church of England, he commented in his *Autobiography* that "it was wasted, as far as academical studies were concerned, as completely as at Edinburgh and at school." Having little scientific preparation, but a growing interest in nature, Darwin joined H.M.S. *Beagle* as a naturalist in 1831. The ostensible mission of the voyage was "to survey the coast of Patagonia and Tierra del Fuego, Chile, Peru, and some Pacific islands and to carry a chain of chronometrical measurements round the world." After five years at sea the *Beagle* returned to England in 1836. Darwin, who had left England little disposed to question the literal truth of Genesis, returned with little left of that belief, and in 1837 opened the first of his notebooks on "Transmutation of Species." His explorations of nature made during the voyage of the *Beagle* provided an enormous store of material, much of which became evidence for his newly emergent belief in the variability of species. Darwin's most important contribution to the theory of evolution is clearly the provision of natural selection as the causal mechanism capable of explaining why chance variations would be preserved, thus creating a new species more adaptable to its environment. The process in nature is slow and hard to observe directly. Darwin was therefore forced to collect large amounts of circumstantial evidence. Although he prepared several manuscript versions of his theory of

[*] From *Journal of the Proceedings of the Linnean Society* (1858).

evolution by natural selection (1842–1844) and discussed his views in correspondence, it was not until the theory was independently proposed by Alfred Russel Wallace that Darwin permitted himself to be persuaded by his friends to commit his manuscript to publication.

Like Darwin, Alfred Russel Wallace (1823–1913) learned his natural history during the course of lengthy voyages of exploration: One in 1848 took him to the Amazon; another voyage, to the Malay Archipelago, began in 1854 and lasted eight years. The paper here reprinted, spelling out the conclusion that natural selection could serve as a mechanism of evolution, was written during the latter voyage sometime after Wallace had read Thomas Robert Malthus's *Essay on Population*. Together with his theory of natural selection, Wallace's studies on the geographical distribution of plants and animals provide a lasting contribution to biology.

The papers of Darwin and Wallace were read for them at a meeting of the Linnean Society of London on July 1, 1858. The Society, honoring the name of Carl Linnaeus (1707–1778), the Swedish naturalist, had as its members the leading botanists, zoologists and geologists in England. Darwin's friends Charles Lyell and Joseph Dalton Hooker (1817–1911), the latter the English plant-systematist, acting to insure the claims of their colleague, wrote the following letter when they presented the papers to the Society:

London, June 30th, 1858.

MY DEAR SIR, — The accompanying papers, which we have the honour of communicating to the Linnean Society, and which all relate to the same subject, viz. the Laws which affect the Production of Varieties, Races, and Species, contain the results of the investigations of two indefatigable naturalists, Mr. Charles Darwin and Mr. Alfred Wallace.

These gentlemen having, independently and unknown to one another, conceived the same very ingenious theory to account for the appearance and perpetuation of varieties and of specific forms on our planet, may both fairly claim the merit of being original thinkers in this important line of inquiry; but neither of them having published his views, though Mr. Darwin has for many years past been repeatedly urged by us to do so, and both authors having now unreservedly placed their papers in our hands, we think it would best promote the interests of science that a selection from them should be laid before the Linnean Society.

Taken in the order of their dates, they consist of: —

1. Extracts from a MS. work on Species,* by Mr. Darwin, which was sketched in 1839, and copied in 1844, when the copy was read by Dr. Hooker, and its contents afterwards communicated to Sir Charles Lyell. The first Part is devoted to "The Variation of Organic Beings under Domestication and in their Natural State;" and the second chapter of that Part, from which we propose to read to the Society the extracts referred to, is headed, "On the Variation of Organic Beings in a state of Nature; on the Natural Means of Selection; on the Comparison of Domestic Races and true Species."

2. An abstract of a private letter addressed to Professor Asa Gray,[1] of Boston, U.S., in October 1857, by Mr. Darwin, in which he repeats his views, and which shows that these remained unaltered from 1839 to 1857.

3. An Essay by Mr. Wallace, entitled "On the Tendency of Varieties to depart indefinitely from the Original Type." This was written at Ternate[2] in February 1858, for the perusal of his friend and correspondent Mr. Darwin, and sent to him with the

---

* This MS. work was never intended for publication, and therefore was not written with care. — C. D. 1858.

1 Asa Gray (1810–1888), professor of botany at Harvard and an early supporter of Darwinian evolution.

2 An island in the Moluccas group, now part of Indonesia.

expressed wish that it should be forwarded to Sir Charles Lyell, if Mr. Darwin thought it sufficiently novel and interesting. So highly did Mr. Darwin appreciate the value of the views therein set forth, that he proposed, in a letter to Sir Charles Lyell, to obtain Mr. Wallace's consent to allow the Essay to be published as soon as possible. Of this step we highly approved, provided Mr. Darwin did not withhold from the public, as he was strongly inclined to do (in favour of Mr. Wallace), the memoir which he had himself written on the same subject, and which, as before stated, one of us had perused in 1844, and the contents of which we had both of us been privy to for many years. On representing this to Mr. Darwin, he gave us permission to make what use we thought proper of his memoir, &c.; and in adopting our present course, of presenting it to the Linnean Society, we have explained to him that we are not solely considering the relative claims to priority of himself and his friend, but the interests of science generally; for we feel it to be desirable that views founded on a wide deduction from facts, and matured by years of reflection, should constitute at once a goal from which others may start, and that, while the scientific world is waiting for the appearance of Mr. Darwin's complete work, some of the leading results of his labours, as well as those of his able correspondent, should together be laid before the public.

We have the honour to be yours very obediently,

CHARLES LYELL.

JOS. D. HOOKER.

J. J. Bennett, Esq.,[3]
Secretary of the Linnean Society.

[3] John Joseph Bennett (1801–1876), a botanist who became secretary of the Linnean Society in 1840, holding the post for twenty years.

I. *Extract from an unpublished Work on Species, by* C. DARWIN, Esq., *consisting of a portion of a Chapter entitled, "On the Variation of Organic Beings in a state of Nature; on the Natural Means of Selection; on the Comparison of Domestic Races and true Species."*[4]

De Candolle,[5] in an eloquent passage, has declared that all nature is at war, one organism with another, or with external nature. Seeing the contented face of nature, this may at first well be doubted; but reflection will inevitably prove it to be true. The war, however, is not constant, but recurrent in a slight degree at short periods, and more severely at occasional more distant periods; and hence its effects are easily overlooked. It is the doctrine of Malthus applied in most cases with tenfold force.[6] As in every climate there are seasons, for each of its in-

[4] Darwin left two early versions of his theory of evolution by natural selection, one a "Sketch" of 35 manuscript pages (1842) and the second an "Essay" of some 230 manuscript pages (1844). These were edited and printed by his son Sir Francis Darwin as *The Foundations of the Origin of Species,* by Charles Darwin (Cambridge: University Press, 1909). They have been re-edited by Sir Gavin de Beer, *Evolution by Natural Selection* (Cambridge: Published for the XV International Congress of Zoology and the Linnean Society of London, at the University Press, 1958).

[5] Augustin Pyrame de Candolle (1778–1841). As Loren Eiseley (*Darwin's Century: Evolution and the Men Who Discovered It* [New York: Doubleday, 1958], p. 101) has suggested, Darwin, whose facility at reading French was slight, probably came upon de Candolle's statement in Lyell's *Principles of Geology.* The following quotation from de Candolle (source unindicated) appears on p. 174 of vol. III of the sixth edition of Lyell: " 'All the plants of a given country,' says de Candolle in his usual spirited style, 'are at war one with another. The first which establish themselves by chance in a particular spot tend, by the mere occupancy of space, to exclude other species — the greater choke the smaller; the longest livers replace those which last for a shorter period; the more prolific gradually make themselves masters of the ground, which species multiplying more slowly would otherwise fill.' " The source is almost certainly de Candolle's *Théorie élémentaire de la Botanique,* Paris, 1813, which is liberally cited in other sections of Lyell's work.

[6] Thomas Robert Malthus (1766–1834), author of *An Essay on Population,*

habitants, of greater and less abundance, so all annually breed; and the moral restraint which in some small degree checks the increase of mankind is entirely lost. Even slow-breeding mankind has doubled in twenty-five years; and if he could increase his food with greater ease, he would double in less time. But for animals without artificial means, the amount of food for each species must, *on an average,* be constant, whereas the increase of all organisms tends to be geometrical, and in a vast majority of cases at an enormous ratio. Suppose in a certain spot there are eight pairs of birds, and that *only* four pairs of them annually (including double hatches) rear only four young, and that these go on rearing their young at the same rate, then at the end of seven years (a short life, excluding violent deaths, for any bird) there will be 2048 birds, instead of the original sixteen. As this increase is quite impossible, we must conclude either that birds do not rear nearly half their young, or that the average life of a bird is, from accident, not nearly seven years. Both checks probably concur. The same kind of calculation applied to all plants and animals affords results more or less striking, but in very few instances more striking than in man.

Many practical illustrations of this rapid tendency to increase are on record, among which, during peculiar seasons, are the extraordinary numbers of certain animals; for instance, during the years 1826 to 1828, in La Plata,[7] when from drought some millions of cattle perished, the whole country actually *swarmed* with mice. Now I think it cannot be doubted that during the breeding-season all the mice (with the exception of a few males or

a pamphlet anonymously published in 1798, was influential upon Darwin though his suggestion of natural checks upon population.

[7] La Plata is an Argentinian seaport south of Buenos Aires.

females in excess) ordinarily pair, and therefore that this astounding increase during three years must be attributed to a greater number than usual surviving the first year, and then breeding, and so on till the third year, when their numbers were brought down to their usual limits on the return of wet weather. Where man has introduced plants and animals into a new and favourable country, there are many accounts in how surprisingly few years the whole country has become stocked with them. This increase would necessarily stop as soon as the country was fully stocked; and yet we have every reason to believe, from what is known of wild animals, that *all* would pair in the spring. In the majority of cases it is most difficult to imagine where the checks fall — though generally, no doubt, on the seeds, eggs, and young; but when we remember how impossible, even in mankind (so much better known than any other animal), it is to infer from repeated casual observations what the average duration of life is, or to discover the different percentage of deaths to births in different countries, we ought to feel no surprise at our being unable to discover where the check falls in any animal or plant. It should always be remembered, that in most cases the checks are recurrent yearly in a small, regular degree, and in an extreme degree during unusually cold, hot, dry, or wet years, according to the constitution of the being in question. Lighten any check in the least degree, and the geometrical powers of increase in every organism will almost instantly increase the average number of the favoured species. Nature may be compared to a surface on which rest ten thousand sharp wedges touching each other and driven inwards by incessant blows. Fully to realize these views much reflection is requisite. Malthus on man should be studied; and all such cases as those of the mice in La Plata, of the cattle and horses when first turned out in South America, of the birds by our calculations, &c., should be well considered. Reflect on the enormous multiplying power *inherent and annually in action* in all animals; reflect on the countless seeds scattered by a hundred ingenious contrivances, year after year, over the whole face of the land; and yet we have every reason to suppose that the average percentage of each of the inhabitants of a country usually remains constant. Finally, let it be borne in mind that this average number of individuals (the external conditions remaining the same) in each country is kept up by recurrent struggles against other species or against external nature (as on the borders of the Arctic regions, where the cold checks life), and that ordinarily each individual of every species holds its place, either by its own struggle and capacity of acquiring nourishment in some period of its life, from the egg upwards; or by the struggle of its parents (in short-lived organisms, when the main check occurs at longer intervals) with other individuals of the *same* or *different* species.

But let the external conditions of a country alter. If in a small degree, the relative proportions of the inhabitants will in most cases simply be slightly changed; but let the number of inhabitants be small, as on an island, and free access to it from other countries be circumscribed, and let the change of conditions continue progressing (forming new stations), in such a case the original inhabitants must cease to be as perfectly adapted to the changed conditions as they were originally. It has been shown in a former part of this work, that such changes of external conditions would, from their acting on the reproductive system, probably cause the organization of those beings which were most affected to become, as under domestication, plastic. Now, can it be doubted, from the struggle each individual has to obtain subsistence, that any minute variation in structure, habits, or instincts, adapting that individual better to the new conditions, would tell upon its vigour and health? In the struggle it would have a better *chance* of surviving; and those of its offspring which inherited the variation, be it ever so slight, would also have a better *chance*. Yearly more are bred than can survive; the smallest grain in the balance, in the long run, must tell on which death shall fall, and which shall survive. Let this work of selection on the one hand, and death on the other, go on for a thousand generations, who will pretend to affirm that it would produce no effect, when we remember what, in a few years, Bakewell effected in cattle, and Western[8] in sheep, by this identical principle of selection?

To give an imaginary example from changes in progress on an island: — let the organization of a canine animal which preyed chiefly on rabbits, but sometimes on hares, become slightly plastic; let these same changes cause the number of rabbits very slowly to decrease, and the number of hares to increase; the effect of this would be that the fox or dog would be driven to try to catch more hares: his organization, however, being slightly plastic, those individuals with the lightest forms, longest limbs, and best eyesight, let the difference be ever so small, would be slightly favoured, and would tend to live longer, and to survive during that time of the year when food was scarcest; they would also rear more young, which would

8 Robert Bakewell (1725–1795), a well-known breeder of sheep and oxen. Charles Callis Western (1767–1844), a politician and agriculturalist active in the improvement of sheep breeding.

tend to inherit these slight peculiarities. The less fleet ones would be rigidly destroyed. I can see no more reason to doubt that these causes in a thousand generations would produce a marked effect, and adapt the form of the fox or dog to the catching of hares instead of rabbits, than that greyhounds can be improved by selection and careful breeding. So would it be with plants under similar circumstances. If the number of individuals of a species with plumed seeds could be increased by greater powers of dissemination within its own area (that is, if the check to increase fell chiefly on the seeds), those seeds which were provided with ever so little more down, would in the long run be most disseminated; hence a greater number of seeds thus formed would germinate, and would tend to produce plants inheriting the slightly better-adapted down.[9]

Besides this natural means of selection, by which those individuals are preserved, whether in their egg, or larval, or mature state, which are best adapted to the place they fill in nature, there is a second agency at work in most unisexual animals, tending to produce the same effect, namely, the struggle of the males for the females. These struggles are generally decided by the law of battle, but in the case of birds, apparently, by the charms of their song, by their beauty or their power of courtship, as in the dancing rock-thrush of Guiana.[10] The most vigorous and healthy males, implying perfect adaptation, must generally gain the victory in their contests. This kind of selection, however, is less rigorous than the other; it does not require the death of the less successful, but gives to them fewer descendants.

[9] Darwin's note of 1858: "I can see no more difficulty in this, than in the planter improving his varieties of the cotton plant."

[10] Here Darwin alludes to an alternate form of competition relying apparently on aesthetic criteria rather than prowess in battle.

[346]

The struggle falls, moreover, at a time of year when food is generally abundant, and perhaps the effect chiefly produced would be the modification of the secondary sexual characters, which are not related to the power of obtaining food, or to defence from enemies, but to fighting with or rivalling other males. The result of this struggle amongst the males may be compared in some respects to that produced by those agriculturists who pay less attention to the careful selection of all their young animals, and more to the occasional use of a choice mate.

II. *Abstract of a Letter from* C. DARWIN, Esq., *to* Prof. ASA GRAY, *Boston, U.S., dated Down, September 5th, 1857.*

1. It is wonderful what the principle of selection by man, that is the picking out of individuals with any desired quality, and breeding from them, and again picking out, can do. Even breeders have been astounded at their own results. They can act on differences inappreciable to an uneducated eye. Selection has been *methodically* followed in *Europe* for only the last half century; but it was occasionally, and even in some degree methodically, followed in the most ancient times. There must have been also a kind of unconscious selection from a remote period, namely in the preservation of the individual animals (without any thought of their offspring) most useful to each race of man in his particular circumstances. The "roguing," as nurserymen call the destroying of varieties which depart from their type, is a kind of selection. I am convinced that intentional and occasional selection has been the main agent in the production of our domestic races; but however this may be, its great power of modification has been indisputably shown in later times. Selection acts only by the accumulation

of slight or greater variations, caused by external conditions, or by the mere fact that in generation the child is not absolutely similar to its parent. Man, by this power of accumulating variations, adapts living beings to his wants — may be said to make the wool of one sheep good for carpets, of another for cloth, &c.

2. Now suppose there were a being who did not judge by mere external appearances, but who could study the whole internal organization, who was never capricious, and should go on selecting from one object during millions of generations; who will say what he might not effect? In nature we have some *slight* variation occasionally in all parts; and I think it can be shown that changed conditions of existence is the main cause of the child not exactly resembling its parents; and in nature geology shows us what changes have taken place, and are taking place. We have almost unlimited time; no one but a practical geologist can fully appreciate this. Think of the Glacial period, during the whole of which the same species at least of shells have existed; there must have been during this period millions on millions of generations.

3. I think it can be shown that there is such an unerring power at work in *Natural Selection* (the title of my book), which selects exclusively for the good of each organic being. The elder De Candolle, W. Herbert,[11] and Lyell have written excellently on the struggle for life; but even they have not written strongly enough. Reflect that every being (even the elephant) breeds at such a rate, that in a few years, or at most a few centuries, the surface of the earth would not hold the progeny of one pair. I have found it hard constantly to bear in mind that the in-

11 William Herbert (1778–1847) a classical scholar, linguist and naturalist, who carried out an early series of experiments in plant hybridization.

crease of every single species is checked during some part of its life, or during some shortly recurrent generation. Only a few of those annually born can live to propagate their kind. What a trifling difference must often determine which shall survive, and which perish!

4. Now take the case of a country undergoing some change. This will tend to cause some of its inhabitants to vary slightly — not but that I believe most beings vary at all times enough for selection to act on them. Some of its inhabitants will be exterminated; and the remainder will be exposed to the mutual action of a different set of inhabitants, which I believe to be far more important to the life of each being than mere climate. Considering the infinitely various methods which living beings follow to obtain food by struggling with other organisms, to escape danger at various times of life, to have their eggs or seeds disseminated, &c. &c., I cannot doubt that during millions of generations individuals of a species will be occasionally born with some slight variation, profitable to some part of their economy. Such individuals will have a better chance of surviving, and of propagating their new and slightly different structure; and the modification may be slowly increased by the accumulative action of natural selection to any profitable extent. The variety thus formed will either coexist with, or, more commonly, will exterminate its parent form. An organic being, like the woodpecker or misseltoe, may thus come to be adapted to a score of contingences — natural selection accumulating those slight variations in all parts of its structure, which are in any way useful to it during any part of its life.

5. Multiform difficulties will occur to every one, with respect to this theory. Many can, I think, be satisfactorily answered.

Natura non facit saltum answers some of the most obvious.[12]
The slowness of the change, and only a very few individuals
undergoing change at any one time, answers others. The extreme imperfection of our geological records answers others.

6. Another principle, which may be called the principle of
divergence, plays, I believe, an important part in the origin of
species. The same spot will support more life if occupied by very
diverse forms. We see this in the many generic forms in a square
yard of turf, and in the plants or insects on any little uniform
islet, belonging almost invariably to as many genera and families
as species. We can understand the meaning of this fact amongst
the higher animals, whose habits we understand. We know that
it has been experimentally shown that a plot of land will yield a
greater weight if sown with several species of genera of grasses,
than if sown with only two or three species. Now, every organic
being, by propagating so rapidly, may be said to be striving its
utmost to increase in numbers. So it will be with the offspring
of any species after it has become diversified into varieties, or
sub-species, or true species. And it follows, I think, from the
foregoing facts, that the varying offspring of each species will
try (only few will succeed) to seize on as many and as diverse
places in the economy of nature as possible. Each new variety or
species, when formed, will generally take the place of, and thus
exterminate its less well-fitted parent. This I believe to be the
origin of the classification and affinities of organic beings at
all times; for organic beings always *seem* to branch and sub-
branch like the limbs of a tree from a common trunk, the
flourishing and diverging twigs destroying the less vigorous —

[12] G. W. Leibniz, *Protogoea*, XXVI: "All advances by degrees in Nature,
and nothing by leaps. . . ."

the dead and lost branches rudely representing extinct genera and families.

This sketch is *most* imperfect; but in so short a space I cannot make it better. Your imagination must fill up very wide blanks.

C. DARWIN.

III. *On the Tendency of Varieties to depart indefinitely from the Original Type.* By ALFRED RUSSEL WALLACE.

One of the strongest arguments which have been adduced to prove the original and permanent distinctness of species is, that *varieties* produced in a state of domesticity are more or less unstable, and often have a tendency, if left to themselves, to return to the normal form of the parent species; and this instability is considered to be a distinctive peculiarity of all varieties, even of those occurring among wild animals in a state of nature, and to constitute a provision for preserving unchanged the originally created distinct species.

In the absence or scarcity of facts and observations as to *varieties* occurring among wild animals, this argument has had great weight with naturalists, and has led to a very general and somewhat prejudiced belief in the stability of species. Equally general, however, is the belief in what are called "permanent or true varieties," — races of animals which continually propagate their like, but which differ so slightly (although constantly) from some other race, that the one is considered to be a *variety* of the other. Which is the *variety* and which the original *species*, there is generally no means of determining, except in those rare cases in which the one race has been known to produce an offspring unlike itself and resembling the other. This, however, would

[351]

seem quite incompatible with the "permanent invariability of species," but the difficulty is overcome by assuming that such varieties have strict limits, and can never again vary further from the original type, although they may return to it, which, from the analogy of the domesticated animals, is considered to be highly probable, if not certainly proved.

It will be observed that this argument rests entirely on the assumption, that *varieties* occurring in a state of nature are in all respects analogous to or even identical with those of domestic animals, and are governed by the same laws as regards their permanence or further variation. But it is the object of the present paper to show that this assumption is altogether false, that there is a general principle in nature which will cause many *varieties* to survive the parent species, and to give rise to successive variations departing further and further from the original type, and which also produces, in domesticated animals, the tendency of varieties to return to the parent form.

The life of wild animals is a struggle for existence. The full exertion of all their faculties and all their energies is required to preserve their own existence and provide for that of their infant offspring. The possibility of procuring food during the least favourable seasons, and of escaping the attacks of their most dangerous enemies, are the primary conditions which determine the existence both of individuals and entire species. These conditions will also determine the population of a species; and by a careful consideration of all the circumstances we may be enabled to comprehend, and in some degree to explain, what at first sight appears so inexplicable — the excessive abundance of some species, while others closely allied to them are very rare.

The general proportion that must obtain between certain

groups of animals is readily seen. Large animals cannot be so abundant as small ones; the carnivora must be less numerous than the herbivora; eagles and lions can never be so plentiful as pigeons and antelopes; the wild asses of the Tartarian deserts[13] cannot equal in numbers the horses of the more luxuriant prairies and pampas of America. The greater or less fecundity of an animal is often considered to be one of the chief causes of its abundance or scarcity; but a consideration of the facts will show us that it really has little or nothing to do with the matter. Even the least prolific of animals would increase rapidly if unchecked, whereas it is evident that the animal population of the globe must be stationary, or perhaps, through the influence of man, decreasing. Fluctuations there may be; but permanent increase, except in restricted localities, is almost impossible. For example, our own observation must convince us that birds do not go on increasing every year in a geometrical ratio, as they would do, were there not some powerful check to their natural increase. Very few birds produce less than two young ones each year, while many have six, eight, or ten; four will certainly be below the average; and if we suppose that each pair produce young only four times in their life, that will also be below the average, supposing them not to die either by violence or want of food. Yet at this rate how tremendous would be the increase in a few years from a single pair! A simple calculation will show that in fifteen years each pair of birds would have increased to nearly ten millions! whereas we have no reason to believe that the number of the birds of any country increases at all in fifteen or in one hundred and fifty years. With such powers of increase the population must have reached its limits, and have become

13 Tartarian deserts — the deserts of Siberia.

stationary, in a very few years after the origin of each species. It
is evident, therefore, that each year an immense number of
birds must perish — as many in fact as are born; and as on the
lowest calculation the progeny are each year twice as numerous
as their parents, it follows that, whatever be the average number
of individuals existing in any given country, *twice that number
must perish annually,* — a striking result, but one which seems
at least highly probable, and is perhaps under rather than over
the truth. It would therefore appear that, as far as the continuance of the species and the keeping up the average number of
individuals are concerned, large broods are superfluous. On the
average all above *one* become food for hawks and kites, wild cats
and weasels, or perish of cold and hunger as winter comes on.
This is strikingly proved by the case of particular species; for we
find that their abundance in individuals bears no relation whatever to their fertility in producing offspring. Perhaps the most
remarkable instance of an immense bird population is that of
the passenger pigeon of the United States, which lays only one,
or at most two eggs, and is said to rear generally but one young
one.[14] Why is this bird so extraordinarily abundant, while others
producing two or three times as many young are much less plentiful? The explanation is not difficult. The food most congenial
to this species, and on which it thrives best, is abundantly distributed over a very extensive region, offering such differences
of soil and climate, that in one part or another of the area the
supply never fails. The bird is capable of a very rapid and long-
continued flight, so that it can pass without fatigue over the

[14] The population once numbered in the billions and the passenger pigeon
was considered among the most numerous of surviving land birds. The extinction of the species was due primarily to exploitation by man. The last
survivor died in a zoo in 1914.

whole of the district it inhabits, and as soon as the supply of food begins to fail in one place is able to discover a fresh feeding-ground. This example strikingly shows us that the procuring a constant supply of wholesome food is almost the sole condition requisite for ensuring the rapid increase of a given species, since neither the limited fecundity, nor the unrestrained attacks of birds of prey and of man are here sufficient to check it. In no other birds are these peculiar circumstances so strikingly combined. Either their food is more liable to failure, or they have not sufficient power of wing to search for it over an extensive area, or during some season of the year it becomes very scarce, and less wholesome substitutes have to be found; and thus, though more fertile in offspring, they can never increase beyond the supply of food in the least favourable seasons. Many birds can only exist by migrating, when their food becomes scarce, to regions possessing a milder, or at least a different climate, though, as these migrating birds are seldom excessively abundant, it is evident that the countries they visit are still deficient in a constant and abundant supply of wholesome food. Those whose organization does not permit them to migrate when their food becomes periodically scarce, can never attain a large population. This is probably the reason why woodpeckers are scarce with us, while in the tropics they are among the most abundant of solitary birds. Thus the house sparrow is more abundant than the redbreast, because its food is more constant and plentiful, — seeds of grasses being preserved during the winter, and our farm-yards and stubble-fields furnishing an almost inexhaustible supply. Why, as a general rule, are aquatic, and especially sea birds, very numerous in individuals? Not because they are more prolific than others, generally the contrary; but because their food never fails, the sea-shores and river-banks daily swarming with a fresh supply of small mollusca and crustacea. Exactly the same laws will apply to mammals. Wild cats are prolific and have few enemies; why then are they never as abundant as rabbits? The only intelligible answer is, that their supply of food is more precarious. It appears evident, therefore, that so long as a country remains physically unchanged, the numbers of its animal population cannot materially increase. If one species does so, some others requiring the same kind of food must diminish in proportion. The numbers that die annually must be immense; and as the individual existence of each animal depends upon itself, those that die must be the weakest — the very young, the aged, and the diseased, — while those that prolong their existence can only be the most perfect in health and vigour — those who are best able to obtain food regularly, and avoid their numerous enemies. It is, as we commenced by remarking, "a struggle for existence," in which the weakest and least perfectly organized must always succumb.

Now it is clear that what takes place among the individuals of a species must also occur among the several allied species of a group, — viz. that those which are best adapted to obtain a regular supply of food, and to defend themselves against the attacks of their enemies and the vicissitudes of the seasons, must necessarily obtain and preserve a superiority in population; while those species which from some defect of power or organization are the least capable of counteracting the vicissitudes of food, supply, &c., must diminish in numbers, and, in extreme cases, become altogether extinct. Between these extremes the species will present various degrees of capacity for ensuring the means of preserving life; and it is thus we account for the abundance or rarity of species. Our ignorance will generally prevent us from accurately tracing the effects to their causes; but could we become perfectly acquainted with the organization and habits of the various species of animals, and could we measure the capacity of each for performing the different acts necessary to its safety and existence under all the varying circumstances by which it is surrounded, we might be able even to calculate the proportionate abundance of individuals which is the necessary result.

If now we have succeeded in establishing these two points — 1st, *that the animal population of a country is generally stationary, being kept down by a periodical deficiency of food, and other checks;* and, 2nd, *that the comparative abundance or scarcity of the individuals of the several species is entirely due to their organization and resulting habits, which, rendering it more difficult to procure a regular supply of food and to provide for their personal safety in some cases than in others, can only be balanced by a difference in the population which have to exist in a given area* — we shall be in a condition to proceed to the consideration of *varieties,* to which the preceding remarks have a direct and very important application.

Most or perhaps all the variations from the typical form of a species must have some definite effect, however slight, on the habits or capacities of the individuals. Even a change of colour might, by rendering them more or less distinguishable, affect their safety; a greater or less development of hair might modify their habits. More important changes, such as an increase in the power or dimensions of the limbs or any of the external organs, would more or less affect their mode of procuring food or the range of country which they inhabit. It is also evident that most

[357]

changes would affect, either favourably or adversely, the powers of prolonging existence. An antelope with shorter or weaker legs must necessarily suffer more from the attacks of the feline carnivora; the passenger pigeon with less powerful wings would sooner or later be affected in its powers of procuring a regular supply of food; and in both cases the result must necessarily be a diminution of the population of the modified species. If, on the other hand, any species should produce a variety having slightly increased powers of preserving existence, that variety must inevitably in time acquire a superiority in numbers. These results must follow as surely as old age, intemperance, or scarcity of food produce an increased mortality. In both cases there may be many individual exceptions; but on the average the rule will invariably be found to hold good. All varieties will therefore fall into two classes — those which under the same conditions would never reach the population of the parent species, and those which would in time obtain and keep a numerical superiority. Now, let some alteration of physical conditions occur in the district — a long period of drought, a destruction of vegetation by locusts, the irruption of some new carnivorous animal seeking "pastures new"[15] — any change in fact tending to render existence more difficult to the species in question, and tasking its utmost powers to avoid complete extermination; it is evident that, of all the individuals composing the species, those forming the least numerous and most feebly organized variety would suffer first, and, were the pressure severe, must soon become extinct. The same causes continuing in action, the parent species would next suffer, would gradually diminish in numbers, and with a recurrence of similar unfavourable conditions

15 Milton, *Lycidas.*

might also become extinct. The superior variety would then alone remain, and on a return to favourable circumstances would rapidly increase in numbers and occupy the place of the extinct species and variety.

The *variety* would now have replaced the *species*, of which it would be a more perfectly developed and more highly organized form. It would be in all respects better adapted to secure its safety, and to prolong its individual existence and that of the race. Such a variety *could not* return to the original form; for that form is an inferior one, and could never compete with it for existence. Granted, therefore, a "tendency" to reproduce the original type of the species, still the variety must ever remain preponderant in numbers, and under adverse physical conditions *again alone survive*. But this new, improved, and populous race might itself, in course of time, give rise to new varieties, exhibiting several diverging modifications of form, any of which, tending to increase the facilities for preserving existence, must, by the same general law, in their turn become predominant. Here, then, we have *progression and continued divergence* deduced from the general laws which regulate the existence of animals in a state of nature, and from the undisputed fact that varieties do frequently occur. It is not, however, contended that this result would be invariable; a change of physical conditions in the district might at times materially modify it, rendering the race which had been the most capable of supporting existence under the former conditions now the least so, and even causing the extinction of the newer and, for a time, superior race, while the old or parent species and its first inferior varieties continued to flourish. Variations in unimportant parts might also occur, having no perceptible effect on the life-preserving powers; and the varieties so furnished might run a course parallel with the parent species, either giving rise to further variations or returning to the former type. All we argue for is, that certain varieties have a tendency to maintain their existence longer than the original species, and this tendency must make itself felt; for though the doctrine of chances or averages can never be trusted to on a limited scale, yet, if applied to high numbers, the results come nearer to what theory demands, and, as we approach to an infinity of examples, become strictly accurate. Now the scale on which nature works is so vast — the numbers of individuals and periods of time with which she deals approach so near to infinity, that any cause, however slight, and however liable to be veiled and counteracted by accidental circumstances, must in the end produce its full legitimate results.

Let us now turn to domesticated animals, and inquire how varieties produced among them are affected by the principles here enunciated. The essential difference in the condition of wild and domestic animals is this, — that among the former, their well-being and very existence depend upon the full exercise and healthy condition of all their senses and physical powers, whereas, among the latter, these are only partially exercised, and in some cases are absolutely unused. A wild animal has to search, and often to labour, for every mouthful of food — to exercise sight, hearing, and smell in seeking it, and in avoiding dangers, in procuring shelter from the inclemency of the seasons, and in providing for the subsistence and safety of its offspring. There is no muscle of its body that is not called into daily and hourly activity; there is no sense or faculty that is not strengthened by continual exercise. The domestic animal, on the other hand, has food provided for it, is sheltered, and often confined, to guard it against the vicissitudes of the seasons, is carefully secured from the attacks of its natural enemies, and seldom even rears its young without human assistance. Half of its senses and faculties are quite useless; and the other half are but occasionally called into feeble exercise, while even its muscular system is only irregularly called into action.

Now when a variety of such an animal occurs, having increased power or capacity in any organ or sense, such increase is totally useless, is never called into action, and may even exist without the animal ever becoming aware of it. In the wild animal, on the contrary, all its faculties and powers being brought into full action for the necessities of existence, any increase becomes immediately available, is strengthened by exercise, and must even slightly modify the food, the habits, and the whole economy of the race. It creates as it were a new animal, one of superior powers, and which will necessarily increase in numbers and outlive those inferior to it.

Again, in the domesticated animal all variations have an equal chance of continuance; and those which would decidedly render a wild animal unable to compete with its fellows and continue its existence are no disadvantage whatever in a state of domesticity. Our quickly fattening pigs, short-legged sheep, pouter pigeons, and poodle dogs could never have come into existence in a state of nature, because the very first step towards such inferior forms would have led to the rapid extinction of the race; still less could they now exist in competition with their wild allies. The great speed but slight endurance of the race horse, the unwieldy strength of the ploughman's team, would both be useless in a state of nature. If turned wild on the pam-

pas, such animals would probably soon become extinct, or under favourable circumstances might each lose those extreme
qualities which would never be called into action, and in a few
generations would revert to a common type, which must be that
in which the various powers and faculties are so proportioned
to each other as to be best adapted to procure food and secure
safety, — that in which by the full exercise of every part of his
organization the animal can alone continue to live. Domestic
varieties, when turned wild, *must* return to something near the
type of the original wild stock, *or become altogether extinct*.

We see, then, that no inferences as to varieties in a state of
nature can be deduced from the observation of those occurring
among domestic animals. The two are so much opposed to each
other in every circumstance of their existence, that what applies
to the one is almost sure not to apply to the other. Domestic
animals are abnormal, irregular, artificial; they are subject to
varieties which never occur and never can occur in a state of
nature: their very existence depends altogether on human care;
so far are many of them removed from that just proportion of
faculties, that true balance of organization, by means of which
alone an animal left to its own resources can preserve its existence and continue its race.

The hypothesis of Lamarck[16] — that progressive changes in
species have been produced by the attempts of animals to increase the development of their own organs, and thus modify
their structure and habits — has been repeatedly and easily refuted by all writers on the subject of varieties and species, and it

[16] Jean Baptiste Pierre Antoine de Monet, Chevalier de Lamarck (1744–1829)
presented his theory of evolution in three different versions: *Système des
Animaux sans Vertèbres* (1801), *Philosophie Zoölogique* (1809), *Histoire Naturelle
des Animaux sans Vertèbres* (1815).

seems to have been considered that when this was done the whole question has been finally settled; but the view here developed renders such an hypothesis quite unnecessary, by showing that similar results must be produced by the action of principles constantly at work in nature. The powerful retractile talons of the falcon- and the cat-tribes have not been produced or increased by the volition of those animals; but among the different varieties which occurred in the earlier and less highly organized forms of these groups, *those always survived longest which had the greatest facilities for seizing their prey.* Neither did the giraffe acquire its long neck by desiring to reach the foliage of the more lofty shrubs, and constantly stretching its neck for the purpose, but because any varieties which occurred among its antitypes with a longer neck than usual *at once secured a fresh range of pasture over the same ground as their shorter-necked companions, and on the first scarcity of food were thereby enabled to outlive them.* Even the peculiar colours of many animals, especially insects, so closely resembling the soil or the leaves or the trunks on which they habitually reside, are explained on the same principle; for though in the course of ages varieties of many tints may have occurred, *yet those races having colours best adapted to concealment from their enemies would inevitably survive the longest.* We have also here an acting cause to account for that balance so often observed in nature, — a deficiency in one set of organs always being compensated by an increased development of some others — powerful wings accompanying weak feet, or great velocity making up for the absence of defensive weapons; for it has been shown that all varieties in which an unbalanced deficiency occurred could not long continue their existence. The action of this principle is exactly like

[363]

that of the centrifugal governor[17] of the steam engine, which checks and corrects any irregularities almost before they become evident; and in like manner no unbalanced deficiency in the animal kingdom can ever reach any conspicuous magnitude, because it would make itself felt at the very first step, by rendering existence difficult and extinction almost sure soon to follow. An origin such as is here advocated will also agree with the peculiar character of the modifications of form and structure which obtain in organized beings — the many lines of divergence from a central type, the increasing efficiency and power of a particular organ through a succession of allied species, and the remarkable persistence of unimportant parts such as colour, texture of plumage and hair, form of horns or crests, through a series of species differing considerably in more essential characters. It also furnishes us with a reason for that "more specialized structure" which Professor Owen[18] states to be a characteristic of recent compared with extinct forms, and which would evidently be the result of the progressive modification of any organ applied to a special purpose in the animal economy.

We believe we have now shown that there is a tendency in nature to the continued progression of certain classes of *varieties* further and further from the original type — a progression to which there appears no reason to assign any definite limits — and that the same principle which produces this result in a state

[17] The centrifugal governor was an early "feedback" control mechanism which assured a constant speed regardless of variations in the load. A typical governor consisted of two attached pendulums deflecting toward the vertical when the engine was at rest and rising toward the horizontal as the engine increased speed. Upon passing some preset limit the governor would reduce the steam pressure, thus automatically reducing the speed of the engine.

[18] Richard Owen (1804–1892), England's greatest comparative anatomist. Presided over the establishment of the Natural History section of the British Museum.

of nature will also explain why domestic varieties have a tendency to revert to the original type. This progression, by minute steps, in various directions, but always checked and balanced by the necessary conditions, subject to which alone existence can be preserved, may, it is believed, be followed out so as to agree with all the phenomena presented by organized beings, their extinction and succession in past ages, and all the extraordinary modifications of form, instinct, and habits which they exhibit.

Ternate, February, 1858.

Bibliographical Notes

Bibliographical Notes

Since our aim has been to provide selections in readable scientific prose, we have presented each selection as an entity complete in itself. Thus we have not indicated omissions by suspension points, nor have we indicated those cases in which what we have presented as a single essay was originally taken from two or more separate chapters of the same book. The following list will guide the reader to the sources from which these selections have been made.

Charles Babbage, *The Ninth Bridgewater Treatise: A Fragment* (London: John Murray, 1838, 2nd edition. 1st edition, London: John Murray, 1837). Selections from Chapter II, "Argument in Favour of Design from the Changing of Laws in Natural Events"; Chapter III, "Argument to Show that the Doctrines in the Preceding Chapter do not Lead to Fatalism"; Chapter XIII, "A Priori Argument in Favour of the Occurrence of Miracles"; Appendix, Note B, "The Calculating Engine."

Charles Bell, *The Anatomy and Philosophy of Expression as Connected with the Fine Arts* (London: Henry G. Bohn, 1865, 5th edition). Selections from Essay V, "Of the Expression of Passion, as Illustrated by a Comparison of the Muscles of the Face in Man and in Animals; and of the Muscles Peculiar to Man, and their Effects in Bestowing Human Expression"; Essay VI "Of Expression (continued)."

Charles Bell, *The Hand, Its Mechanism and Vital Endowments, as*

Evincing Design. The Bridgewater Treatises on the Power, Wisdom, and Goodness of God as Manifested in the Creation. Treatise IV (London: W. Pickering, 1833). Selection from Chapter VI, "The Argument Pursued from the Comparative Anatomy."

Robert Brown, "Additional Remarks on Active Molecules." *The Philosophical Magazine, or Annals of Chemistry, Mathematics, Astronomy, Natural History, and General Science,* Volume 6, new series (July–December, 1829), pp. 161–166.

Robert Chambers, *Vestiges of the Natural History of Creation* (London: John Churchill, 1844, 2nd edition). Selections from "Hypothesis of the Development of the Vegetable and Animal Kingdoms."

Thomas Chalmers, *Discourses on the Christian Revelation, Viewed in Connexion with the Modern Astronomy* (Montpelier: E. P. Walton, 1819. 1st edition, Glasgow: J. Smith & Son, 1817). Selections from Discourse I, "A Sketch of the Modern Astronomy"; Discourse III, "On the Extent of the Divine Condescension"; Discourse VII, "On the Slender Influence of Mere Taste and Sensibility in Matters of Religion."

John Dalton, *A New System of Chemical Philosophy* (Manchester: R. Bickerstaff, 1808). Selections from Part I, Chapter 2, "On the Constitution of Bodies"; Chapter 3, "On Chemical Synthesis."

Charles Darwin and Alfred Russel Wallace, "On the Tendency of Species to Form Varieties; and on the Perpetuation of Varieties and Species by Natural Means of Selection.

I. Extract from an Unpublished Work on Species, by C. Darwin, Esq., Consisting of a Portion of a Chapter Entitled, 'On the Variation of Organic Beings in a State of Nature; on the Natural Means of Selection; on the Comparison of Domestic Races and True Species.'

II. Abstract of a Letter from C. Darwin, Esq., to Prof. Asa Gray, Boston, U.S., Dated Down, September 5th, 1857.

III. On the Tendency of Varieties to Depart Indefinitely from the Original Type, by A. R. Wallace."
Journal of the Proceedings of the Linnean Society, volume III, number 9 (1858), pp. 45–62.

Humphry Davy, "The Bakerian Lecture, On Some New Phenomena of Chemical Changes Produced by Electricity, Particularly the Decomposition of Fixed Alkalies, and the Exhibition of the New Substances Which Constitute their Bases; and on the General Nature of Alkaline Bodies." *Philosophical Transactions of the Royal Society,* London, volume 98 (1808), pp. 1–44.

Michael Faraday, *A Course of Six Lectures on the Chemical History of a Candle. To Which is Added a Lecture on Platinum. Delivered Before a Juvenile Auditory at the Royal Institution of Great Britain During the Christmas Holidays of 1860–61,* edited by W. Crookes (London: Griffin, Bohn & Co., 1861). Selection from Lecture I, "A Candle: The Flame — Its Sources — Structure — Mobility — Brightness."

William Vernon Harcourt, *Report of the First and Second Meetings of the British Association for the Advancement of Science; at York in 1831, and at Oxford in 1832: Including its Proceedings, Recommendations, and Transactions* (London: John Murray, 1833). Selection from "First Report. Proceedings of the General Meeting, 1831."

John Frederick William Herschel, *Outlines of Astronomy* (London: Longmans, Green, and Co., 1875, new edition). Based on edition, London: Longmans, 1849, which in turn was an extension of *A Treatise on Astronomy,* published as Part 43 of *Lardner's Cabinet Cyclopedia* of 1833. Selections from Introduction and Chapter I.

James Prescott Joule, "On Matter, Living Force and Heat." A

Lecture at St. Ann's Church Reading Room, 1847. Reprinted from Osborne Reynolds, *Memoir of James Prescott Joule* (Manchester: Literary and Philosophical Society, 1892).

Charles Lyell, *Principles of Geology, Being an Attempt to Explain the Former Changes of the Earth's Surface, by Reference to Causes Now in Operation* (London: John Murray, 1833). Volume III. Selections from Chapter I and Chapter XXVI.

James Clerk Maxwell, "On Faraday's Lines of Force." *Transactions of the Cambridge Philosophical Society,* Volume X, Part I (1856).

William Paley, *Paley's Natural Theology, with Illustrative Notes, by Henry Lord Brougham and Sir Charles Bell. To Which are Added Supplementary Dissertations by Sir Charles Bell* (London: Charles Knight, 1836). 2 Volumes. Paley's original edition was published in 1802. Selections from Chapter I, "State of the Argument"; XIV, "Prospective Contrivances"; XXVI, "Of the Goodness of the Deity."

John Playfair, *Illustrations of the Huttonian Theory of the Earth* (Edinburgh: William Creech; London: Cadell and Davies, 1802). Selection from Section III, "Of the Phenomena Common to Stratified and Unstratified Bodies."

William Whewell, "Of the Transformation of Hypotheses in the History of Science." *Transactions of the Cambridge Philosophical Society,* volume 9, part 2, pp. 139–146 (1856). Reprinted as Appendix G of *On the Philosophy of Discovery, Chapters Historical and Critical* (London: John W. Parker and Son, 1860).

DATE DUE

OCT 1 1 '78			
NOV 7 '72			
GAYLORD			PRINTED IN U.S.A.